Mathematics Olympiad

Highly useful for all school students participating in Various Olympiads & Competitions

Series Editor Keshav Mohan

Author Sanmeen Kaur

Class 9

arihant

ARIHANT PRAKASHAN, MEERUT

ARIHANT PRAKASHAN, MEERUT

卐 **Administrative & Production Offices**

Corporate Office 'Ramchhaya' 4577/15, Agarwal Road, Darya Ganj New Delhi -110002
Tele: 011- 47630600, 43518550; Fax: 011- 23280316

Head Office Kalindi, TP Nagar, Meerut (UP) - 250002
Tele: 0121-2401479, 2512970, 4004199; Fax: 0121-2401648

All disputes subject to Meerut (UP) jurisdiction only.

卐 **Sales & Support Offices**

Agra, Ahmedabad, Bengaluru, Bhubaneswar, Bareilly, Chennai, Delhi, Guwahati, Haldwani, Hyderabad, Jaipur, Jalandhar, Jhansi, Kolkata, Kota, Lucknow, Meerut, Nagpur & Pune

卐 **ISBN** 978-93-5203-394-2

卐 **Price** ₹75

Typeset by Arihant DTP Unit at Meerut
Printed & Bound by Arihant Publications (I) Ltd. (Press Unit)

Production Team

Publishing Manager	Mahendra Singh Rawat	*Page Layouting*	Diwakar Gaur
Project Head	Karishma Yadav	*DTP Operator*	Akash
Project Coordinator	Divya Gusain	*Cover Designer*	Syed Darin Zaidi
Proof Reader	Reena Garg	*Inner Designer*	Deepak Kumar

For further information about the products from Arihant
log on to www.arihantbooks.com or email to info@arihantbooks.com

Preface

Mathematics Olympiad Series for Class 6th -10th is a series of books which will challenge the young inquisitive minds by the non-routine and exciting mathematical problems.

The main purpose of this series is to make the students ready for competitive exams. The school/board exams are of qualifying nature but not competitive, they do not help the students to prepare for competitive exams, which mainly have objective questions.

- **Need of Olympiad Series**
  This series will fill this gap between the School/Board and Competitive Exams as this series have all questions in Objective format. This series helps students who are willing to sharpen their problem solving skills. Unlike typical assessment books, which emphasis on drilling practice, the focus of this series is on practicing problem solving techniques.
- **Development of Logical Approach**
  The thought provoking questions given in this series will help students to attain a deeper understanding of the concepts and through which students will be able to impart reasoning/Logical/Analytical skills in them.
- **Complement Your School Studies**
  This series complements the additional preparation needs of students for regular school/board exams. Along with, it will also address all the requirements of the students who are approaching National/State level competitions or Olympiads.

We shall welcome criticism from the students, teachers, educators and parents. We shall also like to hear from all of you about errors and deficiencies, which may have remained in this edition and the suggestions for the next edition.

Editor & Author

Contents

1

Number System

A. Types of Numbers, Rational and Irrational Numbers

1. The number $(2+\sqrt{3})(2-\sqrt{3})$ is a

a rational number **b** irrational number
c Can't say **d** None of these

2. The sum of a rational number and an irrational number is a/an

a rational number **b** irrational number
c Not defined **d** None of these

3. For an integer n, a student states

I. If n is odd, $(n+1)^2$ is even.

II. If n is even, $(n-1)^2$ is odd.

III. If n is even, $\sqrt{(n-1)}$ is irrational.

Which of the above statements would be correct?

a I and III **b** I and II
c I, II and III **d** II and III

4. Match the following:

	List I		List II
A.	Decimal representation of a rational number can't be	i.	whole number
B.	0 is a	ii.	non-terminating
C.	$\frac{\sqrt{2}+\sqrt{3}}{\sqrt{3}}$ gives a number, which is	iii.	not defined
D.	$\frac{1}{0}$ is	iv.	irrational

Codes

	A	B	C	D
a	(i)	(ii)	(iii)	(iv)
b	(ii)	(i)	(iv)	(iii)
c	(ii)	(iii)	(iv)	(i)
d	(i)	(iii)	(ii)	(iv)

5. The number of rational numbers between any two rational numbers are

a one **b** zero
c infinite **d** None of these

6. The sum of two irrational numbers always produces an irrational number.

a True **b** False
c Can't say **d** None of these

7. If x and y are two positive real numbers, then which of the following is correct?

a $x > y \Rightarrow -x > -y$

b $x > y \Rightarrow -x < -y$

c $x > y \Rightarrow \frac{1}{x} > \frac{1}{y}$

d $x > y \Rightarrow -\frac{1}{x} < -\frac{1}{y}$

8. As we know that, π is an irrational number. Then, the sum of five times of π and three times of π is subtracted from nine times of π. If two boys A and B gave the answers as rational and irrational, respectively, then who gave the correct answer?

a A **b** B
c Neither A nor B **d** None of these

9. **Assertion** (A) Rational numbers are always closed under division.

Reason (R) Division by zero is not defined.

Which of the following is true?

a (A) is true and (R) is the correct explanation of (A)

b (A) is false and (R) is the correct explanation of (A)

c (A) is true and (R) is false

d Both (A) and (R) are true

B. Properties of Rational and Irrational Numbers

1. The product of a rational number and its reciprocal is

a 0
b 1
c −1
d None of these

2. For any two rational numbers x and y, which of the following properties are correct?

(i) $x > y$ (ii) $x < y$ (iii) $x = y$

a (i) and (ii)
b (i) and (iii)
c (ii) and (iii)
d (i), (ii) and (iii)

3. Two rational numbers A and B, when added result in zero, then A and B are called

a additive inverse
b additive identity
c commutative property
d None of the above

4. Match the following:

	List I		List II
A.	The multiplicative inverse of 0 is	i.	additive inverse
B.	The additive inverse of $\frac{2}{5}$ is	ii.	$-\frac{2}{5}$
C.	$A+B=B+A=0$ is	iii.	not defined
D.	A and $\frac{1}{A}$ are	iv.	multiplicative inverse

Codes

	A	B	C	D
a	(i)	(ii)	(iii)	(iv)
b	(iii)	(ii)	(i)	(iv)
c	(ii)	(iii)	(iv)	(i)
d	(i)	(iii)	(iv)	(ii)

5. The value of $2\sqrt{3}+3\sqrt{3}-4\sqrt{3}$ is

a $3\sqrt{3}$ b $\sqrt{3}$
c $2\sqrt{6}$ d $\sqrt{9}$

6. If $\frac{(2-\sqrt{5})+(3+2\sqrt{5})-(4+\sqrt{5})}{4}=p+q\sqrt{5}$, then the values of p and q are

a $\frac{1}{4}$ and 2 b $-\frac{1}{4}$ and $-\frac{2}{4}$
c $\frac{1}{4}$ and 0 d $-\frac{1}{4}$ and 0

7. The sum of additive and multiplicative inverse of $\frac{2}{3}$ is

a $\frac{13}{6}$ b $\frac{5}{6}$
c $-\frac{5}{6}$ d $\frac{4}{3}$

8. The rationalising factor of $\sqrt[7]{a^4b^3c^5}$ is

a $\sqrt[7]{a^3b^3c^2}$
b $\sqrt[7]{a^3b^4c^2}$
c $\sqrt[7]{a^2b^3c^3}$
d $\sqrt[7]{a^2b^4c^3}$

9. If the number $x = 1.242424\ldots$ can be expressed in the form of $x=\frac{p}{q}$, where p and q are positive integers having no common factor. Then, the value of $(p+q)$ is

a 72 b 74
c 53 d 41

10. Let product of two rational numbers be $-\frac{9}{16}$. If one of the numbers is $-\frac{4}{3}$, then the another number is

a $\frac{36}{48}$ b $\frac{25}{64}$
c $\frac{27}{49}$ d $\frac{27}{64}$

11. By what rational number should $-\frac{4}{39}$ be multiplied to obtain 25?

a $-\frac{979}{4}$ b $-\frac{769}{4}$
c $-\frac{975}{4}$ d $-\frac{265}{4}$

12. If two rational numbers $\frac{p}{q}$ and $\frac{r}{s}$ are compared and it is found that both are equal. Then, which of the following is correct?

a $pq = rs$
b $ps = rq$
c $pr = qs$
d None of the above

13. If $\sqrt{18} \times \sqrt{27} \div \sqrt{12} + \sqrt{\frac{81}{2}}$ of $\sqrt{36} - \sqrt{8} = a + \frac{b}{\sqrt{2}}$.

Then, the value of $\frac{a-b}{a+b}$ is

a 1
b −1
c $\frac{22}{26}$
d $\frac{26}{22}$

14. **Assertion** (A) $\frac{83}{64}$ is a terminating decimal.

Reason (R) If the denominator of a rational number has 2 as a prime factor, then that rational number can be expressed as a terminating decimal.

Which of the following is true?

a (A) is false and (R) is true
b (A) is true and (R) is false
c (A) is true and (R) is the correct explanation of (A)
d (A) is false and (R) is the correct explanation of (A)

15. If $x = \frac{\sqrt{3}-\sqrt{2}}{\sqrt{3}+\sqrt{2}}$ and $y = \frac{\sqrt{3}+\sqrt{2}}{\sqrt{3}-\sqrt{2}}$, then the value of the expression is

$$\left(x+\frac{1}{y}\right)+\left(y+\frac{1}{x}\right)-2y = \frac{1}{p+\sqrt{q}}.$$

What is the value of $\frac{p}{q}$?

a $\frac{5}{12}$
b $\frac{3+2}{\sqrt{6}}$
c 3
d $\frac{5}{2\sqrt{6}}$

16. a, b and c are three positive whole numbers such that their sum is 117 and

(i) a is a prime number.

(ii) b and c are multiples of a.

(iii) $b \le c$

What is the greatest possible value of the product abc?

a 9747
b 15379
c 35152
d 42237

17. If $p = t^{1/2} + t^{-1/2}$ and $q = t^{1/2} - t^{-1/2}$, then the value of $p^2q^2 + 2$ in terms of t, is

a $\frac{1}{2t^2}$
b $2t^2$
c $t^2 + \frac{1}{t^2}$
d $t^2 - \frac{1}{t^2}$

18. If $\sqrt[3]{x^2} - 5\sqrt[3]{x} + 6 = 0$, then the values of x are

a 3 and 8
b 8 and 4
c 8 and 27
d 27 and 5

19. If $(BE)^2 = MPB$, where B, E, M and P are distinct integers. Then, M is

a 2
b 3
c 9
d None of the above

20. If $\sqrt{32 - x\sqrt{15}} = \sqrt{27} + \sqrt{5}$, then what is the value of x?

a −5
b −6
c −4
d −2

21. $\sqrt{\frac{49}{36}\sqrt{\frac{49}{36}\sqrt{\frac{49}{36}\ldots\infty}}}$ is equal to

a $\frac{7}{6}$
b $\frac{49}{6}$
c $\frac{7}{36}$
d $\frac{49}{36}$

22. The value of $\frac{\sqrt{5\sqrt{5\sqrt{5\ldots}}} + \sqrt{7\sqrt{7\sqrt{7\ldots}}}}{\sqrt{3\sqrt{3\sqrt{3\ldots}}}}$ is

a $\frac{35}{3}$
b 4
c 3
d 2

23. $\sqrt{11+2\sqrt{30}} + \sqrt{11-2\sqrt{30}}$ is equal to

a $\sqrt{6}$
b $\sqrt{30}$
c $2\sqrt{6}$
d $2\sqrt{5}$

24. $(\sqrt[6]{15-2\sqrt{56}})(\sqrt[3]{\sqrt{7}+2\sqrt{2}})$ is equal to

a 0
b 1
c 2
d None of the above

C. nth Root of a Real Number and Laws of Exponents with Integral Powers

1. If m and n are positive integers, then for a positive number a, $\{\sqrt[m]{(\sqrt[n]{a})}\}^{mn}$ is

a a^{mn} b a c $a^{m/n}$ d 1

2. If square root of 64 is divided by cube root of 64 gives 2. Then, the statement is

a true b false
c Can't say d None of these

3. If $\left\{\left(\frac{2}{3}\right)^4\right\}^3 = \left(\frac{3}{2}\right)^x$, then x is equal to

a 12 b −12
c 7 d −7

4. If $a=2$ and $b=3$, then the values of $a^a + b^b$ and $a^b + b^a$ are respectively

a 17 and 31 b 31 and 17
c 36 and 25 d 25 and 36

5. Which one is greatest out of $\sqrt{2}, \sqrt[6]{3}, \sqrt[3]{4}$ and $\sqrt[4]{5}$?

a $\sqrt[3]{4}$ b $\sqrt[4]{5}$ c $\sqrt{2}$ d $\sqrt[6]{3}$

6. Match the following:

List I	List II
A. $\left\{\sqrt[m]{\sqrt[n]{\frac{1}{a}}}\right\}^{mn}$ is	i. $\frac{3}{10}\times\frac{3}{10}\times\frac{3}{10}$
B. If $\frac{2^{m+n}}{2^{n-m}} = 16$, then m is	ii. $\frac{xy}{x+y}$
C. $\left(\frac{100}{9}\right)^{-3/2}$ is	iii. $\frac{1}{a}$
D. $(x^{-1}+y^{-1})^{-1}$ is	iv. 2

Codes

	A	B	C	D
a	(i)	(ii)	(iii)	(iv)
b	(iii)	(iv)	(i)	(ii)
c	(iv)	(iii)	(i)	(ii)
d	(iii)	(ii)	(iv)	(i)

7. If $x=2$ and $y=4$, then $\left(\frac{x}{y}\right)^{y-x} + \left(\frac{y}{x}\right)^{x-y}$ is

a 2 b $\frac{1}{2}$ c $\frac{17}{4}$ d $\frac{4}{17}$

8. If $2^a = 3^b = 6^{-c}$, then $\frac{1}{a}+\frac{1}{b}+\frac{1}{c}$ is equal to

a $\frac{7}{32}$ b 0 c $\frac{7}{16}$ d $\frac{7}{18}$

9. If $\sqrt{2^n} = 1024$, then the value of $3^{2\left(\frac{n}{4}-4\right)}$ is

a 3 b 9
c 27 d 81

10. The value of $\frac{5^{n+2} - 6\times 5^{n+1}}{13\times 5^n - 2\times 5^{n+1}}$ is

a $\frac{5}{3}$ b $\frac{-5}{3}$
c $\frac{3}{5}$ d $\frac{-3}{5}$

11. If $25^{x-1} = 5^{2x-1} - 100$, then the value of x is

a 3 b 2 c 4 d 1

12. The value of $\left(\frac{x^a}{x^b}\right)^{a+b} \cdot \left(\frac{x^b}{x^c}\right)^{b+c} \cdot \left(\frac{x^c}{x^a}\right)^{c+a}$ is

a 0 b 1
c x d None of these

13. The value of the given expression $\frac{(x^{-2}y^2)^{1/2}}{\left(\sqrt[4]{\sqrt{x^4+y^4}+x^2}\right)\left(\sqrt[4]{\sqrt{x^4+y^4}-x^2}\right)}$ is

a $\frac{1}{x}$ b $\frac{1}{y}$ c $\frac{1}{xy}$ d $\frac{x}{y}$

14. **Assertion** (A) $a^0 = 1$, where $a \neq 0$.

Reason (R) $a^m \cdot a^n = a^{m+n}$, where m and n being integers.

Which of the following is true?

a Both (A) and (R) are true and (R) is th correct explanation of (A)
b Both (A) and (R) are true but (R) is not th correct explanation of (A)
c (A) is true but (R) is false
d (A) is false but (R) is true

15. If $a^x = c^q = b$ and $c^y = a^z = d$, then which one the following is correct?

a $xy = qz$ b $\frac{x}{y} = \frac{q}{z}$
c $x+y = q+z$ d $x-y = q-z$

16. The volume of cubic shape and the area of a square are equal to 64. A student is asked to find the cost of a boundary of a rectangular field whose length is side of cube and bread is side of square, if the cost is ₹ 15 per unit.

a ₹ 350 b ₹ 400 c ₹ 360 d ₹ 37

D. Rationalisation

1. For rationalising $\frac{\sqrt{5}}{\sqrt{3}-2}$, we multiply the denominator by

a $-\frac{\sqrt{5}}{\sqrt{3}+2}$ b $\frac{\sqrt{5}}{2-\sqrt{3}}$

c $2+\sqrt{3}$ d $2-\sqrt{3}$

2. After rationalisation, the value of $\frac{\sqrt{2}+1}{\sqrt{2}-1}$ is

a $3+2\sqrt{2}$ b $(\sqrt{2}+1)(\sqrt{2}-1)$

c $\frac{(\sqrt{2}+1)^2}{(\sqrt{2}-1)^2}$ d None of these

3. After simplification, the value of

$\frac{3}{5-\sqrt{3}}+\frac{2}{5+\sqrt{3}}$ is

a $\frac{\sqrt{28}}{22}$ b $\frac{\sqrt{28}}{28}$

c $\frac{25+\sqrt{3}}{22}$ d $\frac{\sqrt{25}+\sqrt{3}}{22}$

4. Find the value of x.

$$\frac{x-\sqrt{6}}{\sqrt{3}+\sqrt{2}}=\frac{3\sqrt{3}-4\sqrt{2}}{1}$$

a $\sqrt{2}$ b $\sqrt{3}$

c 1 d None of these

5. The denominator of $\frac{r-\sqrt{r^2-q^2}}{r+\sqrt{r^2-q^2}}+\frac{r+\sqrt{r^2-q^2}}{r-\sqrt{r^2-q^2}}$ is

a r^2 b q^2

c $\sqrt{r^2-q^2}$ d $\sqrt{r^2+q^2}$

6. Which of the following is not correct?

a The product of $\sqrt[3]{2}$ and $\sqrt[4]{3}$ is $(432)^{1/12}$.

b The rational factor of $(\sqrt{a}+\sqrt{b})$ is $-(\sqrt{a}+\sqrt{b})$.

c $(5+\sqrt{5})(5-\sqrt{5})$ is equal to 20.

d $\sqrt{10}\times\sqrt{15}$ is equal to $5\sqrt{6}$.

7. If $\frac{\sqrt{3}-1}{\sqrt{3}+1}=a+b\sqrt{3}$, then the values of a and b are

a 2 and 1

b −2 and 1

c 2 and −1

d −2 and −1

8. What are the values of x and y, if $\frac{5-\sqrt{3}}{2+\sqrt{3}}=x+y\sqrt{3}$?

a $x=13$ and $y=-7$

b $x=-13$ and $y=7$

c $x=-13$ and $y=-7$

d $x=13$ and $y=7$

9. Match the following:

List I	List II
A. $\frac{2}{\sqrt{7}}=\frac{a\sqrt{7}}{7}$, $a=?$	i. $\sqrt[3]{2}$
B. $\left(\sqrt[6]{27}-\sqrt{6\frac{3}{4}}\right)^2=?$	ii. 2
C. The rationalising factor of $\frac{\sqrt{3}+1}{2-\sqrt{3}}$ is	iii. $\frac{3}{4}$
D. The greatest among $\sqrt[9]{4}$, $\sqrt[6]{3}$ and $\sqrt[3]{2}$ is	iv. $2+\sqrt{3}$

Codes

	A	B	C	D
a	(i)	(ii)	(iii)	(iv)
b	(ii)	(iii)	(iv)	(i)
c	(iii)	(ii)	(iv)	(i)
d	(i)	(iii)	(ii)	(iv)

10. If $x=\sqrt{6}+\sqrt{5}$, then the value of $x^2+\frac{1}{x^2}-2$ is

a $2\sqrt{6}$ b $2\sqrt{5}$

c 24 d 20

11. If $a+\frac{1}{a}=\sqrt{3}$, then the value of $a^2+\frac{1}{a^2}$ is

a 0 b 1

c 2 d 3

12. If $x=\frac{\sqrt{5}+\sqrt{3}}{\sqrt{5}-\sqrt{3}}$ and $y=\frac{\sqrt{5}-\sqrt{3}}{\sqrt{5}+\sqrt{3}}$, then the value of x^2+y^2+xy is

a 48 b 57

c 67 d 63

13. The value of the expression

$\frac{1}{1+\sqrt{2}}+\frac{1}{\sqrt{2}+\sqrt{3}}+\frac{1}{\sqrt{3}+\sqrt{4}}+\ldots+\frac{1}{\sqrt{8}+\sqrt{9}}$ is

a 0 b 1

c 2 d 4

14. **Assertion** (A) $(\sqrt{3}-\sqrt{2})$ is a rationalising factor of $\frac{2}{\sqrt{3}+\sqrt{2}}$.

Reason (R) $(\sqrt{a}-\sqrt{b})$ is a rationalising factor of binomial surd $(\sqrt{a}+\sqrt{b})$.

Which of the following is true?

a Both (A) and (R) are true and (R) is the correct explanation of (A)

b Both (A) and (R) are false and (R) is the correct explanation of (A)

c (A) is true but (R) is false

d (A) is false but (R) is true

15. A student is asked to find the ratio of the sum of length and breadth to difference of length and breadth of a rectangular field whose length is a side of square and breadth is the diagonal of the same square. If the area of square is 12 sq units, then the ratio is

a $2\sqrt{3}:2\sqrt{6}$ **b** $3+2\sqrt{2}:1$

c $1:3+2\sqrt{2}$ **d** None of these

16. State 'T' for true or 'F' for false.

I. The value of $\frac{a+\sqrt{a^2-b^2}}{\sqrt{a^2+b^2}+b}+\frac{\sqrt{a^2+b^2}-b}{a-\sqrt{a^2-b^2}}$ is $\frac{a^2}{b^2}$.

II. Between two rational numbers, there exist infinite number of integers.

III. If $4^{44}+4^{44}+4^{44}+4^{44}=4^x$, then the value of x is 44.

IV. The 100th root of $(10^{10})^{10}$ is 10.

V. The square root of a prime number is rational.

Codes

	I	II	III	IV	V
a	F	F	F	T	F
b	F	F	T	F	F
c	F	T	F	T	F
d	T	F	F	T	F

17. $\frac{1}{\sqrt{9}+\sqrt{10}}+\frac{1}{\sqrt{10}+\sqrt{11}}+\frac{1}{\sqrt{11}+\sqrt{12}}+\ldots+\frac{1}{\sqrt{24}+\sqrt{25}}$ is

a 0

b 1

c 2

d None of the above

18. If $a*b*c=\sqrt{\frac{(a+3)(b-3)}{c-1}}$, then the value of $6*12*26$ is

a $\frac{3}{5}$ **b** $\frac{3\sqrt{5}}{5}$

c $\frac{9\sqrt{5}}{5}$ **d** $\frac{9}{5}$

19. $\frac{\sqrt{15+4\sqrt{11}}}{\sqrt{31+8\sqrt{15}}}\times\frac{1}{8+4\sqrt{11}-\sqrt{165}-2\sqrt{15}}$ is

a 0 **b** 1

c 2 **d** $\sqrt{15}+\sqrt{11}$

20. The following are the steps involved in finding the value of $x-y$ from $\frac{\sqrt{11}-\sqrt{6}}{\sqrt{11}+\sqrt{6}}=x-y\sqrt{66}$.

Arrange them in sequential order.

I. $\frac{17-2\sqrt{66}}{5}=x-y\sqrt{66}$

II. $\frac{(\sqrt{11})^2+(\sqrt{6})^2-2(\sqrt{11})(\sqrt{6})}{(\sqrt{11})^2-(\sqrt{6})^2}=x-y\sqrt{66}$

III. $x-y=3$

IV. $x=\frac{17}{5}, y=\frac{2}{5}$

V. $\frac{(\sqrt{11}-\sqrt{6})(\sqrt{11}-\sqrt{6})}{(\sqrt{11}+\sqrt{6})(\sqrt{11}-\sqrt{6})}=x-y\sqrt{66}$

Codes

a V, I, II, IV, III

b V, II, I, IV, III

c I, II, IV, V, III

d IV, V, II, I, III

2 Polynomials

A. Introduction to Polynomials, Degree and Types of Polynomial

1. Pick the odd one out.

a $3x^{1/2} - 4x + 3$ b $4x^2 - 3\sqrt{x} + 5$

c $3x^2y - 2xy + 5x^4$ d $2x^4 + \frac{3}{x^2} - 1$

2. The degree of the polynomial $(7x^2 - 14x + 5) + (3x^3 - 2x + 1) - (x + 1)$ is

a 2 b 3

c 5 d 1

3. The number of terms in a trinomial and a monomial polynomial respectively are

a 1 and 3 b 3 and 2 c 3 and 1 d 3 and 3

4. Biquadratic polynomial is based on

a number of terms

b number of degree

c degree of polynomial

d Either (a) or (b)

5. A rectangular field has its length and breadth in the ratio 3 : 5. To find its sides when area of the field is 1500 sq units, which type of polynomial will be formed?

a Linear polynomial

b Quadratic polynomial

c Biquadratic polynomial

d None of the above

6. The degree of polynomial $5x^3 - 6x^3y + 4y^2 - 8$ is

a 3 b 2

c 4 d Can't say

7. The maximum number of terms a polynomial of degree n can have

a n b $n + 1$

c $n + 2$ d Can't say

8. The degree of expression, when $x - y$ is subtracted from $x^3 - y^3$, will be

a 0 b 3

c 2 d 1

9. The difference of the degree of the polynomial $2x^4y^2 + 5xy^6 - 2x^6$ and $13x^4 - 2x^3 - 2$ is

a 5 b 4

c 3 d 2

10. What is the coefficient of x^3 in the polynomial $x^2 + 5x + 6$?

a 1 b 2

c 0 d Can't say

11. **Assertion** (A) $2x - 6$ is a linear polynomial.
Reason (R) $f(x) = ax^2 + bx + c$ is a general form of a quadratic polynomial.

Which of the following is correct?

a (A) is true and (R) is the correct explanation of (A)

b Both (A) and (R) are true but (R) is not the correct explanation of (A)

c (A) is true and (R) is false

d Both (A) and (R) are false

12. If a piece of cardboard 30 inch by 15 inch is made into an open donut box by cutting out squares of side x from each corner. Then, which expression is equivalent to above statement?

a $4x^3 - 90x^2 + 450x$ b $4x^3 + 90x^2 - 450x$

c $4x^2 + 90x^2 + 450$ d None of these

B. Zeroes of a Polynomial, Factorisation and Remainder Theorem

1. A factor of $x^3 - 1$ is

a $x - 1$

b $x^2 + x + 1$

c Either (a) or (b)

d None of the above

2. If $(x - 2)$ is a factor of $x^2 + 3ax - 2a$, then a is equal to

a 2　　b −2

c 1　　d −1

3. If $(x + a)$ is a factor of $p(x)$, then $p(-a)$ is equal to

a 1　　b 0

c a　　d x

4. What is the zero of the binomial $2x + 4$?

a −3

b 2

c −2

d 0

5. $(x + 1)$ is a factor of $x^n + 1$ only, if

a n is an odd integer.

b n is an even integer.

c n is a negative integer.

d n is a positive integer.

6. If $(x - 3)$ is one factor of $x^2 + ax - 4 = 0$ and $x^2 - 4x + b = 0$, then $2a - b$ is equal to

a $\frac{13}{3}$

b $\frac{-19}{3}$

c 6

d −4

7. If $(x - 2)$ and $\left(x - \frac{1}{2}\right)$ are factors of $px^2 + 5x + r$, then

a $p = r$

b $p + r = 0$

c $2p + r = 0$

d $p + 2r = 0$

8. If $(x + 1)$ is a factor of $ax^4 + bx^3 + cx^2 + dx + e$, then the relation among a, b, c, d and e is

a $a + c + e = b + d$

b $b + d > a + c + e$

c $a + c + e > b + d$

d None of the above

9. What will be the values of a and b, so that the polynomial $x^3 + 10x^2 + ax + b$ is exactly divisible by $x - 1$ as well as $x - 2$?

a 37 and 26

b −37 and 26

c 37 and −26

d −37 and −26

10. For what value of a, polynomials $ax^3 + 4x^2 + 3x - 4$ and $x^3 - 4x + a$ when divided by $(x - 3)$ leave the same remainder?

a 1

b −1

c 0

d −2

11. The remainder, when $p(x) = 4x^4 - 3x^3 - 2x^2 + x - 7$ is divided by $(x - 1)$, is

a −7

b −6

c 7

d 6

12. If $x = 2$ is a solution of $x^3 - 7x + 6 = 0$, then other solutions are

a −1 and 3

b 1 and − 3

c 1 and −2

d −1 and −2

13. When $x^{40} + 2$ is divided by $x^4 + 1$, then what is the remainder?

a 21

b 19

c 3

d −2

14. If $(x - 1)$ and $(x + 1)$ exactly divides $ax^2 - 3bx + 1$, then the values of a and b are

a $a = 0, b = -1$

b $a = b = -1$

c $a = -1, b = 0$

d $a = 1, b = -1$

15. If $(x + a)$ is a factor of polynomial $p(x)$, then $p(a) = 0$ always

a true　　b false

c Can't say　　d None of these

16. If $x^{49} + 49$ is divided by $(x + 1)$, then the remainder is 50.

a True b False
c Partially true d None of these

7. Consider the given statements:

Statement I $a^n + b^n$ is divisible by $a + b$, if $n = 2K + 1$, where K is a positive integer.

Statement II $a^n - b^n$ is divisible by $a - b$, if $n = 2K$, where K is a positive integer.

Which of the statement(s) is/are correct?

a I and II b Only I
c Only II d None of these

8. Match the following:

List I	List II
A. If $(ax + b)$ is a factor of $p(x)$, then	i. $n \in$ positive odd integer
B. $(x + a)$ is a factor of $(x^n + a^n)$, if	ii. $p\left(\frac{-b}{a}\right) = 0$
C. If $p(x)$ is divided by $(ax - b)$, then remainder is	iii. $\frac{4}{3}$
D. Zeroes of polynomial $3x - 4$ is	iv. $p\left(\frac{b}{a}\right)$

Codes

	A	B	C	D
a	(i)	(ii)	(iii)	(iv)
b	(ii)	(i)	(iv)	(iii)
c	(i)	(iii)	(ii)	(iv)
d	(i)	(ii)	(iv)	(iii)

The remainder, when $p(x) = x^4 + 2x^3 - 3x^2 + x - 1$ is divided by $(x - 2)$, is

a 21 b −21
c 47 d −47

Assertion (A) $4x^2 - 8x + 4$ leaves remainder 0, when it is divided by $(x - 1)$.

Reason (R) If $p(x)$ is divided by $(x - a)$, then remainder is $p(a)$.

Which of the following is true?

a Both (A) and (R) are true and (R) is the correct explanation of (A)
b (A) is true and (R) is false
c (A) is false and (R) is true
d Both (A) and (R) are true and (R) is not the correct explanation of (A)

21. If $9x^2 + 3px + 6q$ when divided by $(3x + 1)$ leaves a remainder $\left(\frac{-3}{4}\right)$ and $qx^2 + 4px + 7$ is exactly divided by $(x + 1)$, then the values of p and q respectively will be

a $\frac{7}{4}, 0$ b $2, \frac{1}{3}$
c 4, 6 d $\frac{4}{7}, \frac{6}{7}$

22. If $(x - a)$ is a factor of $x^8 - ax^7 + x^6 - ax^5 + x^4 - ax^3 + 3x - a + 2 = 0$, then the value of a is

a −2 b 2
c 1 d −1

23. If zeroes of $f(x) = x^2 + 2x + 1$ is a factor of $px^5 + qx^4 + rx^3 + sx^2 + tx + u$, then which of the following is true?

a $p + q + r = s + t + u$
b $p + r + t = q + s + u$
c $p + r - t = q + s - u$
d $p + q - r = s + t - u$

24. If two polynomials $ax^3 + 3x^2 - 3$ and $3x^3 - 7x + a$, when divided by $(x - 1)$ each leave remainders m and n, respectively such that $m + n = 0$, then the value of a is

a 0 b 1
c 2 d 3

25. If $(x - a)$ and $\left(x - \frac{1}{a}\right)$ are factors of $px^2 + 5x + q = 0$, where $a \neq \pm 1$, then

a $p = q$ b $p < q$
c $p > q$ d $p + q = 0$

26. If $(x + a)$ is a common factor of $(x^2 + px + q)$ and $(x^2 + lx + m)$, then the value of a is

a $m - q$
b $m + q$
c $\frac{m + q}{l - p}$
d $\frac{m - q}{l - p}$

27. Square root of the polynomial $m^4 + 6m^3 + 11m^2 + 6m + 1$ is

a $\sqrt{m^2 + 6m + 1}$ b $m^2 + 3m + 1$
c $\sqrt{m^2 + 3m + 2}$ d $m^2 + 11m + 6$

C. Factorisation and Algebraic Identities

1. $x^3 + y^3 + z^3 = 3xyz$ if and only if

a $x = y = z$ **b** $x + y = z$
c $x + y = -z$ **d** None of these

2. The factors of $6x^2 + 17x + 5$ are

a $(3x - 1)(2x - 5)$ **b** $(3x + 1)(2x - 5)$
c $(2x + 5)(3x - 1)$ **d** $(3x + 1)(2x + 5)$

3. If $a + b + c = 0$, then $a^3 + b^3 + c^3 - 3abc$ is equal to

a 0
b $6abc$
c $a^2 + b^2 + c^2 - ab - bc - ca$
d None of the above

4. The value of 101×99 can be calculated by using which of the following algebraic identity?

a $a^2 + b^2 + 2ab = (a + b)^2$
b $a^2 + b^2 = (a + b)^2 - 2ab$
c $(a + b)(a - b) = a^2 - b^2$
d None of the above

5. Which of the following is/are the factor(s) of expression $2(m+3)+3(3-m)$?

a $m+3$
b $m-3$
c Both (a) and (b)
d None of the above

6. In the quadratic equation $x^2 - 4x + 3 = 0$, the coefficients of the terms obtained by splitting the middle term are

a (1, 3) **b** (–3, –1)
c (1, – 3) **d** (3, –1)

7. If $x + \frac{1}{x} = 13$, then the value of $x^2 + \frac{1}{x^2}$ is

a 165 **b** 169 **c** 167 **d** 170

8. If $a = 225$, $b = 226$ and $c = 227$, then the value of $a^3 + b^3 + c^3 - 3abc$ is

a 2304 **b** 2430
c 2034 **d** 2240

9. The value of $\frac{(1.5)^2 + (4.7)^2 + 2 \cdot (1.5)(4.7)}{6.2}$ is

a 3.2 **b** 6.2 **c** 4.7 **d** 1.5

10. If $p = (2 - a)$, then the value of $a^3 + 6ap + p^3 - 8$ is

a 0 **b** 1 **c** 2 **d** 3

11. The roots of quadratic equation $\sqrt{3}x^2 + 11x + 6\sqrt{3} = 0$ are obtained by using which of the following factors?

a $(x - 3\sqrt{3})(\sqrt{3}x + 2)$
b $(x - 3\sqrt{3})(\sqrt{3}x - 2)$
c $(x + 3\sqrt{3})(\sqrt{3}x - 2)$
d $(x + 3\sqrt{3})(\sqrt{3}x + 2)$

12. $(p - q)^6 - 27r^3$ is equal to

a $\{(p - q)^3 + 3r\}\{(p - q)^3 - 3r^2\}$
b $\{(p - q)^2 - 3r\}\{(p - q)^4 + 9r^2 + (p - q)^2 3r\}$
c Both (a) and (b)
d None of the above

13. The value of $(p + q)^3 - (p - q)^3 - 6q(p^2 - q^2)$ is

a $8p^3$
b $8q^3$
c 0
d None of the above

14. If $(a + b + c) = 9$ and $ab + bc + ca = 23$, then the value of $a^3 + b^3 + c^3 - 3abc$ is

a 108 **b** 207
c 669 **d** 729

15. Match the following:

List I	List II
A. 98×102 is equal to	i. $a^3 + b^3 + c^3 - 3ab$
B. $\frac{1}{2}(a + b + c)\{(a - b)^2 + (b - c)^2 + (c - a)^2\}$ is	ii. 18
C. If $a^{1/3} + b^{1/3} + c^{1/3} = 0$, then	iii. 9996
D. $(-1)^3 - (2)^3 + (3)^3$ is equal to	iv. $(a + b + c)^3 = 27a$

Codes

	A	B	C	D		A	B	C
a	(i)	(ii)	(iii)	(iv)	**b**	(iii)	(i)	(iv)
c	(ii)	(iv)	(i)	(iii)	**d**	(iv)	(ii)	(i)

16. Which of the following is a possible expres for the length and breadth of the rectangle whose area is given by $4a^2 + 4a - 3$?

a $(2a + 1)(2a + 3)$
b $(2a - 1)(2a + 3)$
c $(a + 1)(2a + 3)$
d None of the above

17. If $\frac{a}{b}+\frac{b}{a}=1$, then the value of a^3+b^3 is

a 1 b −1
c 1/2 d 0

18. If $x^3+\frac{1}{x^3}=110$, then the value of $x+\frac{1}{x}$ is

a 5 b 10
c 15 d 17

19. If $a+b+c=0$ and $ab+bc+ca=5$, then the value of $a^3+b^3+c^3$ is

a 0 b 4
c $3abc$ d 2

20. Which of the following is correct quadratic equation, whose roots are $\frac{\alpha}{\beta}$ and $\frac{\beta}{\alpha}$, where α and β are roots of the quadratic equation $4a^2+8a+3=0$?

a $3x^2-10x+3=0$
b $3x^2+10x+3=0$
c $x^2-\frac{10}{3}x+3=0$
d None of the above

21. If $x^3-3x^2+3x+7=(x+1)(ax^2+bx+c)$, then the value of $a+b+c$ is

a 4 b 12
c −10 d 3

22. If we write $2x^2+4x+1=p(x+1)^2-q$, then the value of (p, q) will be

a (2, 1) b (2, −1)
c (−2, 1) d (−2, −1)

23. **Assertion** (A) $25^3-15^3=(10)(1225)$
Reason (R) $a^3-b^3=(a-b)(a^2+ab+b^2)$
Which of the following is true?

a Both (A) and (R) are true and (R) is the correct explanation of (A)
b Both (A) and (R) are false and (R) is not the correct explanation of (A)
c (A) is true and (R) is false
d (R) is true and (A) is false

24. In a school, there are some boys and girls in class IX. If difference between the squares of number of boys and girls is 400 and when the number of boys multiplied with the number of girls, result is 375. If difference in their numbers is 10. Then, the total number of students and ratio of boys to girls are, respectively

a 40 and 5 : 3
b 30 and 3 : 5
c 50 and 4 : 5
d None of the above

25. The sum of digits of a two-digit number is 9. If 9 is added to the number, then its digits interchange their place. What is the difference in cube of the digits?

a 65 b 61
c 89 d 125

26. State 'T' for true or 'F' for false.

I. Zero (0) is always a zero of a polynomial.
II. When x^3-6x^2+9x+7 is divided by $(x-1)$, then the remainder is 11.
III. If $x=3$ and $\frac{1}{2}$ are factors of px^2+5x+r, then $p\neq r$.
IV. The value of following expression $\frac{0.76\times0.76\times0.76+0.24\times0.24\times0.24}{0.76\times0.76-0.76\times0.24+0.24\times0.24}$ is 1.

Codes

	I	II	III	IV
a	T	T	T	T
b	T	F	T	T
c	T	F	T	F
d	F	F	T	T

27. If $x=\frac{1}{a}$, $y=\frac{1}{b}$ and $z=\frac{1}{c}$, then

$$\left(\frac{1}{x}+\frac{1}{y}+\frac{1}{z}\right)^2-\left(\frac{2}{xy}+\frac{2}{yz}+\frac{2}{zx}\right)$$

is equal to

a $a^2+b^2+c^2$
b $\frac{1}{a^2}+\frac{1}{b^2}+\frac{1}{c^2}$
c 0
d 1

28. If $p+q+r+s=9$, $q+r+s=0$, $pq+qr+rs=14$ and $qr+rs+sq=19$, then $q^3+r^3+s^3$ is equal to

a $3pqr$ b 0
c $3qrs$ d $-3pqr$

29. If $a^2+b^2+c^2+3=2a-2b+2c$, then $(a+b-c)^3$ is equal to

a 0
b −1
c −2
d None of the above

3 Linear Equations in Two Variables

A. Introduction to Linear Equations in Two Variables and Their Solutions using Algebraic Methods

1. $ax + by + c = 0$ does not represent an equation in two variables, if

a $a = c = 0$ and $b \neq 0$
b $b = c = 0$ and $a \neq 0$
c $a = b = 0$
d $c = 0, a \neq 0$ and $b \neq 0$

2. A system of a pair of linear equations in two variables is said to be inconsistent, if it has

a a unique solution
b infinitely many solutions
c no solution
d None of the above

3. Which of the following is correct?

a Linear equation in two variables is in the form $ax + by + c = 0$, where $a = 0$
b Linear equation in two variables is $px + qy + c = 0$
c It is in the form of $sx + ty + r = 0$, where s, t and r are constants not equal to zero
d $ax + by + c = 0, a + b \neq 0$, is an example of linear equation in three variables

4. The option which is not a solution of the equation $2x + 3y = 6$, is

a (3, 0)
b (0, 2)
c (− 3, 4)
d (1, 1)

5. Which equation satisfies the data in the table?

x	−1	0	1	2
y	−3	−1	1	3

a $y = x - 2$ b $y = 2x - 1$
c $y = 3x - 3$ d $y = x + 1$

6. Which of the following points lies on the line $y = 2x + 3$?

a (2, 8) b (3, 9)
c (4, 12) d (5, 15)

7. If (2, 0) is a solution of the linear equation $3x + 2y = k/2$, then the value of k is

a 4 b 3
c 2 d 12

8. The number of linear equations in x and y which can be satisfied by $x = 1$ and $y = 3$, is/are

a only one b two
c infinite d three

9. If the point (1, 3) lies on the graph of the equation $3y = ax + 7$, then the value of a is

a 1 b 2
c 3 d 4

10. The linear equation $2(x - y) + 3(y - x) = 5$ has

a a unique solution
b two solutions
c infinitely many solutions
d no solution

11. If we multiply or divide both sides of a linear equation with a non-zero number, then the solution of the linear equation

a changes

b remains the same

c changes in case of multiplication only

d changes in case of division only

12. Sonam has x bags more than Deepika. If together they have y number of bags, then the number of bags Deepika has, is

a $y + x$ **b** $y - x$

c $\frac{y - x}{2}$ **d** $2y - x$

13. If linear equation $2x + cy = 8$ has equal values of x and y, then the value of c, when value of $x = 1$, will be

a 6 **b** 3

c 4 **d** 1

14. The taxi fare in a city is as follows: For the first kilometre, the fare is ₹ 8 and for the subsequent distance, it is ₹ 5 per kilometre. Taking the distance covered as x km and total fare as ₹ y. The linear equation for this information is

a $5x + y + 3 = 0$ **b** $5x - y + 3 = 0$

c $5x + y - 3 = 0$ **d** $5x - y - 3 = 0$

15. In an isosceles right angled triangle, the angles are in the ratio, if one of the angles is $x°$ and other angle is $y°$ (apart from right angle)

a 1 : 2 : 3 **b** 1 : 1 : 2

c 2 : 1 : 2 **d** 1 : 1 : 1

16. If α and β are the solutions of the linear equation $ax + by + c = 0$. Then, the value of $a\alpha + b\beta$ is

a c **b** 0

c $-b$ **d** None of these

17. Match the following:

	List I		List II
A.	The degree of a linear equation is	i.	3, −1
B.	One of the solutions of $2x + 3y = 3$ is	ii.	1
C.	A linear equation of $ax + by + c = 0$ have	iii.	$x - 2y = 0$
D.	The cost of a book is twice the cost of a pen, is represented by	iv.	infinitely many solutions

Codes

	A	B	C	D
a	(i)	(ii)	(iii)	(iv)
b	(ii)	(i)	(iv)	(iii)
c	(iii)	(iv)	(i)	(ii)
d	(iv)	(i)	(ii)	(iii)

18. If the values of k are given such that $x = 1, y = 1$ is a solution of the equation $2x + 3y = k$. Then, which of the following is the correct value for k?

a 4

b 5

c 7

d 8

19. The solutions of the equations $\frac{p}{x} + \frac{q}{y} = m$ and $\frac{q}{x} + \frac{p}{y} = n$ are

a $x = \frac{q^2 - p^2}{mp - nq}$ and $y = \frac{p^2 - q^2}{np - mq}$

b $x = \frac{p^2 - q^2}{mp - nq}$ and $y = \frac{q^2 - p^2}{np - mq}$

c $x = \frac{p^2 - q^2}{mp - nq}$ and $y = \frac{p^2 - q^2}{np - mq}$

d $x = \frac{q^2 - p^2}{mp - nq}$ and $y = \frac{q^2 - p^2}{np - mq}$

20. For what value of k, the given equation

$$\left(\frac{k+2}{k-1}\right)x - \left(\frac{3k-2}{k+2}\right)y - 3 = 0$$

has a solution (1, 0)?

a 3/2

b 5/2

c 2/5

d 2/3

21. Assertion (A) There are infinite number of lines which are satisfied by the point (2, 4).

Reason (R) A linear equation in two variables has infinitely many solutions.

Which of the following is correct?

a Both (A) and (R) are true and (R) is the correct explanation of (A)

b Both (A) and (R) are true and (R) is not the correct explanation of (A)

c (A) is true and (R) is false

d (A) is false and (R) is true

B. Graphical Representation of Linear Equation in Two Variables and Their Solutions

1. The graph of a linear equation in two variables is a

a straight line
b curve
c straight line parallel to X-axis
d straight line parallel to Y-axis

2. Which of the following statements is true for $x+1=0$?

a Parallel to X-axis
b Parallel to Y-axis
c Passing through the origin
d None of the above

3. The equation of the line passing through the origin (0, 0) is

a $y = mx + c$ b $y = mx$
c $y = 0$ d $x = 0$

4. The graph of the linear equation $y = x$ passes through the point

a (0, 2) b (2, 0)
c (3, 0) d None of these

5. Match the following:

	List I		List II
A.	$x = a$	i.	$y = 0$
B.	Line parallel to X-axis	ii.	Straight line parallel to Y-axis
C.	$y = mx + c$	iii.	$y = a$
D.	Equation of X-axis	iv.	Equation of line in two variables

Codes

	A	B	C	D
a	(i)	(ii)	(iii)	(iv)
b	(ii)	(iii)	(iv)	(i)
c	(iii)	(ii)	(iv)	(i)
d	(ii)	(i)	(iii)	(iv)

6. The graph of the equation $3x - 4y = 8$ cuts the Y-axis at the point

a (2, 0) b (0, 2) c (3, 0) d (0, − 2)

7. If a linear equation has solutions $(-2, 2)$, $(0, 0)$ and $(2, -2)$, then it is of the form

a $y - x = 0$ b $x + y = 0$
c $-2x + y = 0$ d $-x + 2y = 5$

8. The linear equation is drawn on graph. If the sum of ordinate and abscissa of the equation is 0, then

a $x = y$ b $x - y = 0$
c $x + y = 0$ d None of these

9. The distance between the two points on graph (4, 0) and (−5, 0) is

a −1 b 9
c −9 d None of these

10. If the point on the graph of the linear equation $2x + 4y = 8$, whose ordinate is 1.5 times, its abscissa, is

a $\left(\frac{3}{2}, 1\right)$ b $\left(1, \frac{3}{2}\right)$
c $\left(-1, \frac{3}{2}\right)$ d $\left(1, \frac{-3}{2}\right)$

11. Fill in the blanks with the help of options, given in the box.

(i) 7/2, (ii) first, (iii) second, (iv) unaffected, (v)5/2

I. The negative solution of the equation $ax + by + c = 0$ always lies in the___ quadrant.
II. x-intercept of the equation $2x + 5y = 7$ is ___ unit.
III. When a non-negative number is added to both sides of a linear equation, then its solution is ___.

Codes

	I	II	III
a	(iii)	(i)	(iv)
b	(ii)	(iii)	(i)
c	(iv)	(v)	(i)
d	(iii)	(v)	(iv)

12. The area of a triangle formed by the line $2x + 3y = 6$ and axes, is

a 5 sq units
b 3 sq units
c 6 sq units
d 8 sq units

13. Two friends Ram and Mohan standing on the respective axes walk along the straight lines $x = 7$ and $y = 3$, respectively. After some time, they meet on a line $2x + 3y = 23$. What will be the area of triangle formed by meeting origin, meeting point and point from where Ram starts walking?

a 9.5 sq units b 10 sq units
c 10.5 sq units d None of these

C. Application Based Problems on Linear Equations in Two Variables

1. If cost of a pen is 3 more than twice the cost of a pencil, then equation that describes the statement is

a $2x = y + 3$
b $x = 2y + 3$
c $2x + y = 0$
d Both (a) and (b)

2. If $x > 0$ and $y < 0$, then the point (x, y) lies in

a quadrant I
b quadrant II
c quadrant III
d quadrant IV

3. In a bag, there are some balls of two colours, red and blue. If the ratio of number of red balls to number of blue balls is 3 : 2 and total number of balls is 50. Then, the number of red balls is

a 20 b 30
c 25 d 40

4. Five years ago, Raju told Rita that he was 10 yr older than your age. Taking Raju's and Rita's present age as x yr and y yr, respectively. Then, the linear equation which represents their age 5 yr ago, is

a $x + y = 10$
b $x - y = 20$
c $x - y = 10$
d $x + y = 20$

5. During vegetable purchase, a shopkeeper tells that cost of 3 kg of potatoes is equal to 2 kg of tomatoes. If the total cost of 3 kg potatoes and 2 kg tomatoes is ₹ 90. Then, what will be the cost of tomato per kg?

a ₹ 45 b ₹ 15
c ₹ 22.5 d ₹ 30

6. A rectangular field has its length and breadth such that length is 3/4th of its breadth. If its area is equal to 25/3 sq units, then the length of rectangular is

a $\frac{10}{3}$ b $\frac{5}{3}$
c $\frac{5}{2}$ d 5

7. If the linear equation that converts Fahrenheit to Celcius is $(F - 32)25 = 9C \times 5$. Then, match the following:

	List I		List II
A.	26°C in F	i.	17.8° C
B.	64°F in C	ii.	78.8° F
C.	32°C in F	iii.	32° F
D.	0°C in F	iv.	32° C

Codes

	A	B	C	D
a	(i)	(ii)	(iii)	(iv)
b	(ii)	(i)	(iv)	(iii)
c	(ii)	(i)	(iii)	(iv)
d	(iii)	(ii)	(iv)	(i)

8. Mohan has ₹ 25 in the form of 50 paisa and one rupee coins. He has half as many 50 paisa coins as he has one rupee coins. The number of one rupee coins is

a 10 b 20
c 15 d 30

9. A certain distance is covered at a certain speed (s_1). If half of this distance is covered in double the time at speed (s_2). Find the ratio of two speeds s_1, s_2. If $s_1 = 40$ km/h, then find the value of s_2.

a 1 : 4 and 10 km/h
b 4 : 1 and 10 km/h
c 1 : 2 and 20 km/h
d 2 : 1 and 20 km/h

10. If a person travels from A to B through C in 10 min and from B to D in 5 min, then what will be his average speed throughout journey?

$$\left[\text{given, speed} = \frac{\text{distance}}{\text{time}}\right]$$

a 64 km/h
b 24 km/h
c 40 km/h
d 45 km/h

Directions (Q. Nos. 11-13) In a class of some students, books are distributed according to the following equation.

$$x + 2y = 80$$

where, x is number of boys and y is number of girls in the class.

11. If there are 40 boys, then the number of girls in that class is

a 40 **b** 20
c 30 **d** 10

12. Total number of students in the class is

a 50 **b** 60
c 40 **d** 80

13. If we make a group of 2 boys and 1 girl, then the number of groups will be

a 30 **b** 20
c 10 **d** 40

Directions (Q. Nos. 14-16) *Given, two statements* A *and* B. *Study the statements carefully and answer according to the options given below.*

a If both the statements are needed to answer the question
b If any of the two statements is sufficient to answer the question
c If both the statements together are not sufficient to answer the question
d None of the above

14. What will be the cost of 4 pens and 5 pencils?

A. Cost of 5 pens and 3 pencils is ₹ 35.
B. Cost of 5 pens is equal to the cost of 4 pencils.

15. What is the age of Ajay after 5 yr from now?

A. Combined age of Ajay and Nisha is 50 yr.
B. Neha is as many year older than Nisha as Nisha is older than Mohit.

16. What is the number of girls in class IX of the school?

A. Total number of students in class IX is 64.
B. The difference between number of boys and number of girls in class IX is 10.

17. The ratio of cars to motorbikes in a car park is 10 cars to 4 motorbikes. There total 140 vehicles in the parking. Then, how many cars are there?

a 100 **b** 50
c 40 **d** 90

18. State 'T' for true or 'F' for false.

I. Equation $y = 3x + 5$ has a unique solution.
II. The solution of a linear equation is not affected when the same number is added to both sides of the equation.
III. The line parallel to Y-axis at a distance a units to the left of Y-axis is given by the equation $x = -a$.
IV. If $x = 2$ and $y = 1$ is the solution of equation $2x - 3y = k$, then the value of k is -1.

Codes

	I	II	III	IV		I	II	III	IV
a	T	F	T	F	**b**	F	T	T	F
c	T	T	T	F	**d**	F	F	T	T

19. This formula can be used to calculate a child's dose of medicine, when the adult dose is known.

$$\text{Child dose} = \text{Adult dose} \times \frac{\text{Age}}{\text{Age} + 12}$$

A nurse calculated that a 4 yr old child's dose would be 6 mL of medicine.
What was the adult dose?

a 1.5 mL **b** 2 mL
c 18 mL **d** 24 mL

4

Lines and Angles

A. Angles, Types of Angles and Angle on a Straight Line

1. If sum of two adjacent angles is 180°, then the figure formed by non-common arms of angle is

a parallel lines
b a straight line
c perpendicular lines
d None of the above

2. The sum of angles which form a linear pair, is

a 90° **b** 180°
c 0° **d** 360°

3. An angle which is less than 360° and more than 180° is called

a a reflex angle **b** a straight angle
c an acute angle **d** an obtuse angle

4. This picture shows the face of a clock. When the time is 10:10, the hour hand and the minute hand form angle x and minute hand and second hand form angle z, whereas hour hand and second hand form angle y. Then, which of the following is correct?

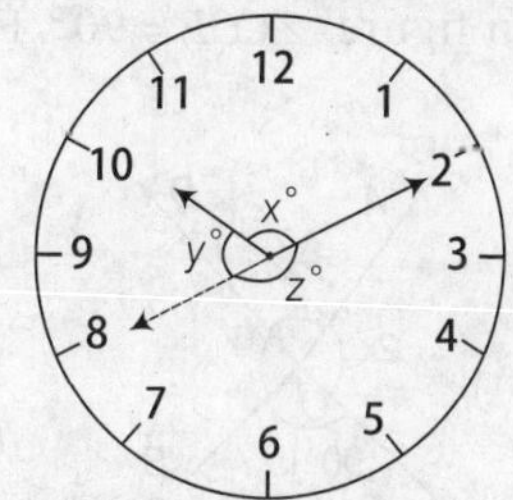

a $x = y + \frac{z}{2}$ **b** $x = \frac{y+z}{2}$
c $y = x + \frac{z}{3}$ **d** None of these

5. If two complementary angles are such that one angle is $1\frac{1}{2}$ times the other, then the smallest angle among them is

a 36° **b** 54°
c 72° **d** 18°

6. If two supplementary angles A and B are such that the difference between them is 30°, then the angles are, respectively

a 110° and 80° **b** 75° and 105°
c 80° and 100° **d** 30° and 60°

7. In the given figure, find the value of $\angle EOD$.

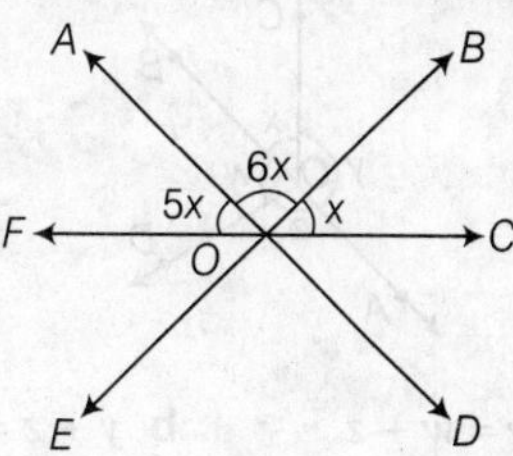

a 15° **b** 70°
c 45° **d** 90°

8. In the given figure, $\angle COD$ is a right angle. If $\angle AOC : \angle BOD = 3:2$, then $\angle BOD$ is equal to

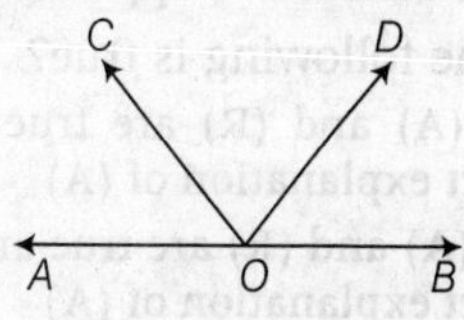

a 40° **b** 50°
c 54° **d** 36°

9. The angle formed between bisectors of angles, of a linear pair is

a 180° **b** 90°
c 45° **d** 30°

10. If two angles A and B such that A is complementary of itself and B is supplementary of itself. Then, the values of $\angle A$ and $\angle B$ are, respectively

a 45° and 180° **b** 45° and 90°
c 90° and 45° **d** 180° and 0°

11. If angle A is 5 times its complementary angle and $\frac{5}{7}$ of its supplementary angle. Then, measure of $\angle A$ is

a 105° **b** 75°
c 60° **d** 90°

12. In the given figure, PQ and RS are two intersecting lines. If $\angle POS = 75°$, then x will be

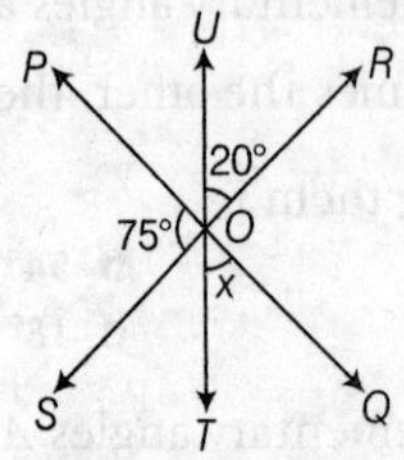

a 120° **b** 130°
c 140° **d** 85°

13. If AOB is a line, then the relation between x, y, z and w will be

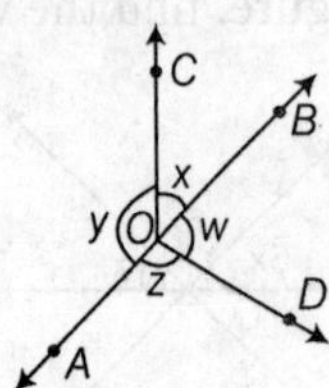

a $x + y = w + z$ **b** $y + z = x + w$
c $x + y + w + z = 180°$ **d** None of these

14. Assertion (A) Two adjacent angles always form a linear pair.
Reason (R) In a linear pair of angles, two non-common arms are opposite rays.
Which of the following is true?

a Both (A) and (R) are true and (R) is the correct explanation of (A)
b Both (A) and (R) are true and (R) is not the correct explanation of (A)
c (A) is true and (R) is false
d (A) is false and (R) is true

Directions (Q.Nos. 15-16) *Read the following information carefully and answer by choosing the correct option.*

In a circle, AB is its diameter of length 14 cm and OC is a ray originating from centre O. Two angle bisectors OP and OQ are drawn. OP bisects $\angle BOC$ and OQ bisects $\angle AOC$.

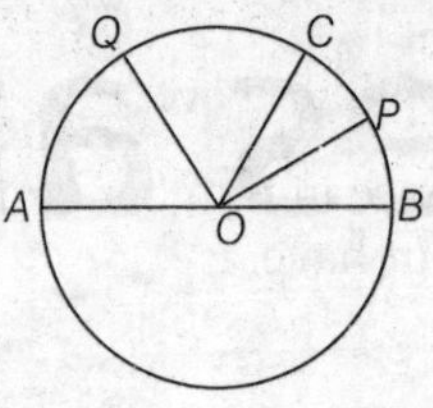

15. $\angle POQ$ is equal to

a 75° **b** 90°
c 60° **d** 120°

16. The relation between $\angle POC$ and $\angle QOC$, if $\angle AOQ$ and $\angle BOP$ are $x°$ and $y°$ respectively, is

a supplementary **b** complementary
c < 90° **d** None of the above

17. Choose the correct statement.

a The angle between the bisectors of a linear pair of angles is a right angle.
b The angle between the bisectors of a linear pair of angles is a complementary angle to itself.
c If two lines intersect, then the vertically opposite angles are supplementary.
d All of the above.

18.

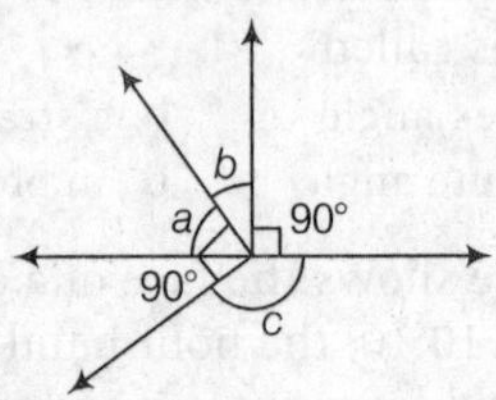

In the above figure, if $a : b = 2 : 3$, then $\angle c$ is equal to

a 54° **b** 126° **c** 36° **d** 144°

19. In the given figure, $\angle COE = 90°$. Find the value of x.

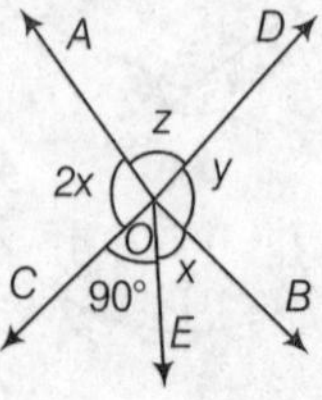

a 60° **b** 30°
c 45° **d** 10°

B. Perpendicular and Parallel Lines, Collinear and Non-collinear Points, Angles of a Triangle

1. The sum of all the angles of a three-sided polygon is

a 180°
b 360°
c 90°
d None of the above

2. The difference in number of points, a ray and line segment have, is

a 0
b 2
c 1
d infinite

3. The angles made between two perpendicular and parallel lines are, respectively

a 90° and 90°
b 90° and 180°
c 0° and 0°
d 90° and 0°

4. If the angles of a triangle are in the ratio of 2 : 3 : 4. Then, the difference between greatest and smallest angles is

a 60° **b** 40°
c 120° **d** 90°

5. The maximum number of obtuse angles a triangle can have, is

a 0
b 1
c 2
d more than 2

6. In an equilateral triangle, if one of the angles is 60°. Then, the difference between other two angles is

a 60°
b 120°
c 30°
d 0°

7. In an isosceles triangle, if the third angle is 80°, then the remaining two angles are equal to

a 50° **b** 80°
c 40° **d** 100°

8. If the angles of a triangle are in the ratio 3 : 5 : 4, then the triangle formed will be

a right angled triangle
b isosceles triangle
c scalene triangle
d obtuse angled triangle

9. Match the following:

	List I		List II
A.	In an equilateral triangle	i.	55°
B.	If (figure: 35°, x°) then, $\angle x°$ is equal to	ii.	45°
C.	A right angled isosceles triangle has other angles equal to	iii.	All angles are equal
D.	Sum of interior angles of a pentagon is	iv.	540°

Codes

	A	B	C	D
a	(i)	(ii)	(iii)	(iv)
b	(ii)	(iv)	(i)	(iii)
c	(iii)	(i)	(ii)	(iv)
d	(iv)	(iii)	(i)	(ii)

10. If the greatest angle of a triangle is 30° more than the least angle and the third angle is 15° less than the greatest angle. Then, angles of the triangle are, respectively

a 40°, 60° and 80°
b 50°, 50° and 80°
c 45°, 75° and 60°
d 30°, 60° and 90°

11. If the sides of ΔABC are produced and exterior angles are formed. Then, the sum of all three exterior angles, is

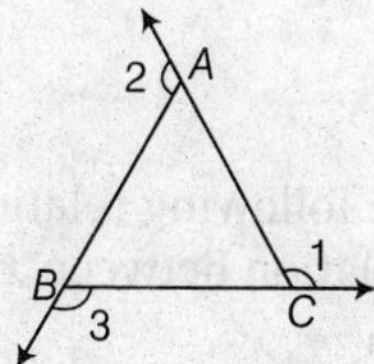

a 180°
b 360°
c 90°
d 0°

12. A triangle is formed using three points (vertices). If area of the triangle is calculated to be zero, then the points are

a non-collinear
b collinear
c Can't say
d None of the above

13. In the given figure, if OCD is a triangle in which OD and OC are equal, then what will be the value of $\angle OCD$?

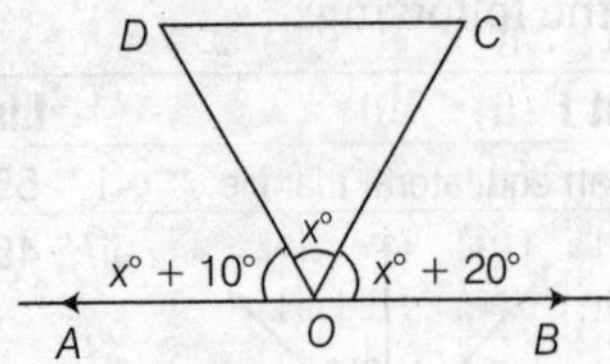

a 70°
b 50°
c 65°
d 45°

Directions (Q.Nos.14-15) *Read the following information carefully and answer by choosing the correct option.*

In the given figure, ABO is a triangle whose angles are such that

$$\frac{\angle A}{\angle AOB} = \frac{5}{2} \text{ and } \frac{\angle B}{\angle AOB} = \frac{3}{2}.$$

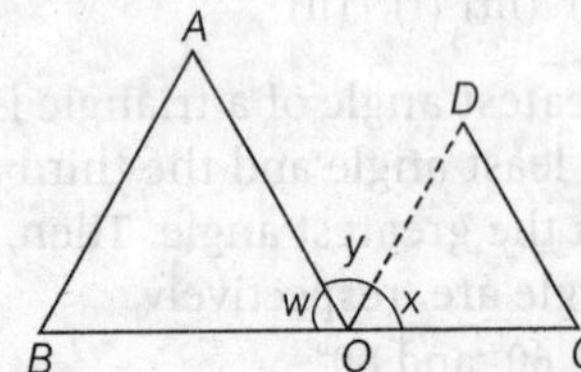

OD is angle bisector of $\angle AOC$, which is exterior angle of ΔAOB. Also, ΔOCD is an isosceles triangle in which sides OD and CD are equal.

14. What is the value of $\angle x$?
a 90°
b 72°
c 60°
d 65°

15. Which of the following relations correctly shows the relation between x and w?
a $\angle x = \angle w$
b $2\angle x = \angle w$
c $\angle x = 2\angle w$
d $\angle x = \angle w = 180°$

16.

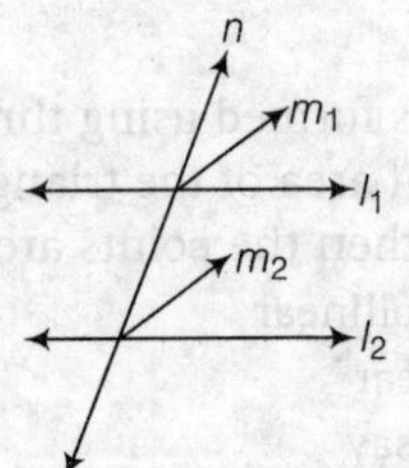

Assertion (A) If l_1 and l_2 are parallel lines and n is the transversal such that m_1 and m_2 are respectively bisector of their corresponding angles, then m_1 is parallel to m_2.

Reason (R) If a transversal intersects two lines in such a way that corresponding angles are equal, then the lines are parallel.

Which of the following is correct?
a (A) and (R) are true and (R) is the correct explanation of (A)
b (A) and (R) are true and (R) is not the correct explanation of (A)
c (A) is true and (R) is false
d Both (A) and (R) are false

17. Consider the following box and answer accordingly:

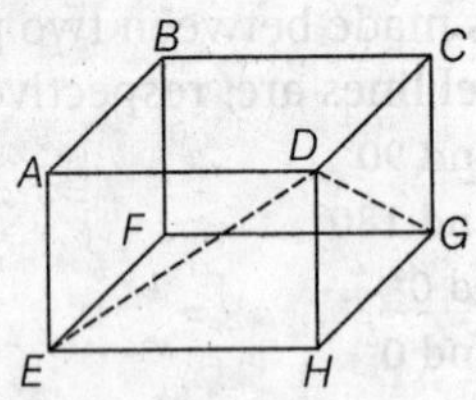

Match the following:

	List I		List II
A.	Line parallel to $\overleftrightarrow{AB}$ and contains D.	i.	AD
B.	Line perpendicular to $\overleftrightarrow{AB}$ and contains D.	ii.	CDH
C.	Plane parallel to plane ABE and contains D.	iii.	CD
		iv	DBC

Codes

	A	B	C		A	B	C
a	(i)	(ii)	(iii)	**b**	(iv)	(ii)	(i)
c	(iii)	(i)	(ii)	**d**	(ii)	(iv)	(iii)

18.

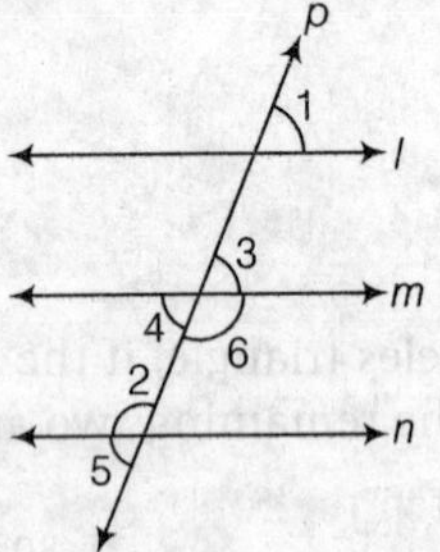

In the above figure, if $\angle 1 = 60°$, $\angle 5 = \left(\frac{2}{3}\right)$rd of right angle and $\angle 6 = \left(\frac{4}{3}\right)$rd of a right angle, then which of the following is true?
a $l \parallel m$
b $l \parallel n$
c $m \parallel n$
d All of these

C. Intersection of Two Lines, Intersection of Two Parallel Lines by a Transversal, Angles Formed and Their Properties

1. If two lines intersect each other at point O. Then, which of the following angles are equal?

- **a** Adjacent angles
- **b** Vertically opposite angles
- **c** Complementary angles
- **d** Supplementary angles

2. In the given figure, the value of y is

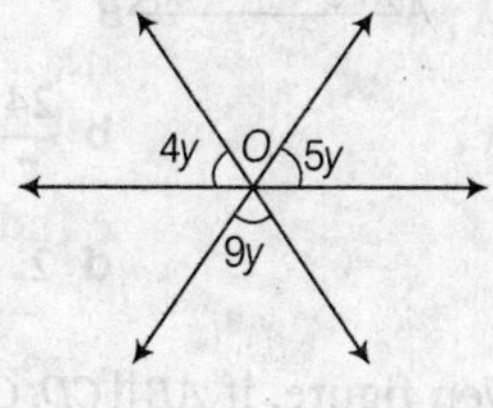

a 24° **b** 22°
c 20° **d** 10°

3. In the given figure, if $x:y=2:3$, then the value of $x+y$ is

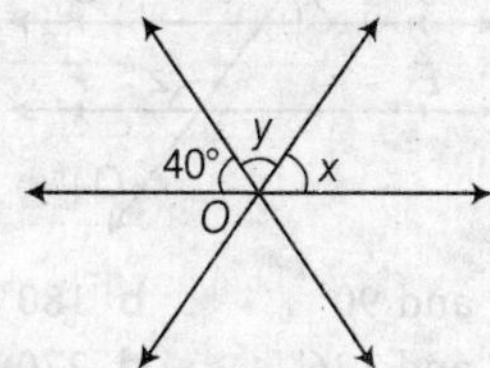

- **a** 60°
- **b** 140°
- **c** 50°
- **d** 80°

4. If a transversal intersects two parallel lines.

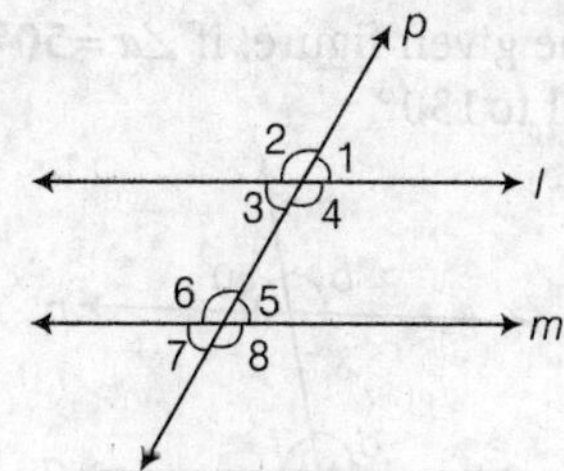

Then, match the following:

List I	List II
A. $\angle 3+\angle 6=?$	i. $\angle 2$ and $\angle 8$
B. Corresponding angle pair	ii. $\angle 3$ and $\angle 7$
C. Vertically opposite angles	iii. $\angle 5$ and $\angle 7$
D. Alternate angles	iv. $\angle 4+\angle 5$

Codes

	A	B	C	D
a	(i)	(ii)	(iii)	(iv)
b	(iv)	(ii)	(iii)	(i)
c	(ii)	(iii)	(iv)	(i)
d	(iii)	(iv)	(ii)	(i)

5. In the given figure, the value of d is

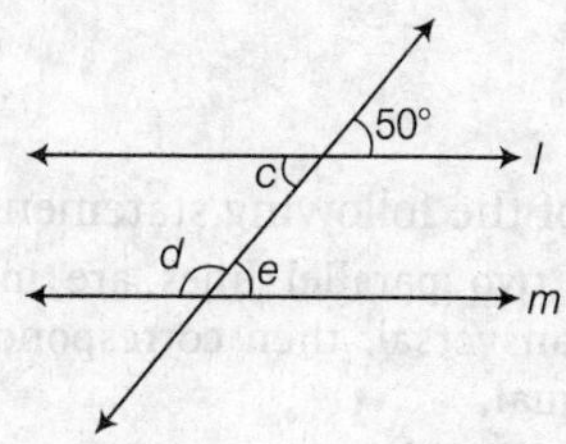

a 50° **b** 130°
c 90° **d** 100°

6. In the given figure, if $\angle A=60°$, $CE \parallel BA$ and $\angle ECD=65°$, then the value of $\angle ACB$ is

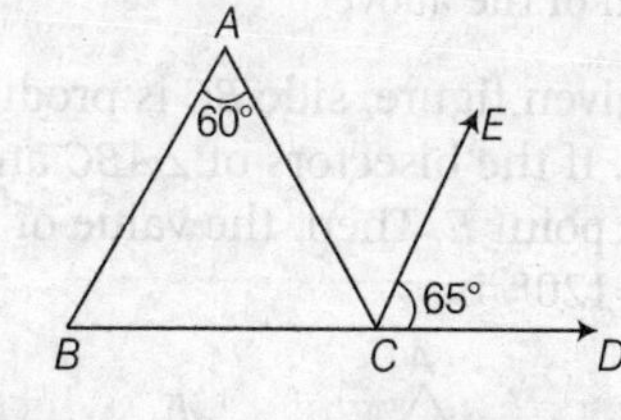

a 60° **b** 55°
c 70° **d** 90°

7. If a transversal intersects three parallel lines at different points. Then, which of the following pairs are equal?

- **a** Corresponding angles
- **b** Alternate interior angles
- **c** Vertically opposite angles
- **d** All of the above

8. In the given figure, if $PQ \perp PS$, $PQ \parallel SR$, $\angle SQR=38°$ and $\angle QRT=75°$, then the value of $|x-y|$ is

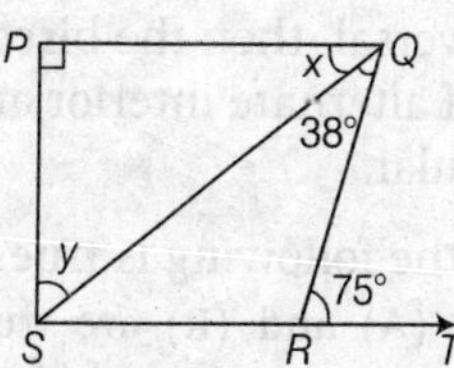

- **a** 47°
- **b** 16°
- **c** −16°
- **d** 75°

9. In the given figure, if $AB || CD$, $\angle APQ = 50°$ and $\angle PRD = 127°$, then the value of $(x + y)$ is

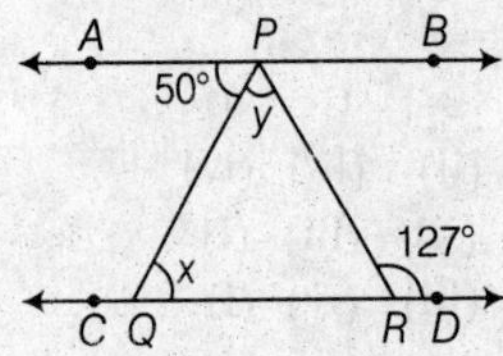

a 137°
b 127°
c 53°
d 27°

10. Which of the following statements is/are true?
a If two parallel lines are intersected by a transversal, then corresponding angles are equal.
b If two parallel lines are intersected by a transversal, then alternate interior angles are equal.
c If two parallel lines are intersected by a transversal, then interior angles on the same side are supplementary.
d All of the above

11. In the given figure, side BC is produced to a point D. If the bisectors of $\angle ABC$ and $\angle ACD$ meet at point E. Then, the value of $\angle E$, when $\angle BAC = 120°$, is

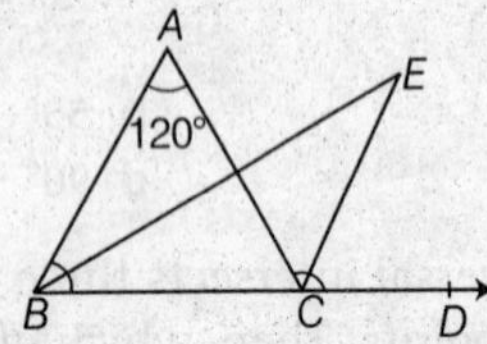

a 120°
b 60°
c 30°
d 90°

12. **Assertion** (A) If a line is perpendicular to one of the two given parallel lines, then it is also perpendicular to the other line.

Reason (R) If two lines are intersected by a transversal, then the bisectors of any pair of alternate interior angles are perpendicular.

Which of the following is true?
a Both (A) and (R) are true and (R) is the correct explanation of (A)
b Both (A) and (R) are true and (R) is not the correct explanation of (A)
c (A) is true and (R) is false
d (A) is false and (R) is true

13. In the given figure, if $l || m$, then the value of $\frac{y}{x}$ is

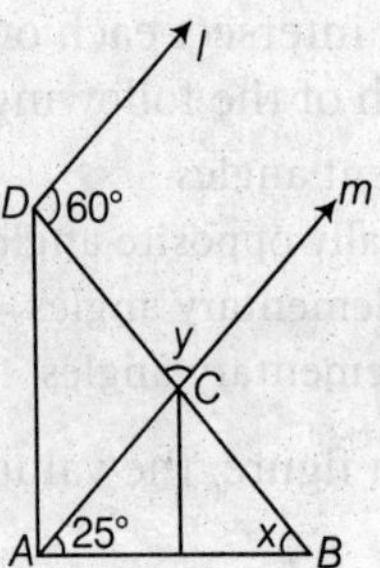

a $\frac{1}{2}$
b $\frac{24}{7}$
c $\frac{7}{24}$
d 2

14. In the given figure, if $AB || CD$, $CD || EF$ and $y : z = 3 : 7$, then the values of $(\angle x + \angle y)$ and $(\angle x + \angle z)$ are, respectively

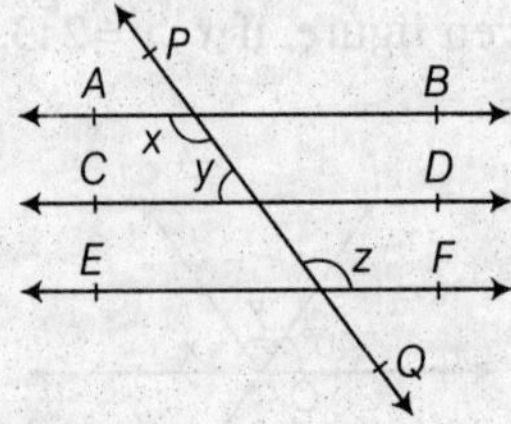

a 250° and 90°
b 180° and 252°
c 180° and 126°
d 270° and 252°

15. State 'T' for true or 'F' for false.
I. Angles forming a linear pair are complementary.
II. If two lines are perpendicular to the third line, then those two lines are perpendicular to each other.
III. In the given figure, if $\angle a = 50°$, then $\angle f$ is equal to 130°.

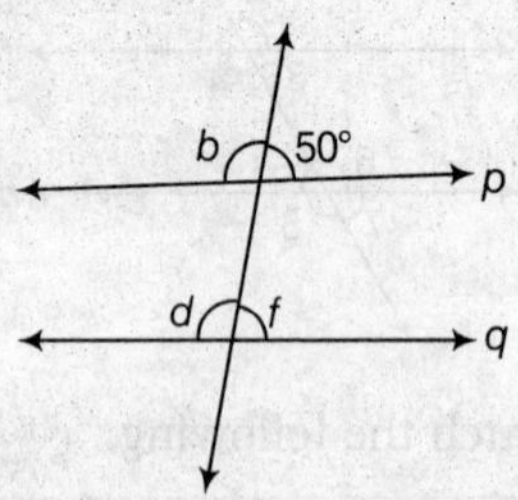

IV. A rotating ray after making a complete rotation coincides with its initial position. The angle formed is reflex angle.

Codes

	I	II	III	IV
a	F	F	F	F
b	T	T	T	T
c	F	F	T	F
d	T	T	F	F

Triangles

A. Triangles, Its Properties and Types of Triangles

1. Polygon formed by three non-collinear points having sum of interior angles equal to half of sum of angles of a rectangle is

a triangle
b circle
c pair of straight lines
d None of the above

2. Which of the following sets of measures can form a triangle?

a 70°, 90° and 25° **b** 65°, 85° and 40°
c 70°, 90° and 30° **d** 45°, 55° and 80°

3. The maximum number of acute angles, a triangle can have

a 2 **b** 1
c 3 **d** None of these

4. The maximum number of obtuse angles, a triangle can have

a 2 **b** 3 **c** 1 **d** 0

5. If two angles of a triangle are equal, then the type of triangle formed is

a an equilateral triangle
b a scalene triangle
c an isosceles triangle
d a right angled triangle

6. Which of the following statements is incorrect?

a Each angle of an isosceles right angled triangle other than right angle is 45°.
b Two triangles are congruent, if the ratio of their areas is not equal to 1.
c In a ΔABC, if $AC^2 = 2AB^2$, then ΔABC is a right angled isosceles triangle.
d None of the above

7. Which of the following figures represent isosceles triangles?

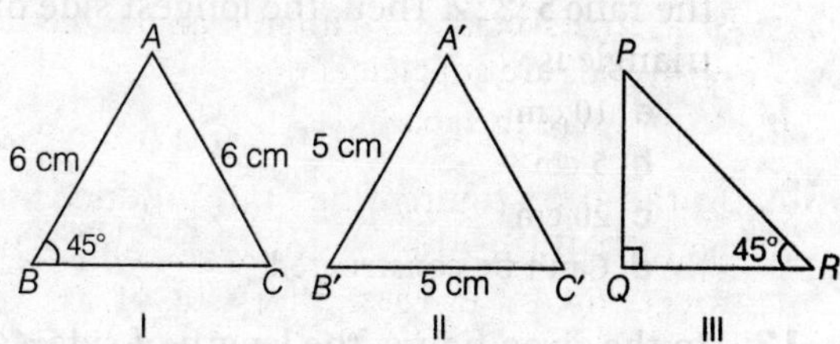

a Only I
b Both I and II
c Both II and III
d All I, II and III

8. If a triangle has lengths $AB = 4$ cm, $BC = 5$ cm and $\angle ABC = 90°$. Then, the side which is greatest among all the sides, is

a AB **b** AC
c BC **d** Can't say

9. In the given figure, if bisector of $\angle A$ divides BC in the ratio $1:1$ and $\angle D = 90°$. Then, ΔABC is of the type

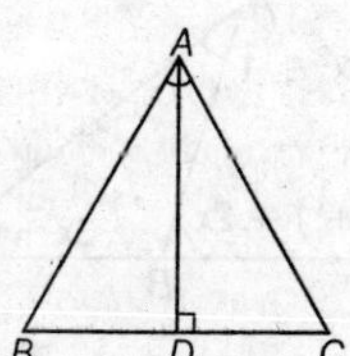

a a right angled triangle
b an isosceles triangle
c an equilateral triangle
d None of the above

10. Match the following:

List I	List II
A. Equilateral triangle is	i. Right isosceles triangle
B. In any ΔPQR, if $PQ > QR$, then	ii. $\angle R > \angle P$
C. In ΔPQR, if $\angle P = 30^\circ$, $\angle Q = 40^\circ$, then the longest side of ΔPQR is	iii. PQ
D. The triangle in which one angle is 90° and other two sides are equal, is	iv. Acute angled triangle

Codes

	A	B	C	D
a	(iv)	(ii)	(iii)	(i)
b	(i)	(ii)	(iii)	(iv)
c	(ii)	(i)	(iii)	(iv)
d	(iv)	(i)	(ii)	(iii)

11. If the sides of a triangle are in the ratio 2 : 3 : 5 and its perimeter is 20 cm and angles are in the ratio 5 : 3 : 2. Then, the longest side of the triangle is

a 10 cm
b 5 cm
c 20 cm
d Can't be constructed

12. In the given figure, the length of side AC is equal to

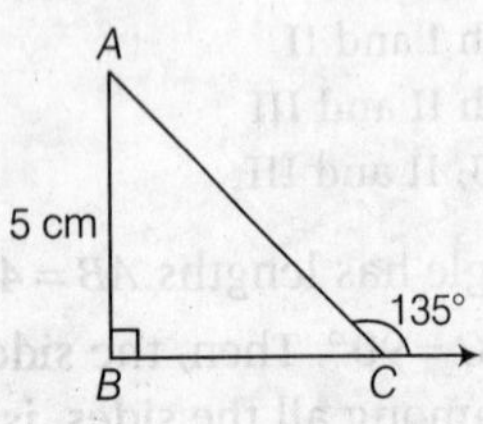

a $5\sqrt{2}$ cm
b 4 cm
c 3 cm
d 5 cm

13.

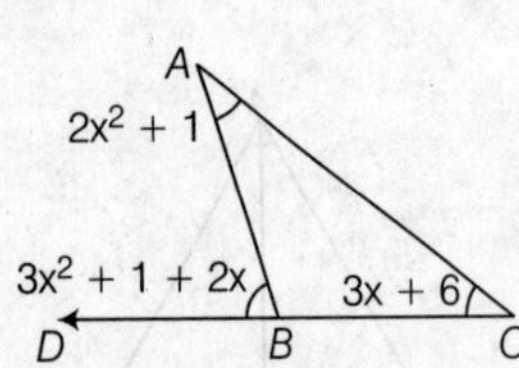

In the above figure, find the value of $\angle ABC$.

a 146°
b 126°
c 106°
d 34°

14. Which of the following figures are right angle triangles?

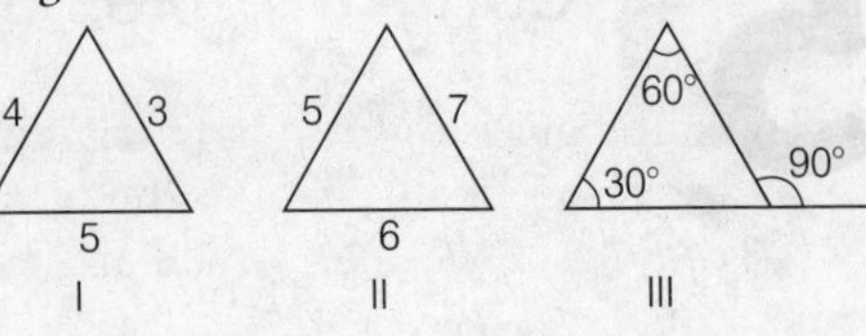

a Both I and II
b Both I and III
c Both II and III
d All I, II and III

15. In the given figure, $\angle ABC = 90^\circ$ and $AB = BC$. If BD is bisector of $\angle ABC$, then in ΔBDC, the longest side is

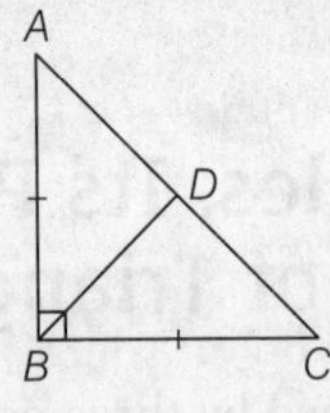

a BC
b BD
c CD
d None of these

16. Match the following :

List I	List II
A. 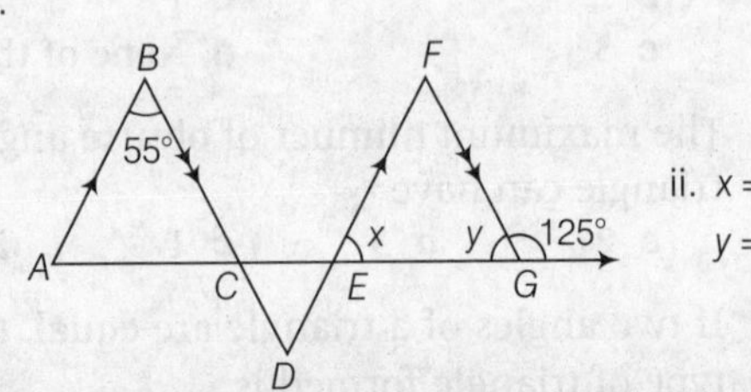	i. $x = 37^\circ$, $y = 53^\circ$
B. 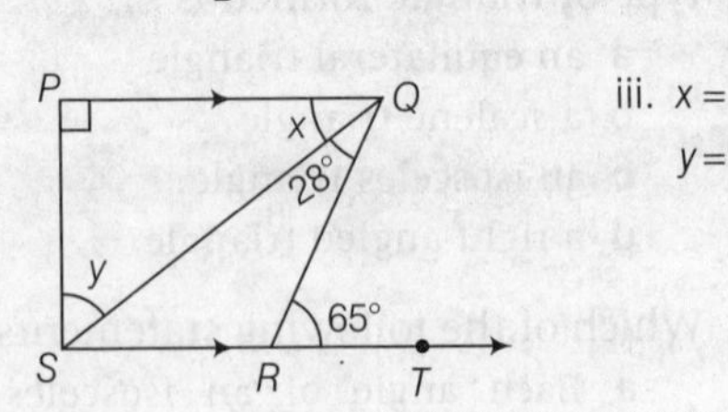	ii. $x = 12$, $y = 11$
C.	iii. $x = 70^\circ$, $y = 55^\circ$

Codes

	A	B	C
a	(i)	(ii)	(iii)
b	(ii)	(iii)	(i)
c	(i)	(iii)	(ii)
d	(ii)	(i)	(iii)

B. Congruency of Triangles, Various Criterion of Congruencies like SSS, SAS, ASA and RHS

1. In the given figures, both triangles, AB and BC are respectively equal to the PQ and QR. If $\Delta ABC \cong \Delta PQR$, then which angles must not be equal?

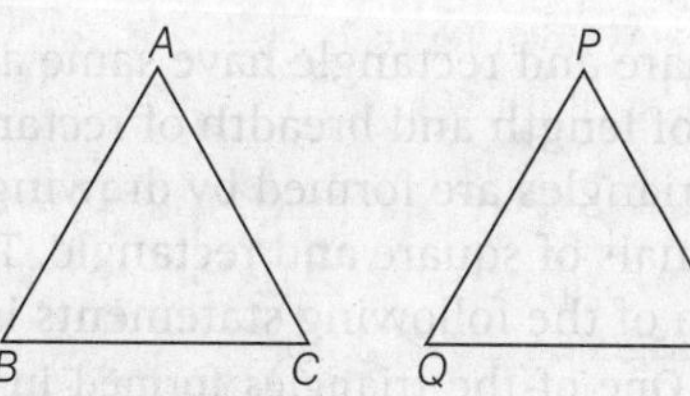

a $\angle A$ and $\angle Q$

b $\angle B$ and $\angle Q$

c $\angle A$ and $\angle P$

d $\angle C$ and $\angle R$

2. Pick the odd one out.

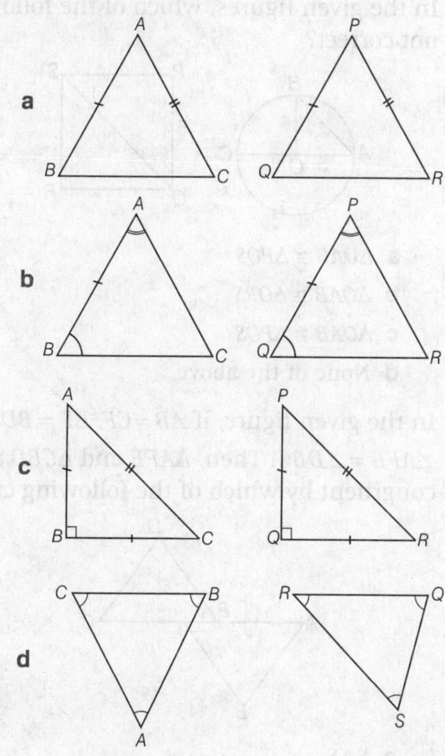

3. Which of the following criteria of congruency is shown?

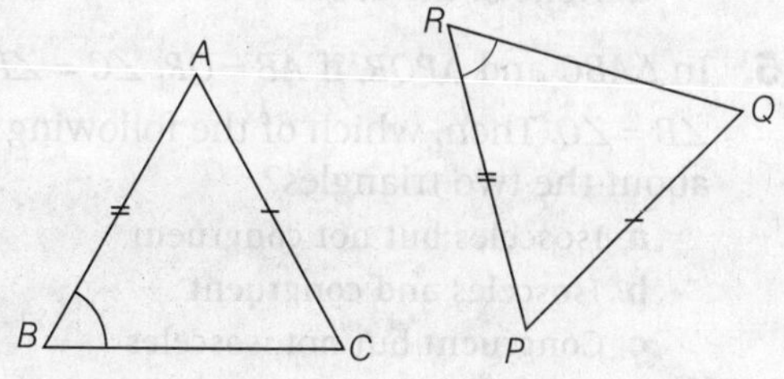

a ASA

b SSS

c SAS

d None of the above

4. In the given figure, if $\angle 1 = \angle 2$ and $\angle 3 = \angle 4$.

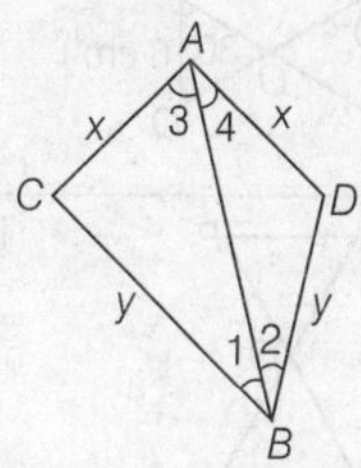

Then, by which congruence property, two ΔABC and ΔABD shown in figure are congruent?

a SAS

b SSS

c RHS

d SSA

5. If $AB = DE$, $AC = DF$, $\angle A = \angle D = 90°$ and $BC = 5$ cm, then DF is equal to

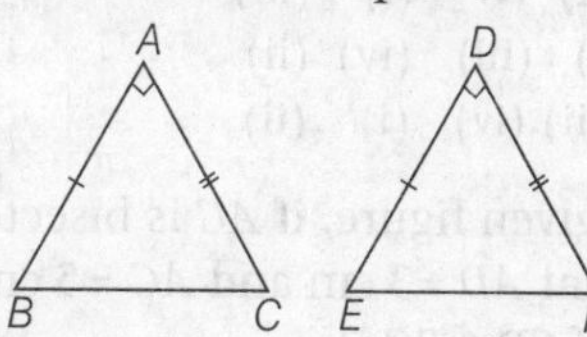

a 5 cm

b 4.5 cm

c 5.5 cm

d Can't say

6. In ΔABC and ΔDEF, $AB = DE$ and $\angle A = \angle D$. Two triangles are congruent by SAS, if

a $BC = EF$

b $AC = DF$

c $AC = EF$

d $BC = DE$

7. In the given figure, the value of $\angle z$ will be

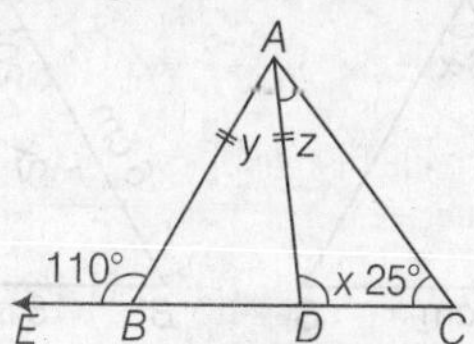

a 40°

b 110°

c 45°

d None of the above

8. Match the following:

	List I		List II
A.	A, 7 cm, 7 cm, B, M, C	i.	SAS
B.	A, P, 6 cm, 30°, 30°, 6 cm, O, B, Q	ii.	RHS
C.	A, P, O, Q, B	iii.	SSS
D.	A, 5 cm, 5 cm, B 4 cm M 4 cm C	iv.	ASA

Codes

	A	B	C	D
a	(i)	(ii)	(iii)	(iv)
b	(ii)	(iv)	(i)	(iii)
c	(i)	(iii)	(iv)	(ii)
d	(iii)	(iv)	(i)	(ii)

9. In the given figure, if AC is bisector of $\angle BAD$ such that $AD = 3$ cm and $AC = 5$ cm, then the value of $CD + BC$ is

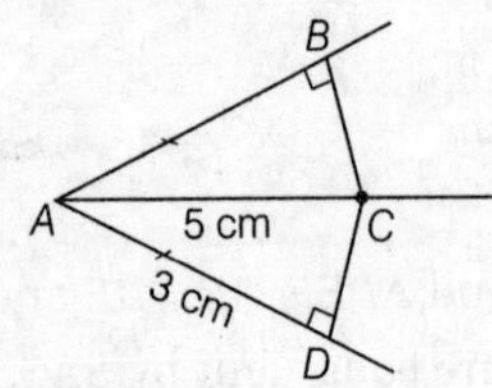

a 4 cm **b** 6 cm
c 8 cm **d** 5 cm

10. In the given figures, the value of x is

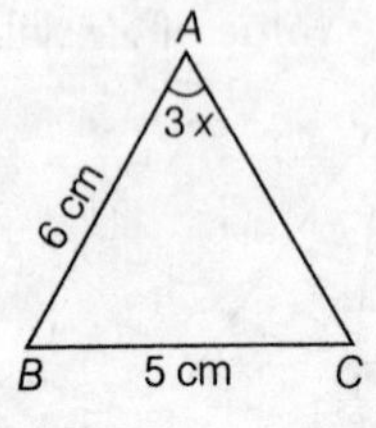

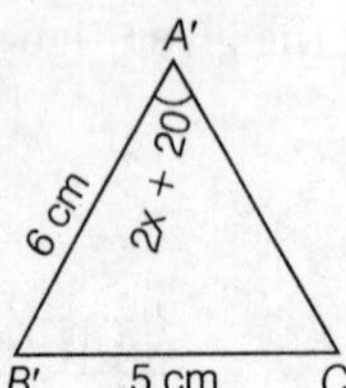

a 50°
b 60°
c 70°
d Can't say

11. In the given figure, if $ABCD$ is a square and BD and AC are two diagonals of square. Then, the number of pairs of congruent triangles is

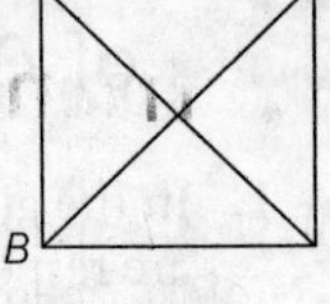

a 4 **b** 6
c 3 **d** None of these

12. A square and rectangle have same area. If the ratio of length and breadth of rectangle is 4 : 9 and triangles are formed by drawing the diagonals of square and rectangle. Then, which of the following statements is true?

a One of the triangles formed in rectangle is congruent to one formed in square
b No triangle is congruent to another
c Triangles formed in square and rectangle are congruent to its complementary part
d None of the above

13. In the given figures, which of the following is not correct?

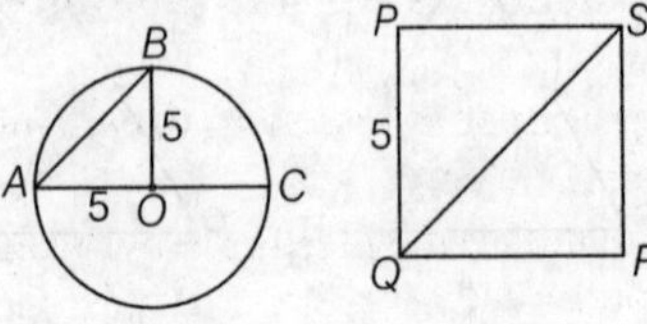

a $\Delta OAB \cong \Delta PQS$
b $\Delta OAB \cong \Delta QRS$
c $\Delta OAB \ncong \Delta PQS$
d None of the above

14. In the given figure, if $AB = CF$, $EF = BD$ and $\angle AFE = \angle DBC$. Then, ΔAFE and ΔCBD are congruent by which of the following criterion?

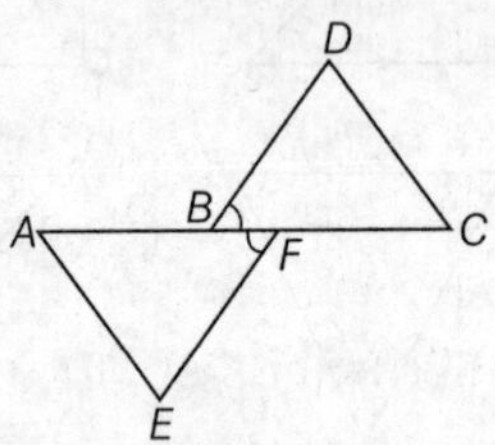

a SAS
b SSS
c ASA
d None of the above

15. In ΔABC and ΔPQR, if $AB = QR$, $\angle C = \angle P$ and $\angle B = \angle Q$. Then, which of the following is true about the two triangles?

a Isosceles but not congruent
b Isosceles and congruent
c Congruent but not isosceles
d Neither congruent nor isosceles

C. Triangle Inequalities

1. If a, b and c are sides of a triangle, then which of the following is true?

a $a - b > c$
b $c > a + b$
c $c = a + b$
d $c + a > b$

2. If measure of two sides of an isosceles triangle is 5 and 2. Then, which of the following can be the measure of the third side?

a 5
b 2
c 7
d None of the above

3. Which of the following regarding a right angled triangle is true?

a Hypotenuse is equal to the sum of other two sides
b Hypotenuse is less than the difference of the other two sides
c Sum of its two sides is always greater than its hypotenuse
d All of the above

4. In the given figure, if $AC > AB$, then which of the following is correct?

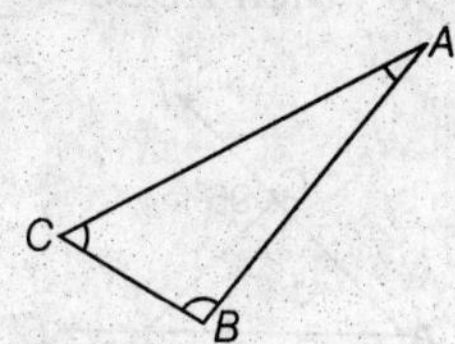

a $\angle A < \angle C$
b $\angle A < \angle B$
c $\angle C < \angle B$
d Both (b) and (c)

5. In the given figure, the value of range of x to form a triangle is

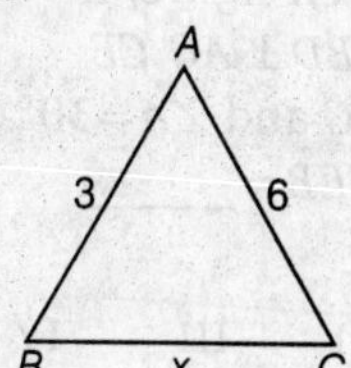

a $x \in$ real number
b $x \in [3, 6]$
c $x \leq 6$
d $3 < x < 9$

6. In the given figure, D and E are mid points of the sides AB and AC of ΔABC. If DE is line segment joining D and E and is parallel to BC. Then, what will be the value of DE, if $BC = 6$ cm?

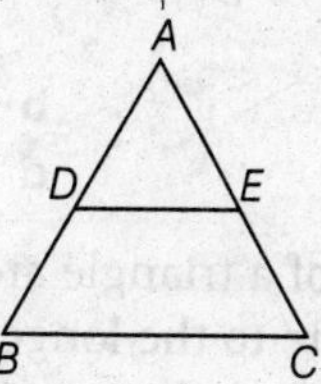

a 6 cm
b 3 cm
c 4 cm
d Can't say

7. In the given figure, if $\angle A : \angle B = 2:3$, then the value of $\angle A + \angle B - \angle C$ is

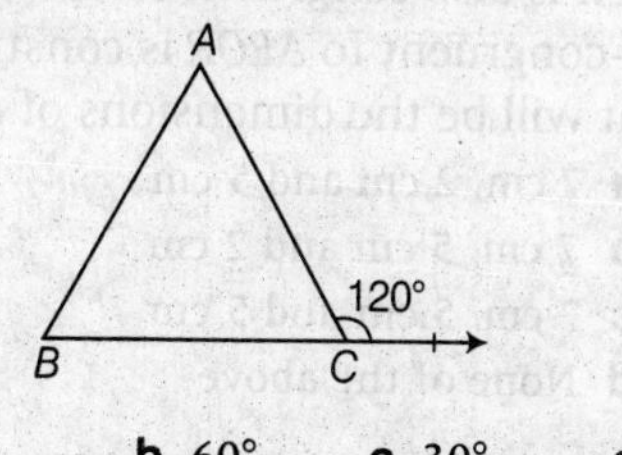

a 70° **b** 60° **c** 30° **d** 50°

8. Find the odd one from given figures.

a (A; 90°; 3; 4; B; C; 5)

b

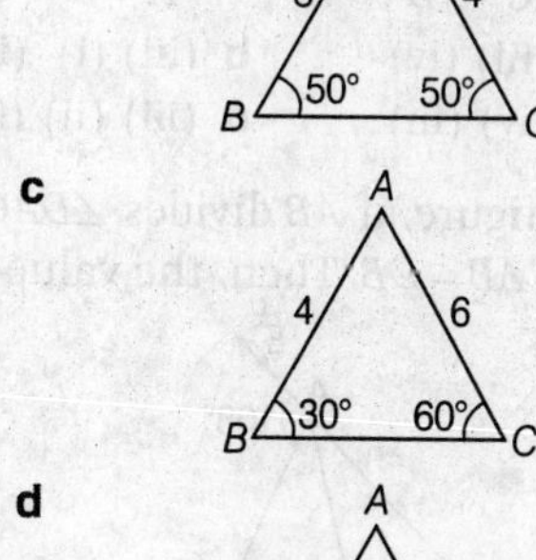

c

d (A; 3; 3; 50°; 40°; B; C)

9. 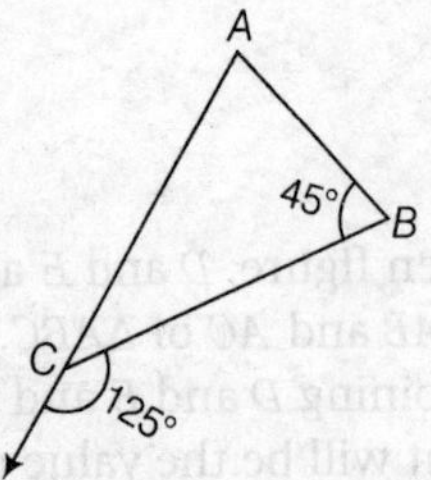

Which is the longest side of the above triangle?

a AB **b** AC

c BC **d** Can't say

10. If two sides of a triangle are unequal, then the angle opposite to the longer side is ___ and angle opposite to shorter side is ___ respectively.

a smaller, greater **b** greater, smaller

c equal, equal **d** None of these

11. Two ΔABC and ΔPQR are congruent having dimensions 7 cm, 5 cm and 2 cm. A ΔDEF, which is also congruent to the ΔABC and non-congruent to ΔPQR is constructed, then what will be the dimensions of ΔDEF?

a 7 cm, 2 cm and 5 cm

b 7 cm, 5 cm and 2 cm

c 7 cm, 5 cm and 5 cm

d None of the above

12. In ΔPQR, if $\angle P = 70°$, $\angle R = 30°$, then match the following:

List I	List II
A. PQ __ QR	i. Can't say
B. $PQ - QR$ __ $QR - PR$	ii. >
C. $\angle P - \angle R$ __ $\frac{\angle Q}{2}$	iii. <
D. $PQ + PR$ __ QR	iv. =

Codes

	A	B	C	D		A	B	C	D
a	(i)	(ii)	(iii)	(iv)	**b**	(iii)	(i)	(iv)	(ii)
c	(i)	(ii)	(iv)	(iii)	**d**	(iii)	(ii)	(i)	(iv)

13. In the given figure, if AB divides $\angle DAC$ in the ratio $1:2$ and $AB = DB$. Then, the value of x is

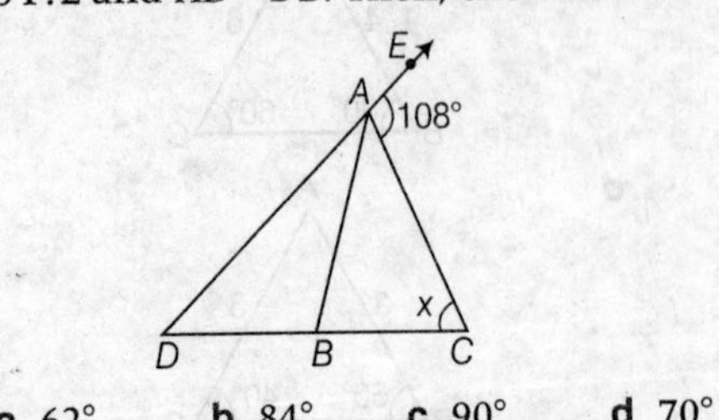

a 62° **b** 84° **c** 90° **d** 70°

14. State 'T' for true or 'F' for false.

I. If two triangles have their corresponding sides equal, then they are always congruent.

II. Two triangles are said to be congruent, if the ratio of corresponding sides is always 1.

III. If the sides of any triangle are 3 : 4 : 5, then the greatest angle is opposite to the side 5.

IV. O is a point inside the ΔABC, then $\angle BOC = \angle BAC + \angle ABO + \angle ACO$.

V. Two right angled triangles are congruent, if hypotenuse and a side of one triangle are respectively equal to the hypotenuse and a side of the other triangle.

Codes

	I	II	III	IV	V		I	II	III	IV	V
a	T	T	F	F	T	**b**	T	F	T	F	T
c	T	T	T	T	T	**d**	F	T	F	T	T

15. Fill in the blanks with the help of options, given in the box.

(i) equal, (ii) unequal, (iii) 96°, (iv) 64°, (v) isosceles, (vi) equilateral, (vii) 4 cm, (viii) 3 cm, (ix) 60°, (x) 30°

I. Sides opposite to equal angles of a triangle are ______.

II. In the given figure, if $AD = CD = BC$ and $\angle BCF = 96°$, then $\angle DBC =$ ______ .

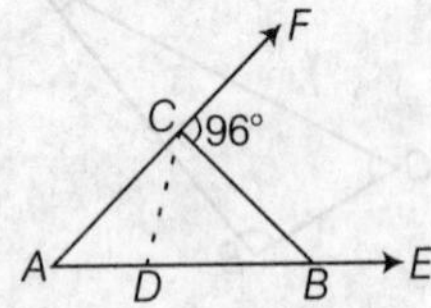

III. If a, b, c are sides of a triangle and $a^2 + b^2 + c^2 = bc + ca + ab$, then the triangle is ______ .

IV. In ΔABC, if $\angle B$ is right angle, $AC = 6$ cm and D is the mid-point of AC. Then, length of BD is ______.

V. In the given figure, if $AB \perp BC, BD \perp AC, CE$ bisects $\angle C$ and $\angle A = 30°$. Then, $\angle CEB =$ ______ .

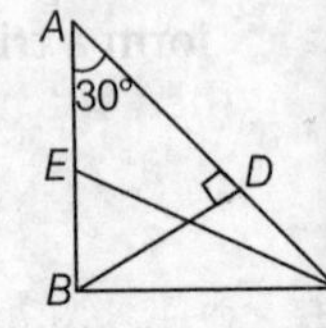

Codes

	I	II	III	IV	V
a	(i)	(iv)	(vi)	(viii)	(ix)
b	(ii)	(iii)	(iv)	(v)	(vi)
c	(vii)	(viii)	(i)	(ii)	(iii)
d	(iv)	(v)	(vi)	(vii)	(viii)

6 Quadrilaterals

A. Introduction to Quadrilaterals and Their Types

1. If the angles of a quadrilateral are in the ratio 1 : 2 : 3 : 4. Then, the angles in ascending order are

- **a** 36°, 108°, 72° and 144°
- **b** 144°, 108°, 72° and 36°
- **c** 36°, 72°, 108° and 144°
- **d** None of the above

2. A quadrilateral in which the measure of each angle is less than 180° is called

- **a** convex quadrilateral
- **b** concave quadrilateral
- **c** rectangle
- **d** trapezium

3. If two sides of a quadrilateral have a common point, then the sides are

- **a** parallel
- **b** adjacent
- **c** perpendicular
- **d** Can't say

4. In a concave quadrilateral, out of all angles, the number of angles whose measure is more than 180°, is

- **a** 2 **b** 1
- **c** 3 **d** 0

5. If the angles of a quadrilateral are x, $x-10°$, $x+30°$ and $2x$. Then, the difference between greatest angle and the smallest angle is

- **a** 20°
- **b** 10°
- **c** 40°
- **d** None of the above

6. If two segments AC and BD bisect each other at O, then $ABCD$ is a

- **a** trapezium
- **b** parallelogram
- **c** Both (a) and (b)
- **d** None of the above

7. Match the following:

List I	List II
A. A quadrilateral having all angles and sides equal.	i. Rectangle
B. A quadrilateral having one pair of parallel sides.	ii. Square
C. A quadrilateral having all sides equal.	iii. Trapezium
D. A quadrilateral whose opposite sides and opposite angles are equal.	iv. Rhombus

Codes

	A	B	C	D		A	B	C	D
a	(i)	(ii)	(iii)	(iv)	**b**	(ii)	(iii)	(iv)	(i)
c	(ii)	(iv)	(i)	(ii)	**d**	(ii)	(iii)	(i)	(iv)

8. In the following figure, the values of x and y are

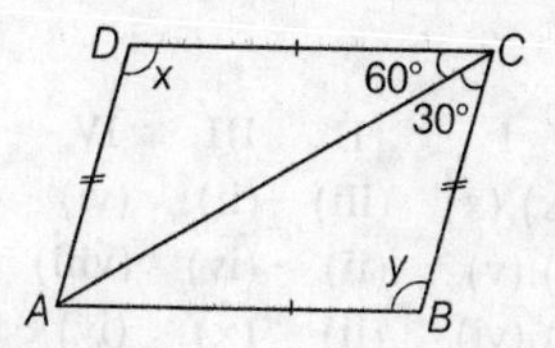

- **a** $x = y = 90°$ **b** $x + y = 90°$
- **c** $y - x = 100°$ **d** $x - y = 90°$

9. In the given figure, $AE = BC$ and $AE \parallel BC$ and the three sides AB, CD and ED are equal in length. If $\angle A = 102°$, then the value of $\angle BCD$ is

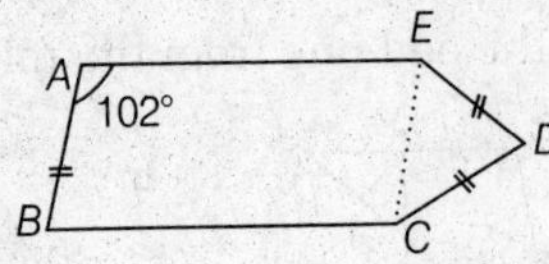

a 138° **b** 162°
c 88° **d** None of these

10. If the difference between the interior and exterior angles of a regular polygon is 120°, then the number of sides in the polygon is

a 4 **b** 6 **c** 8 **d** 12

11. In the following quadrilateral $ABCD$, AO and BO are the bisectors of $\angle A$ and $\angle B$, respectively. If $\angle A : \angle B : \angle C : \angle D = 1:2:3:4$, then the value of $\angle AOB$ is

a 108° **b** 125° **c** 126° **d** 60°

12. In a parallelogram, if two opposite angles are $(3x - 10°)$ and $(50° - 3x)$. Then, the difference between greatest and smallest angles is

a 0 **b** 140° **c** 120° **d** 180°

13. Fill in the blanks with the help of options, given in the box.

(i) adjacent, (ii) parallelogram, (iii) congruent, (iv) quadrilateral, (v) 180°, (vi) 130°, (vii) 6 cm, (viii) 5 cm, (ix) equal, (x) right, (xi) left, (xii) unequal

I. The diagonals of a square are ___ and bisect each other at ___ angle.

II. The diagonals of a square divide it in two ___ triangles.

III. The figure formed by joining the mid-points of the consecutive sides of a quadrilateral having opposite sides parallel is ___.

IV. In a trapezium $ABCD$, $AB \parallel CD$. If $\angle A = 50°$, then $\angle D =$ ___.

V. In a rectangle $ABCD$, two diagonals AC and BD intersect at O. If $AC = 5$ cm, then the length of BD is ___.

Codes

	I	II	III	IV	V
a	(ix),(x)	(iii)	(ii)	(vi)	(viii)
b	(i),(v)	(ii)	(iv)	(viii)	(x)
c	(i),(vi)	(ii)	(x)	(iv)	(viii)
d	(iii),(i)	(vi)	(iv)	(x)	(ii)

14. State 'T' for true or 'F' for false.

I. Every square is a rectangle.

II. If all angles of a quadrilateral are equal, then it is a parallelogram.

III. The sum of all interior angles of a quadrilateral is 180°.

IV. A rhombus is a quadrilateral, whose all sides are equal and each angle is 90°.

V. If three angles of a quadrilateral are equal, then it is a parallelogram.

Codes

	I	II	III	IV	V
a	T	T	T	T	F
b	T	F	T	F	T
c	T	T	F	F	T
d	F	F	T	F	F

15. If the sides BA and DC of quadrilateral $ABCD$ are produced as shown in the following figure, then the value of $x + y$ is

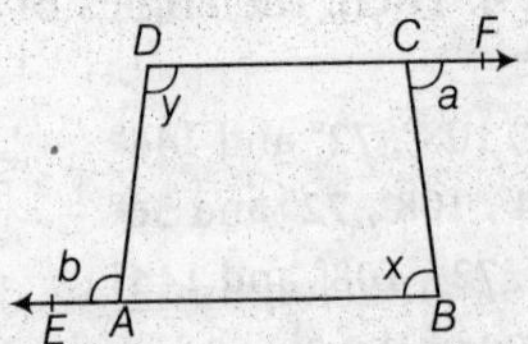

a $2a$

b $2b$

c $a - b$

d $a + b$

16. $ABCD$ is a parallelogram. E and F are mid-points of AB and CD, respectively. If GH is any line intersecting AD, EF and BC at G, P and H respectively such that $GH \parallel AB$. Then, the point P is dividing GH in the ratio

a 1 : 2 **b** 2 : 1
c 1 : 1 **d** 2 : 3

17. **Assertion** (A) If an angle of a parallelogram is two-third of the adjacent angle, then two angles of parallelogram are 106° and 74°.

Reason (R) Adjacent angles of a parallelogram are supplementary.

Which of the following is true?

a (A) is true and (R) is false

b (A) is false and (R) is true

c Both (A) and (R) are true and (R) is correct explanation of (A)

d Both (A) and (R) are true and (R) is not correct explanation of (A)

B. Properties of Parallelogram and Mid-point Theorem

1. In a ΔABC, if D and E are the mid-points of sides AB and AC respectively, the quadrilateral formed is a

a rectangle
b rhombus
c trapezium
d square

2. In the parallelogram shown below, each of its diagonals has maximum value (length) is

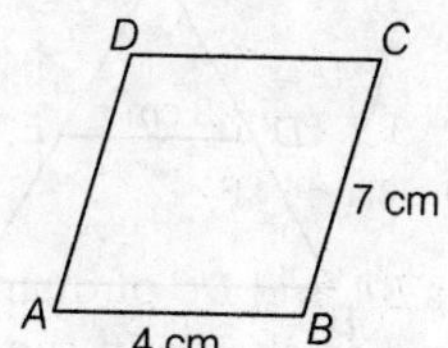

a <11 cm
b <7 cm
c $<\sqrt{65}$ cm
d >12 cm

3. *ABCD* is a parallelogram. If its diagonals are equal, then the value of $\angle ABC$ is

a 90° **b** 120° **c** 75° **d** 60°

4. In a parallelogram *ABCD*, if $AB = y+1$, $CD = 2x+5$, $AD = y+5$ and $BC = 3x-4$. Then, $AB : BC$ is equal to

a 12 : 11 **b** 71 : 21
c 31 : 35 **d** 4 : 7

5.

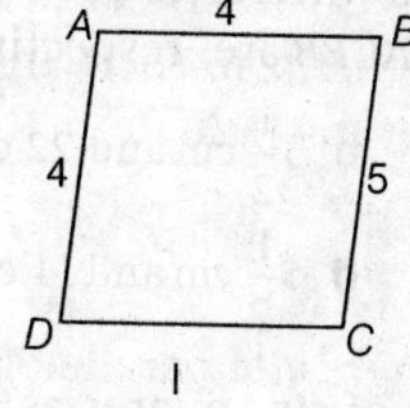

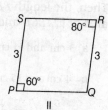

I

S R 80° 3 3 60° P Q

II

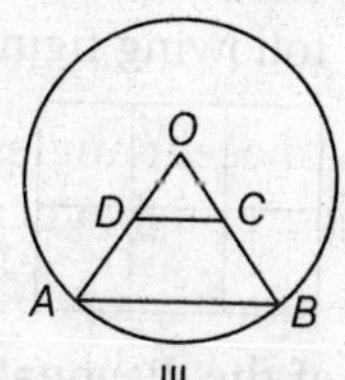

III

Which of the following is/are not a parallelogram?

a I
b II
c III
d All of the above

6. Choose the odd one from the following figures.

a

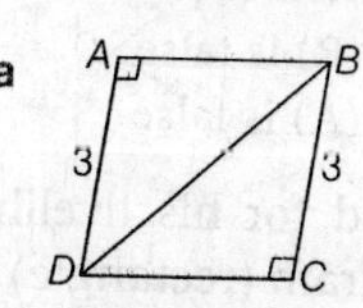

b

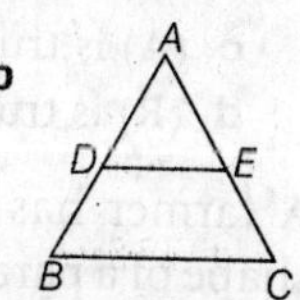

c

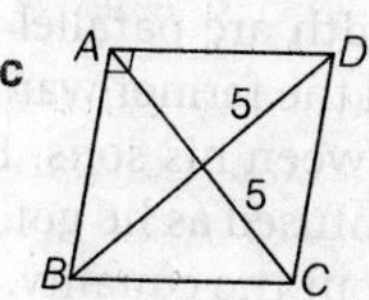

d

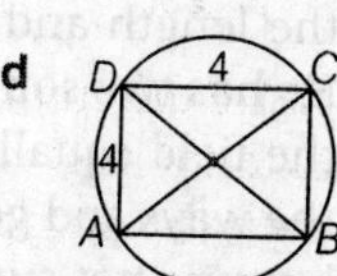

7. In the following figure, if *ABCD* is a rectangle and *P*, *Q* are the mid-points of *AD*, *DC* respectively. Then, the ratio of lengths *PQ* and *AC* is equal to

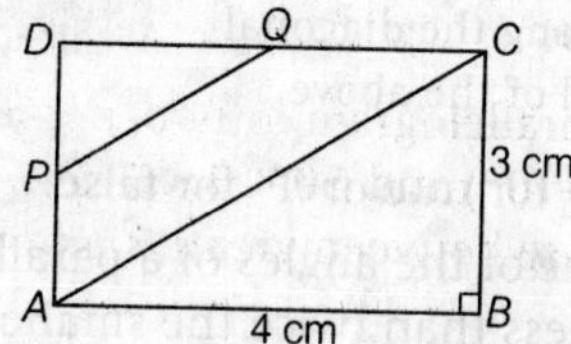

a 1 : 1 **b** 1 : 2
c 2 : 1 **d** 3 : 2

8. In the following figure, if *D*, *E* and *F* are respectively the mid-points of the sides *BC*, *AC* and *AB* of ΔABC. Then, which of the following is/are true?

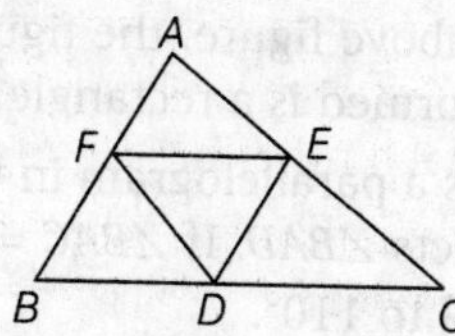

I. *BDEF* is a parallelogram.

II. ar $(\Delta DEF) = \frac{1}{4}$ ar (ΔABC)

III. ar $(\square BDEF) = \frac{1}{4}$ ar (ΔABC)

IV. ar $(\square BDEF)$ = ar $(\square DEAF)$

a Only I
b I and III
c I, II and IV
d All I, II, III and IV

9. **Assertion** (A) The area of two triangles formed by diagonals of a parallelogram are equal.

Reason (R) Diagonals of a parallelogram divide it into two congruent triangles.

Which of the following is true?

a Both (A) and (R) are true and (R) is the correct explanation of (A)

b Both (A) and (R) are true and (R) is not the correct explanation of (A)

c (A) is true and (R) is false

d (R) is true and (A) is false

10. A farmer has a field for his livelihood in the shape of a parallelogram (rectangle) that means the length and breadth are parallel and equal. He has two sons and the farmer wants to divide the field equally between his sons. He thought the ways and got confused as he got three ideas but was not sure about the equality. Finally, he gave all the options to his sons and asked them to choose the best way. What will be the best way so that no dispute should occur?

a Half way along the length

b Half way along the breadth

c Along the diagonal

d All of the above

11. State 'T' for true or 'F' for false.

I. If one of the angles of a parallelogram is $60°$ less than twice the smallest angle, then the smallest angle is $80°$.

II. The line segment joining the mid-points of the sides of an equilateral triangle divides it into three congruent triangles.

III. In the given figure, if the radius of circle is 4 cm, then the length of CD is 8 cm.

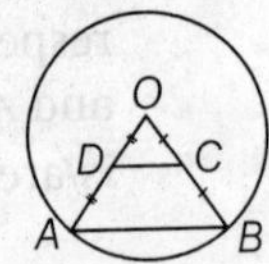

IV. In the above figure, the figure $ABCD$ formed is a rectangle.

V. $ABCD$ is a parallelogram in which diagonal AC bisects $\angle BAD$. If $\angle BAC = 35°$, then $\angle ABC$ is equal to $110°$.

Codes

	I	II	III	IV	V
a	F	F	T	F	F
b	T	F	F	F	T
c	T	F	T	T	T
d	F	F	F	F	T

12. Fill in the blanks with the help of options, given in the box.

(i) 1.5 cm, (ii) square, (iii) $40°$, (iv) 3 cm, (v) 6 cm, (vi) trapezium, (vii) $60°$, (viii) 4 cm

I. In the following figure, S, T and U are mid-points of the given sides. If the line joining QT and RS intersect SU and TU at L and M respectively, then $LM =$ ____ .

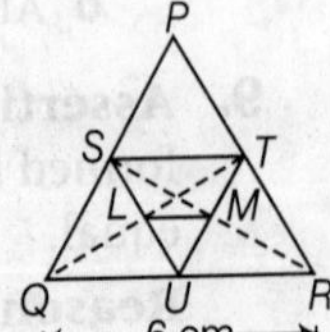

II. In the following figure, $ABCD$ is parallelogram in which P is mid-point of CD and PA is bisector of $\angle DAB$, then $PC =$ ____, if $BC = 4$ cm.

III. In the following figure, $ABCD$ is a parallelogram. If $\angle DAB = 60°$ and $\angle DBC = 80°$, then $\angle CDB =$ ____ .

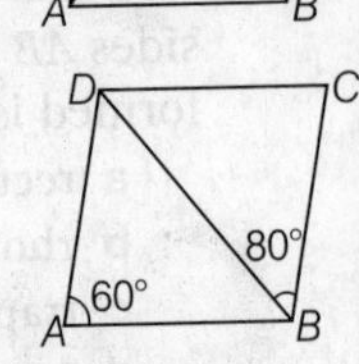

IV. In the following figure, if D and E are mid-points of AB and AC, then $BC =$ ____.

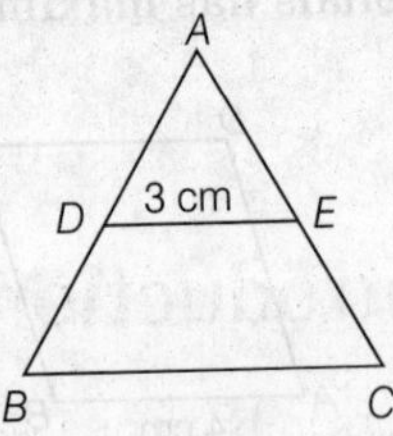

Codes

	I	II	III	IV
a	(i)	(viii)	(iii)	(v)
b	(ii)	(iii)	(iv)	(v)
c	(v)	(iv)	(iii)	(ii)
d	(i)	(ii)	(iv)	(v)

13. In the following figure, DC is parallel to AB and DA is perpendicular to AB. If $DC = 1$ cm, $DA = 4$ cm, $AB = 10$ cm and the area of quadrilateral $APCD$ equals the area of ΔCPB is equal to half of area of quadrilateral $ABCD$.

Then, the length PB and difference between area of $\square ABCD$ and as ΔCPB are, respectively

a 3 cm and 11 cm^2

b $3\frac{1}{2}$ cm and 22 cm^2

c 4 cm and 15 cm^2

d $5\frac{1}{2}$ cm and 11 cm^2

14. A rectangle is made up of six squares as shown in the following figure.

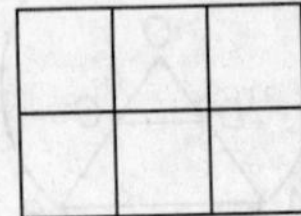

If the length of the diagonal of one of the squares is 2. Then, the length of diagonal of rectangle is

a $2\sqrt{6}$

b $3\sqrt{2}$

c $\sqrt{26}$

d 5

Circle

A. Introduction to Circle and Basic Terminology

1. If a person is on one side of circle and another is exactly at the point which is vertically (through centre) opposite. Then, the distance between them is called

a radius
b centre
c diameter
d chord

2. From three non-collinear points, how many circles can be drawn?

a 0
b 1
c 2
d Infinite

3. Two circles are congruent. If the radius of one circle is 5 cm, then the diameter of second circle is

a 5 cm
b 10 cm
c 15 cm
d Can't say

4. If the measure of an arc is 170°, then the arc is

a major arc
b minor arc
c semi-circle
d None of the above

5. Two circles having different radii intersect each other at various points. The maximum number of points can be

a 1 **b** 2
c 3 **d** many

6. Match the following:

List I | **List II**

A.
A r_1 r_2 B

i. $r_1 + r_2 > AB$

B.

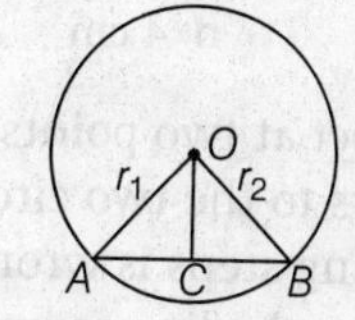

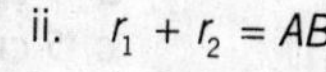

C.

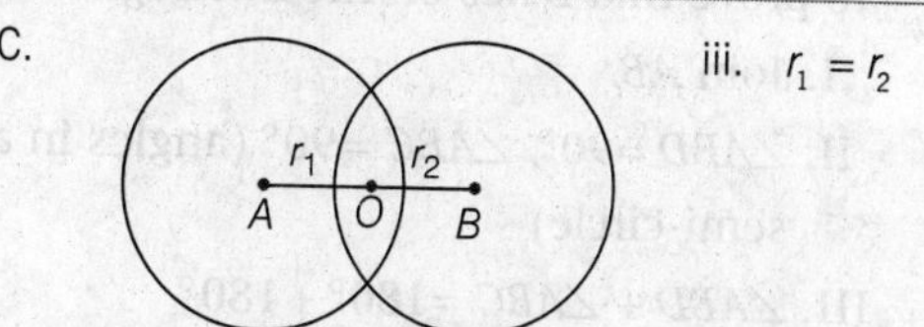

iii. $r_1 = r_2$

D.

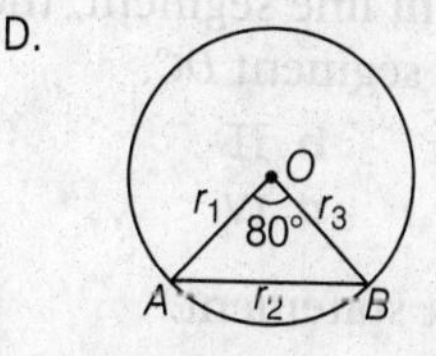

iv. $r_1 < r_2$

Codes

	A	B	C	D
a	(i)	(ii)	(iii)	(iv)
b	(ii)	(iii)	(i)	(iv)
c	(ii)	(iii)	(iv)	(i)
d	(ii)	(iv)	(i)	(iii)

7. Length of the chord of a circle is 1.5 times its radius. If the diameter of the circle is 6 m, then the length of the chords, which is equidistant from the centre w.r.t. to the given chord, is

a equal
b different
c sum of both chords is less than the third chord
d Can't say

8. If AB is a chord of length 24 cm of a circle with centre O and radius 13 cm, then the distance of the chord from the centre is

a 5 cm
b 6 cm
c $\sqrt{407}$ cm
d 7 cm

9. In the following figure, if $AB = 8$ cm, $DE = 8$ cm and $CD = 5$ cm, then CF is equal to

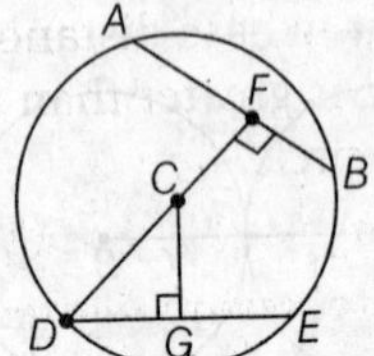

a 3 cm **b** 2 cm
c 5 cm **d** 4 cm

10. If two circles intersect at two points A, B and AD, AC are diameters to the two circles. Then, which of the following steps is wrong in order to prove that B lies on the line segment DC?

I. Join AB.
II. $\angle ABD = 90°$, $\angle ABC = 90°$ (angles in a semi-circle)
III. $\angle ABD + \angle ABC = 180° + 180°$
IV. If DBC is a straight line segment, then B lies on the line segment DC.

a I **b** II
c III **d** IV

11. Choose the incorrect statement.

a If two circles intersect at two points, then the line through the centres is the perpendicular bisector of the common chord.
b Of any two chords of a circle, the one which is nearer to the centre, is larger.
c The arc of a circle subtending a right angle at any point of the circle in its alternate segment is a semi-circle.
d None of the above.

12. PQ and RS are two parallel chords of circle whose centre is at O and radius is 10 cm. If $PQ = 16$ cm and $RS = 12$ cm, then find out the distances between PQ and RS, when they lie on the same side and on opposite side of O, respectively.

a 14 cm and 4 cm
b 2 cm and 12 cm
c 2 cm and 14 cm
d None of the above

13. In the following figure, if two chords AB and CD are at equal distance from centre O of the circle. Then, the area of ΔOCD, when area of ΔAOB is 12 cm^2 and radius is 4 cm, is

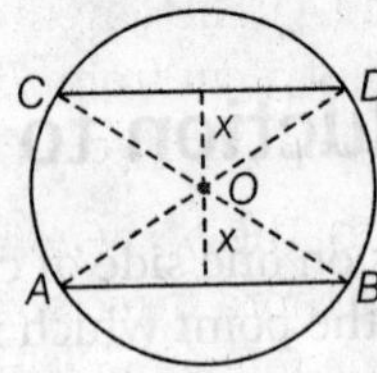

a 24 cm^2
b 12 cm^2
c 6 cm^2
d Can't say

14. In the following figure, two intersecting circles with centres O and O', intersect each other at points A and B. The length of their common chords is 12 cm and the radii are respectively 10 cm and 8 cm. Find the distance between their centres.

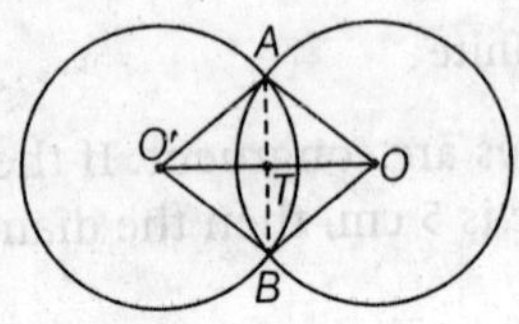

a $(\sqrt{8} + \sqrt{28})$ cm
b $(8 + \sqrt{28})$ cm
c $(8 + 2\sqrt{7})$ cm
d None of the above

15. In a circle of radius 17 cm, two parallel chords are drawn on opposite side of diameter. The distance between the chords is 23 cm. If the length of one chord is 16 cm and the perpendicular distance from centre to the chords are equal. Then, the length of the other chord is

a 34 cm
b 15 cm
c 16 cm
d 30 cm

16. In the following figure, $\angle AOB$, the angle subtended by chord AB of the circle, is 60°. If $OA = 5$ cm, then the length of chord AB is

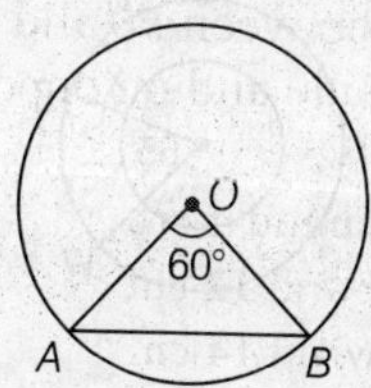

a $\frac{5}{2}$ cm **b** $\frac{5\sqrt{3}}{2}$ cm

c 5 cm **d** $\frac{5\sqrt{3}}{4}$ cm

17. Assertion (A) The length of a chord, which is at distance of 5 cm from the centre of a circle of radius 10 cm, is 17 cm (approx).

Reason (R) The perpendicular from centre of a circle to a chord bisects the chord.

Which of the following is true?

a Both (A) and (R) are true and (R) is the correct explanation of (A)

b Both (A) and (R) are true and (R) is not the correct explanation of (A)

c (A) is true and (R) is false

d (A) is false and (R) is true

18. In the following figure, if $AB = 7$ cm, $BC = 8$ cm and $CA = 5$ cm. Then, the radius of circles are in the ratio

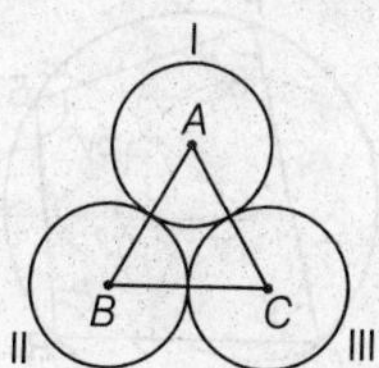

a 1 : 2 : 3

b 5 : 7 : 8

c 2 : 5 : 3

d None of the above

19. State 'T' for true or 'F' for false.

I. Diameter is the shortest chord of the circle.

II. Of any two chords of circle, the one which is nearer to the centre, is longer.

III. Two chords of a circle which are equidistant from the centre of the circle, are equal.

IV. Two congruent circles have equal perimeter and different area.

V. Two circles can intersect at more than two points.

Codes

	I	II	III	IV	V
a	F	T	T	F	F
b	T	T	F	T	T
c	F	T	F	T	F
d	T	F	T	F	T

20. Fill in the blanks with the help of options, given in the box.

(i) interior, (ii) exterior, (iii) radius, (iv) diameter, (v) 4 cm, (vi) 2 cm, (vii) 12 cm (chord), (viii) 16 cm (chord length), (ix) 1:1, (x) 1:2

I. A point, whose distance from the centre of a circle is greater than its radius, lies on the ___ of circle.

II. The longest chord of the circle is ___.

III. In the following figure, if $PQ = 4$ cm, then $QR =$ ___.

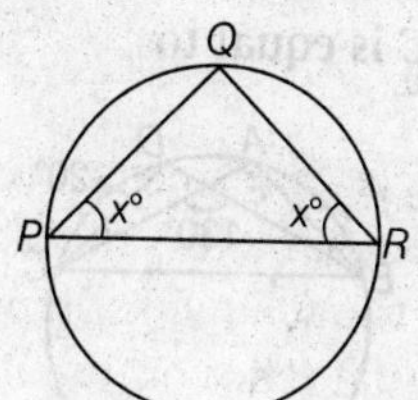

IV. If two chords of a circle are 16 cm and 12 cm long, then the greater angle subtended at centre made is by ___ chord.

V. In a circle with centre O, if AB and CD are two diameters perpendicular to each other. Then, the length of chord AC to length of chord BD is ___.

Codes

	I	II	III	IV	V
a	(i)	(ii)	(iii)	(iv)	(v)
b	(ii)	(iv)	(v)	(viii)	(ix)
c	(ii)	(v)	(vi)	(ix)	(i)
d	(iii)	(ix)	(iv)	(ii)	(vi)

B. Arc Properties of a Circle and Cyclic Quadrilateral

1. Angle made between the minute and hour hands of a watch (circular dial) when the time is 3 O'clock, is

a 60°
b 90°
c 120°
d 30°

2. In the following figure, AB and BC are two chords of the circle with centre O, where $\angle BAO = 40$; $\angle BCO = 30°$, then $\angle AOC$ is equal to

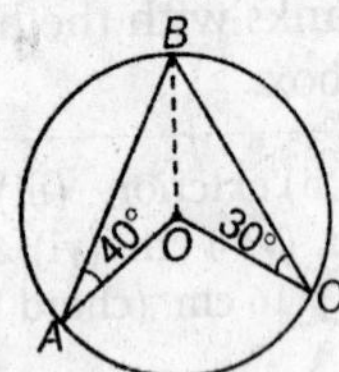

a 120°
b 70°
c 140°
d None of the above

3. In the following figure, A, B, C and D are four points on the circle. If AC and BD intersect at a point E such that $\angle BEC = 130°$ and $\angle ECD = 20°$. Then, $\angle BAC$ is equal to

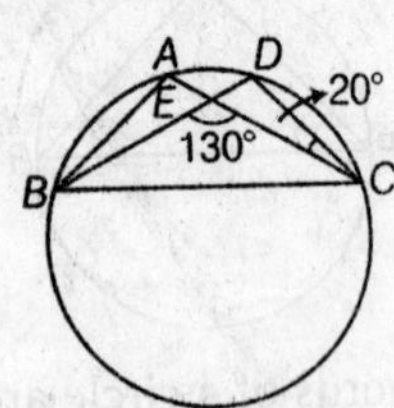

a 50°
b 160°
c 110°
d None of the above

4. Pick the odd one out.

a

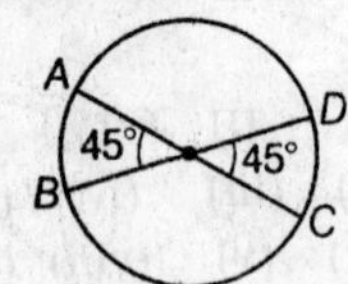

b

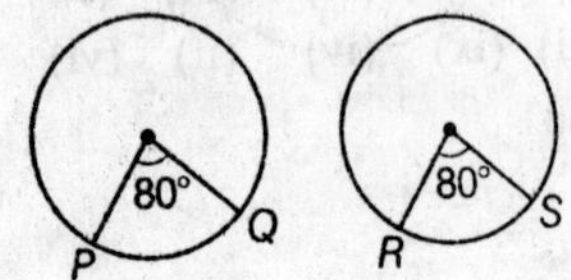

c

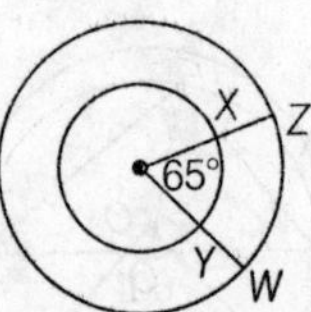

d Can't say

5. The circumference of a circle is 40 cm. Then, the length of an arc of 90° is

a 12 cm
b 11 cm
c 24 cm
d 10 cm

6. In the following figure, if two chords AB and CD of a circle intersect each other at a point E (not the centre) such that $\angle BAC = 45°$ and $\angle BED = 120°$. Then, the value of $\angle ABD$ is

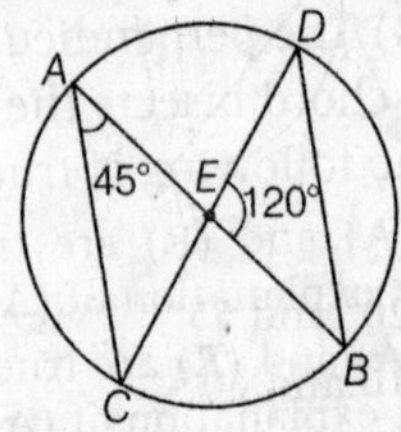

a 15°
b 30°
c 45°
d 60°

7. In the following figure, if $PQRS$ is a cyclic quadrilateral with respective angles shown in the figure. Then, the ratio of x and y is

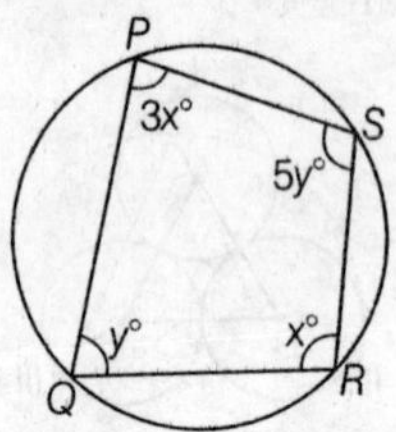

a 2:3
b 3:2
c 1:2
d None of these

8. In the following figure, the values of x and y are, respectively

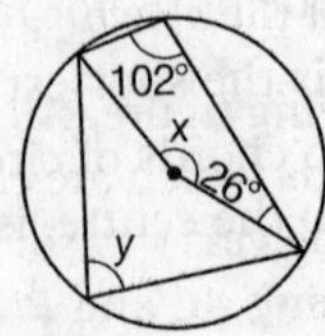

a 160° and 78°
b 156° and 78°
c 160° and 80°
d 144° and 72°

9. In the following figure, if AC is a diameter of the circle and $\widehat{AXB}$ is equal to one-third of $\widehat{BYC}$. Then, $\angle BOC$ is equal to

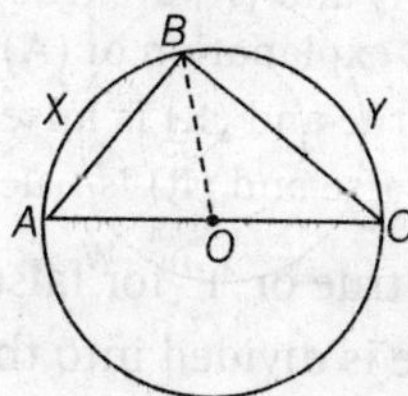

a 90° **b** 45°
c 135° **d** 75°

10. In the following figure, the values of $\angle 4$, $\angle 5$ and $\angle 6$ are, respectively

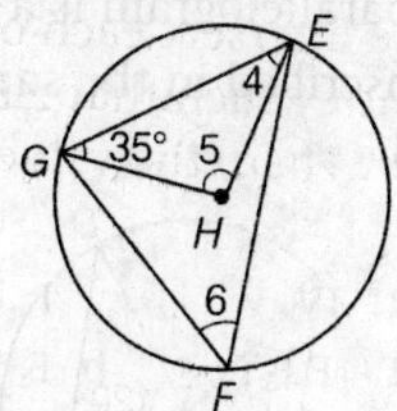

a 35°, 120° and 55°
b 35°, 110 and 60°
c 30°, 120° and 55°
d 35°, 110° and 55°

11. In the following figure, a quadrilateral is drawn in the circle with centre O. If $\angle AOC = 140°$ and $\angle P$, $\angle B$ are x, y respectively, then the value of $y - x$ will be

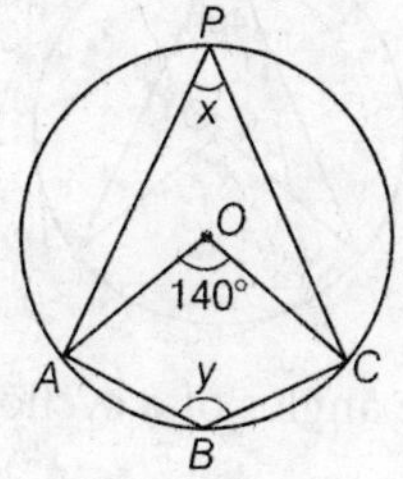

a 70°
b 110°
c 40°
d None of the above

12. In the following figure, AB and CD are two parallel chords which are equidistant from centre O of the circle. Also, the two chords made by joining AC and BD are also equidistant from centre, such that a quadrilateral is formed. The points B and C are connected. If two triangles are formed, then two triangles are

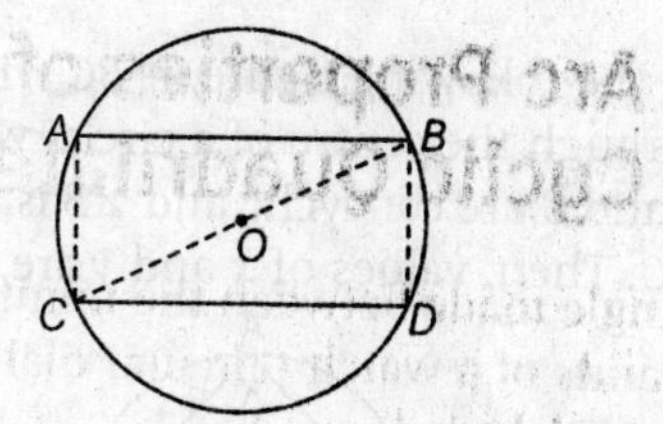

a congruent and have equal area
b non-congruent and have equal area
c neither congruent nor have equal area
d congruent and non-equal area

13. In the following figures, find the odd one out.

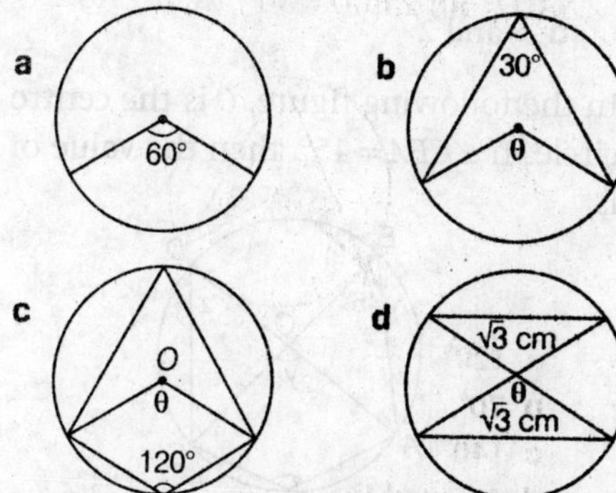

14. In the following figure, if ratio of the areas of regions 1 and 2 are 2 : 1. Then, the value of θ is

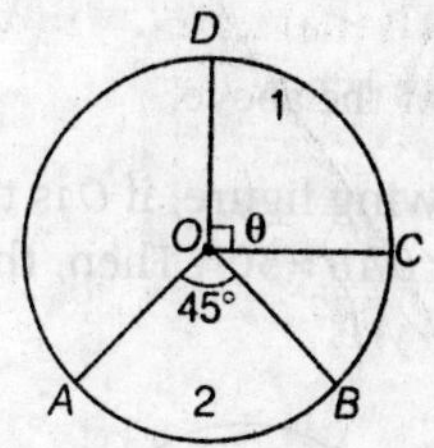

a 60° **b** 90°
c 75° **d** 135°

15. In the following figure, P and Q are centres of two circles, intersecting at B and C. ACD is a straight line. If $\angle APB = 120°$ and $\angle BQD = x$, then value of x is equal to

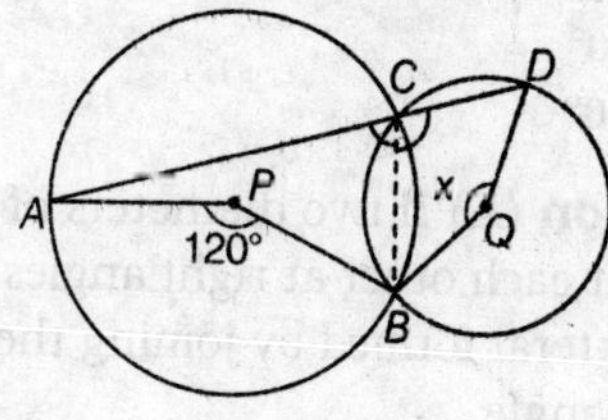

a 60°
b 120°
c 30°
d 90°

16. In the following figure, if BC will pass through the centre of a circle, where points A, B and C are concyclic and $\angle B$ is $44°$ more than $\angle C$. Then, values of x and y are, respectively

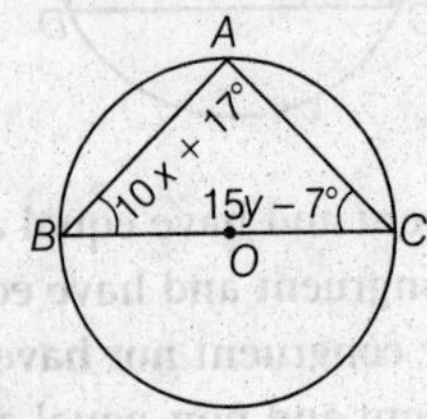

a 4 and 3
b 3 and 5
c 7 and 2
d 5 and 2

17. In the following figure, O is the centre of the circle. If $\angle CEA = 45°$, then the value of $x + y - z$ is

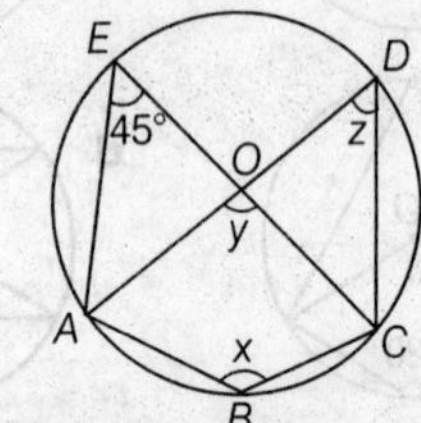

a 90°
b 45°
c 135°
d None of the above

18. In the following figure, if O is the centre of circle and $\angle DAB = 50°$. Then, the value of $(x + y) - (x - y)$ is

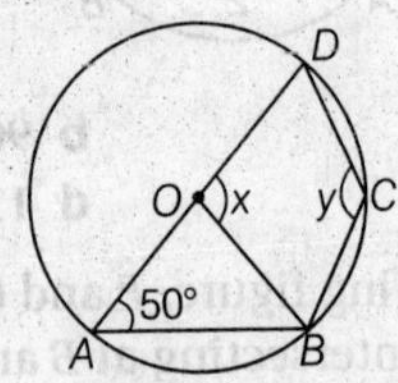

a 160°
b 200°
c 260°
d 180°

19. **Assertion** (A) If two diameters of a circle intersect each other at right angles. Then, the quadrilateral formed by joining their end point is a rectangle.

Reason (R) Angle in a semi-circle is a right angle.

Which of the following is true?

a Both (A) and (R) are true and (R) is the correct explanation of (A)
b Both (A) and (R) are true and (R) is not the correct explanation of (A)
c (A) is true and (R) is false
d (A) is false and (R) is true

20. State 'T' for true or 'F' for false.

I. If a circle is divided into three equal arcs, then each is a major arc.
II. The sum of a pair of opposite angles of a cyclic quadrilateral is 360°.
III. Segment is a region between the chord and its corresponding arc.
IV. A cyclic parallelogram is a rectangle.
V. Angles inscribed in the same arc of a circle are equal.

Codes

	I	II	III	IV	V		I	II	III	IV	V
a	T	F	T	F	T	**b**	F	F	T	T	T
c	T	T	F	F	T	**d**	F	T	F	T	T

21. Fill in the blanks with the help of options, given in the box.

(i) 45°, (ii) 90°, (iii) supplementary, (iv) complementary, (v) chord, (vi) centre, (vii) quadrant of circle, (viii) chord, (ix) opposite angle, (x) opposite angles of its interior angle

I. In the following figure, the value of x ___ .

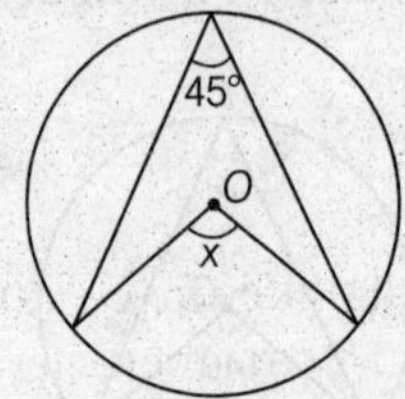

II. Opposite angles of a cyclic quadrilateral are ___ .
III. Congruent arcs of a circle subtend equal angles at the ___ .
IV. The arc of a circle subtending a right angle at the centre is called the ___ .

Codes

	I	II	III	IV
a	(i)	(ii)	(iii)	(iv)
b	(vi)	(vii)	(viii)	(ix)
c	(ii)	(iii)	(vi)	(vii)
d	(ii)	(v)	(viii)	(x)

8

Area of Parallelograms and Triangles

A. Area of Triangle using Heron's Formula (Various Types of Triangles and Perimeter of Plane Figures)

1. The area of a triangle whose perimeter is 144 cm and ratio of the sides is 3 : 5 : 4, is

a 864 cm^2
b 764 cm^2
c 854 cm^2
d 754 cm^2

2. A triangle have its sides in the ratio 2 : 3 : 5 and value of s is 35 cm. Then, perimeter of the triangle is

a 70 cm **b** 35 cm
c 105 cm **d** 140 cm

3. Two triangles ABC and PQR are congruent and have their sides in the ratio 1 : 2 : 3 and 2 : 3 : 5 respectively. If perimeter of ΔABC is 120 cm and area of ΔPQR is 127 cm^2 (approx), then area of ΔABC will be

a 100 cm^2 **b** 125 cm^2
c 127 cm^2 **d** 254 cm^2

4. The percentage increase in the area of a triangle, if its each side is doubled, is

a 100% **b** 200%
c 300% **d** 400%

5. If an isosceles triangle has a perimeter 30 cm and sum of its two equal sides is 24 cm. Then, area of the triangle is

a $\sqrt{135}$ cm^2
b $9\sqrt{15}$ cm^2
c $15\sqrt{9}$ cm^2
d None of the above

6. If the area of a triangle which is made by dividing a rectangle diagonally is 25 cm^2. Then, perimeter of rectangle will be

a 100 cm **b** 50 cm
c 40 cm **d** Can't say

7. In the given figure, the two circles intersect at points C and D. A triangle is formed by joining its centre to the intersection point and to other centre. The radii of circles are 6 cm and 8 cm. Then, the length of CD, if $AB = 10$ cm, is

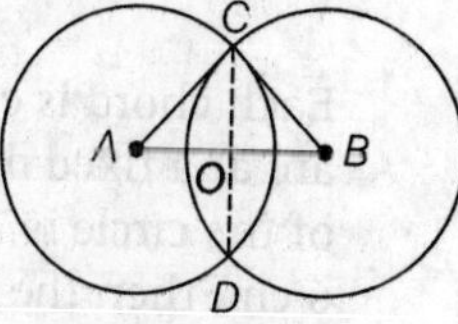

a 4.8 cm **b** 2.8 cm
c 9.6 cm **d** 2.4 cm

8. A triangle and a parallelogram have the same base and same area. If the sides of the triangle are 26 cm, 28 cm and 30 cm and the parallelogram stands on the base 28 cm, then the height of the parallelogram is

a 6 cm **b** 12 cm **c** 18 cm **d** 9 cm

9. In the given figure, AB and CD are two parallel and equidistant chords. BC is joined. O is the centre of the circle and its radius is 4 cm. If one of the parallel sides is 6 cm, then distance between AB and CD is

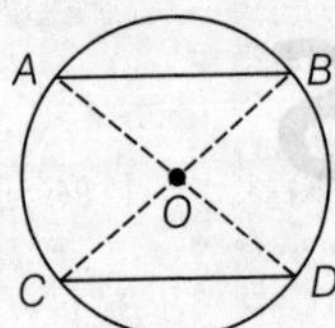

a $\sqrt{7}$ cm **b** $2\sqrt{7}$ cm

c $4\sqrt{7}$ cm **d** $3\sqrt{7}$ cm

10. Assertion (A) If the sides of a triangle are 3 cm, 4 cm and 5 cm, then its area is 6 sq cm.

Reason (R) If $2s = (a + b + c)$, where a, b and c are sides of triangle, then

$$\text{Area} = \sqrt{s(s-a)(s-b)(s-c)}$$

Which of the following is true?

a Both (A) and (R) are true and (R) is the correct explanation of (A)

b Both (A) and (R) are true and (R) is not the correct explanation of (A)

c (A) is true and (R) is false

d (A) is false and (R) is true

11. Ram made a diagram by using circle and their properties as follows:

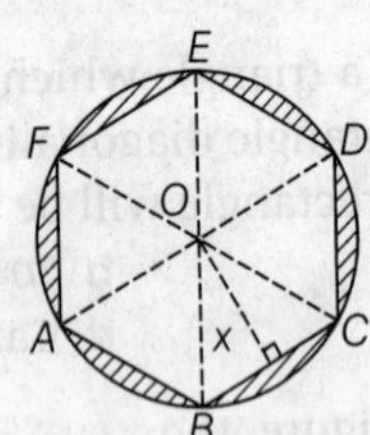

Each chord is equidistant from centre i.e. they are at a fixed distance (say x cm). If the radius of the circle is 7 cm and the length of chord is 6 cm, then the perpendicular distance from centre to any chord is

a 2 cm **b** 4 cm

c 6.3 cm **d** 6 cm

12. State 'T' for true or 'F' for false.

I. Area of a quadrilateral whose sides and one diagonal are given, can be calculated by dividing the quadrilateral into two triangles and using the Heron's formula.

II. Area of a triangle with sides a, b and c is $\sqrt{s(s-a)(s-b)(s-c)}$, where $s = \frac{a+b+c}{2}$.

III. A median of a triangle divides it into two equal triangles of unequal area.

IV. The area of triangle with base 4 cm and altitude 5 cm is same as the area of square whose side is 3 cm.

V. The area of any triangle is

$2 \times \text{base} \times \text{height}$.

Codes

	I	II	III	IV	V
a	T	T	F	F	F
b	T	F	T	F	F
c	T	T	F	F	T
d	T	F	F	F	F

13. Fill in the blanks with the help of options, given in the box.

(i) 4 cm, (ii) 8 cm, (iii) 1:1, (iv) 2:1, (v) $8\sqrt{4}$ cm², (vi) two, (vii) three, (viii) 5 cm, (ix) 10 cm, (x) 12 cm²

I. A diagonal of parallelogram divides the parallelogram into ___ triangles of equal areas.

II. If the base of an isosceles triangle is 6 cm and its perimeter is 16 cm, then area of triangle is ___ .

III. Perimeter of a square and a rectangle are in the ratio of 2 : 3. If breadth of rectangle is 10 cm and side of square is 5 cm. Then, length of rectangle is ___ .

IV. The length of each side of an equilateral triangle of area $4\sqrt{3}$ cm² is ___ .

Codes

	I	II	III	IV
a	(vii)	(iii)	(vii)	(ii)
b	(vi)	(iii)	(viii)	(ii)
c	(vii)	(x)	(vi)	(i)
d	(vi)	(x)	(viii)	(i)

B. Area of Circle and Parallelogram (Using Area of Triangle and Its Properties)

1. A circle having its perimeter equal to 132 cm. Then, area of the same circle is

a 286 cm^2 **b** 1386 cm^2
c 1420 cm^2 **d** 1836 cm^2

2. A circle is of diameter 14 cm. Then, the length of wire to measure its length (total) for the purpose of making a boundary, is equal to

a 308 cm **b** 44 cm
c 77 cm **d** 218 cm

3. In the given figure, *OCDE* is a rectangle inscribed in a quadrant of circle of radius 10 cm. If $OE = 2\sqrt{5}$ cm, then area of ΔODE : area of rectangle *OCDE* is equal to

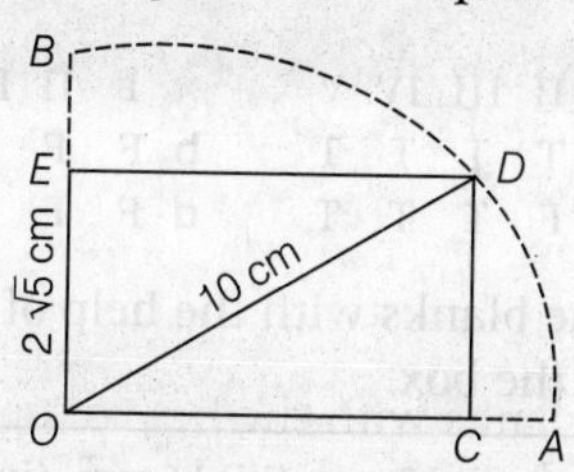

a 2 : 1 **b** 1 : 2
c 1 : 1 **d** 1 : 3

Directions (Q. Nos. 4-6) *Which of the following statements are required to solve the questions?*

4. Area of a ΔABC is

I. the sum of two equal sides is 20 cm.

II. the angle between equal side is 90°.

a Only I **b** Only II
c Both I and II **d** Neither I nor II

5. The area of parallelogram is

I. the triangle and the parallelogram are on the same base and between the same parallel lines.

II. the angles of triangle are equal and its one side is 6 cm.

a Only I **b** Only II
c Both I and II **d** Neither I nor II

6. The circumference of circle

I. the length of longest chord is 14 cm.

II. the area of the circle is 154 cm^2.

a Only I **b** Only II
c Both I and II **d** Either I or II

7. In a trapezium *PQRS* with $RS = 8$ cm, $RQ = 17$ cm and $PQ \| RS$, *RT* is the perpendicular bisector of *PQ*, then area of trapezium *PQRS* is

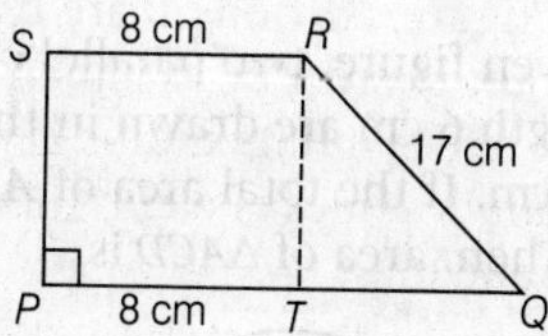

a 120 cm^2 **b** 150 cm^2
c 180 cm^2 **d** 80 cm^2

8. In the given figure, if *ABCD* is a trapezium in which $AB = 7$ cm, $AD = BC = 5$ cm, $DC = x$ cm and distance between *AB* and *DC* is 4 cm. Then, the value of *x* and the area of trapezium are respectively

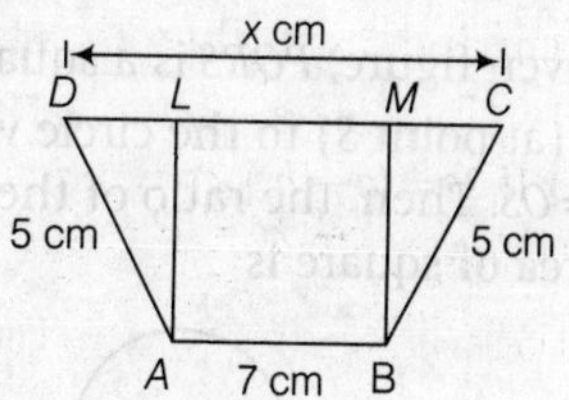

a 6 cm and 40 cm^2
b 9 cm and 40 cm^2
c 13 cm and 40 cm^2
d None of the above

9. A farmer was having a field in the form of a parallelogram *PQRS*. He took any point *A* on *RS* (=10 cm) and joined it to points *P* and *Q* such that the height of ΔAPQ is 8 cm. He also wants to sow pulses and maize in equal portions of the field separately. Then, the area of the region in which he sow the pulses, is

a 80 cm^2 **b** 20 cm^2
c 40 cm^2 **d** None of these

10. **Assertion** (A) If area of ΔABD is equal to 24 cm^2, then area of parallelogram *ABCD* is 24 cm^2.

Reason (R) If a triangle and a parallelogram are on the same base and between the same parallel lines, then area of the triangle is equal to half of the area of parallelogram.

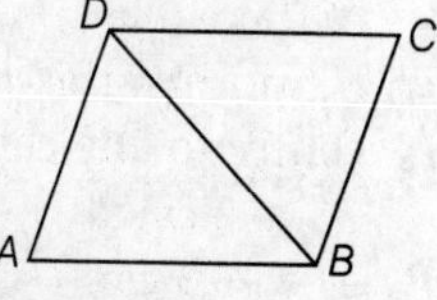

Which of the following is true?

a Both (A) and (R) are true and (R) is the correct explanation of (A)

b Both (A) and (R) are true and (R) is not the correct explanation of (A)

c (A) is true and (R) is false

d (A) is false and (R) is true

11. In the given figure, two parallel chords AB and CD of length 6 cm are drawn in the circle of radius 7 cm. If the total area of $ABCD$ is 66 cm^2. Then, area of ΔACD is

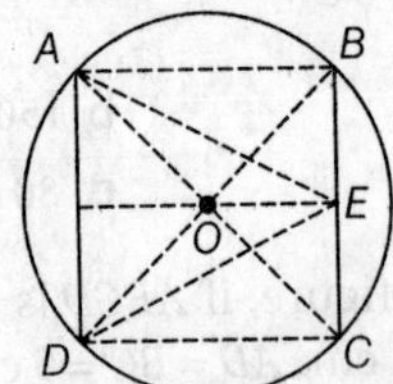

a 30 cm^2 **b** 33 cm^2

c 22 cm^2 **d** 36 cm^2

12. In the given figure, $PQRS$ is a square. SR is a tangent (at point S) to the circle with centre O and $TR = OS$. Then, the ratio of the area of circle to the area of square is

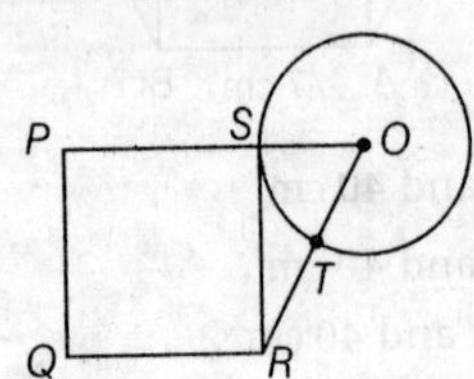

a $\frac{11}{7}$ **b** $\frac{\pi}{3}$

c $\frac{3}{\pi}$ **d** $\frac{7}{11}$

13. In the given figure, two concentric circles are shown with centre O. $PQRS$ is a square inscribed in the outer circle. It also circumscribes the inner circle, touching it at points B, C, D and A. What is the ratio of the perimeter of the outer circle to that of quadrilateral $ABCD$?

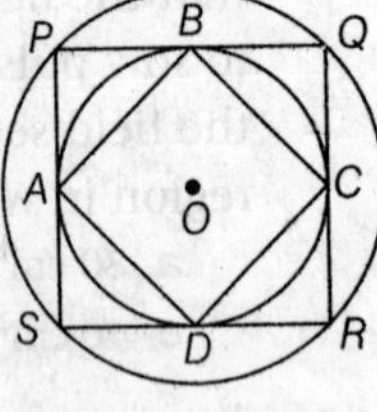

a $\frac{\pi}{4}$ **b** $\frac{3\pi}{2}$

c $\frac{\pi}{2}$ **d** π

14. State 'T' for true or 'F' for false.

I. Two parallelograms are on the same base and between the same parallel lines. Then, they are of unequal areas.

II. If the diagonal of a square is 8 cm. Then, its area is 32 cm^2.

III. The area of a parallelogram is the product of its base and the corresponding altitude.

IV. If two triangles inscribed in a circle are congruent, then their areas are equal.

V. A triangle and a parallelogram are on the same base and between the same parallel lines. The area of triangle is equal to the half of the area of parallelogram.

Codes

	I	II	III	IV	V
a	F	T	T	T	T
b	F	F	T	T	T
c	T	F	T	T	T
d	F	F	F	T	T

15. Fill in the blanks with the help of options, given in the box.

(i) 16cm^2, (ii) 12cm^2, (iii) 16cm^2, (iv) 9cm^2, (v) altitude, (vi) equal, (vii) hypotenuse, (viii) equal, (ix) different, (x) 2cm

I. In ΔABC, D, E and F are the mid-points of its sides. If $ar(\Delta ABC) = 16\text{ cm}^2$, then ar(trapezium $FBCE$) is ____ .

II. Medians of ΔABC intersect at G. If $ar(\Delta ABC)$ is 27 cm^2, then $ar(\Delta BCG)$ is ____ .

III. Area of triangle $= \frac{1}{2} \times$ base $\times$ ____ .

IV. Two triangles having same base and between same parallel lines, have ____ area.

Codes

	I	II	III	IV
a	(ii)	(iv)	(v)	(viii)
b	(iv)	(ii)	(viii)	(v)
c	(i)	(iv)	(vii)	(ix)
d	(iii)	(x)	(v)	(v)

Statistics

A. Introduction to Statistics – Different Terminology, Bar Graphs Representation and Frequency Distribution

1. In an experiment, the data is given below:
15, 20, 6, 5, 30, 35, 92, 35, 40, 90, 18, 82
The range of the above data is

a 87 **b** 15
c 18 **d** 26

2. Pick the odd one out.

a Mean **b** Median
c Mode **d** Bar graph

3. In a frequency distribution, if the class marks are 15, 20, 25, 30, … , then the class corresponding to the class mark 25, is

a 12.5-17.5
b 20.5-29.5
c 18.5-23
d 22.5-27.5

4. If the range of the data with minimum value 16, is 87, then the maximum value is

a 103 **b** 51
c 71 **d** 51.5

5. In a frequency distribution, if the mid value of class is 10 and width of the class is 6, then the lower limit of the class is

a 6 **b** 7
c 8 **d** 12

6. The width of each of the five continuous classes in a frequency distribution is 5 and the upper class limit of upper class is 60. The lower class limit of the lowest class is

a 45 **b** 25
c 35 **d** 40

7. A random survey of a number of children in various age groups playing in a park was found as follows:

Age (in years)	Number of children
1-2	5
2-3	3
3-5	6
5-7	12
7-10	9
10-15	10
15-17	4

By analysing the above table, the class interval in which the maximum number of children lies is

a 7-10 **b** 2-3
c 10-15 **d** 5-7

Directions (Q. Nos. 8-10) *Read the following information and table carefully and then answer the questions that follow:*

The weight of 50 boxes picked at random from consignment, is given below. The mid value of the first class corresponds to 70 g.

Weight (in g)	Tally marks	Frequency
60-80	𝍸	5
80-100	…	13
100-120	𝍸 𝍸 𝍸 II	17
120-140	𝍸 𝍸	…
140-160	IIII	4
160-180	…	…

8. The values in blanks given are

- **a** 𝍸 𝍸 𝍸 |||, 11, (1, 1)
- **b** 𝍸 𝍸 |||, 10, (|, 1)
- **c** 𝍸, 15, 𝍸, 5
- **d** None of the above

9. The number of boxes and their corresponding tally marks which have weight more than 100 g, are respectively

- **a** 24 and 𝍸 𝍸 𝍸 𝍸 ||||
- **b** 32 and 𝍸 𝍸 𝍸 𝍸 𝍸 𝍸 ||
- **c** 18 and 𝍸 𝍸 𝍸 |||
- **d** 15 and 𝍸 𝍸 𝍸

10. The range and number of classes in this distribution, are respectively

- **a** 20 and 5
- **b** 10 and 6
- **c** 30 and 6
- **d** Can't say and 6

11. A table shows the heights of students of Class IX of a school:

Heights	Number of students
150-155	12
155-160	9
160-165	14
165-170	10
170-175	5

By analysing the table, the per cent of number of students having heights shorter than 165 cm, is

- **a** 25%
- **b** 40%
- **c** 50%
- **d** 70%

Directions (Q. Nos. 12-15) *The bar graph shows the export/import for 5 consecutive years for any goods. Answer the following questions based on the graph.*

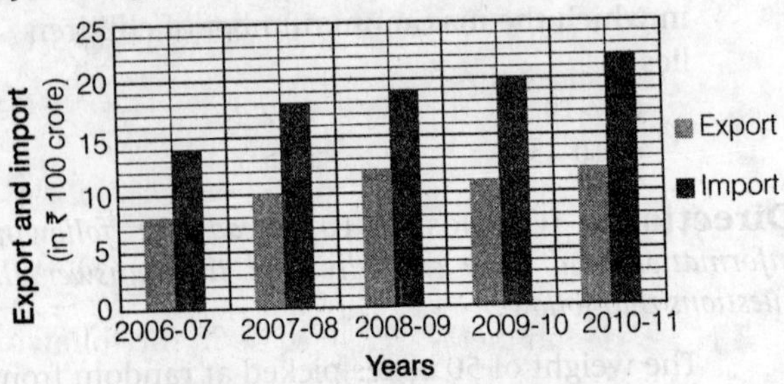

12. In which year import is minimum?

- **a** 2007-08
- **b** 2006-07
- **c** 2008-09
- **d** None of these

13. In which year export is maximum?

- **a** 2008-09
- **b** 2010-11
- **c** Both (a) and (b)
- **d** None of these

14. In which year the difference of the values of export and import is maximum?

- **a** 2007-08
- **b** 2009-10
- **c** 2010-11
- **d** 2006-07

15. The percentage change in export and import together from year 2007-08 to 2009-10 is

- **a** 8.71%
- **b** 10.71%
- **c** 9.5%
- **d** 11.25%

16. Match the following:

List I	List II
A. Class mark of 90-120 is	i. 17.5-22.5
B. Range of the data 25, 18, 20, 22, 16, 6, 17, 15, 12, 30, 32 and 10 is	ii. 60-70
C. Class corresponding to class mark 20 in 15, 20, 25, ... is	iii. 105
D. Class interval 40-50, 50-60, 60-70, the number 60 is included in	iv. 26

Codes

	A	B	C	D
a	(i)	(ii)	(iii)	(iv)
b	(iii)	(iv)	(i)	(ii)
c	(iii)	(iv)	(ii)	(i)
d	(ii)	(iv)	(iii)	(i)

17. State 'T' for true or 'F' for false.

I. After four vertical lines for a tally mark, if the tally mark occurs for the fifth time, then the fifth line is put vertically with previous four lines.

II. The range is the difference between the greatest and the least values of the variate

III. Class size $= \dfrac{\text{Upper limit + Lower limit}}{2}$

Codes

	I	II	III
a	F	T	T
b	T	F	F
c	F	F	F
d	T	T	T

18. Fill in the blanks with the help of options, given in the box.

(i) class mark, (ii) class size, (iii) lower limit, (iv) mid value of class, (v) *Y*-axis, (vi) *X*-axis, (vii) 30-40, (viii) 4, (ix) 5,(x) 20-30

I. The difference between the upper limit and lower limit of a class is ___.

II. A frequency polygon is constructed by plotting frequency of the class interval and the ___.

III. In a histogram, the class intervals or the groups are taken along ___.

IV. The tallies are usually marked in a bunc of ___.

Codes

	I	II	III	IV
a	(i)	(ii)	(iii)	(iv)
b	(vi)	(vii)	(viii)	(ix)
c	(ii)	(iv)	(vi)	(ix)
d	(ix)	(x)	(i)	(ii)

B. Measure of Central Tendencies – Mean, Median, Mode and Relation among Them

1. The mean of prime numbers between 1 and 20 is

a 9.5
b 10.5
c 9.6
d 10.6

2. If the mean of 10 observations is 20 and that of another 15 observations is 16. Then, the mean of 25 observations is

a 18
b 18.2
c 17.6
d 17

3. In a class test, in Maths, 10 students scored 75 marks, 12 students scored 60 marks, 8 students scored 40 marks and 3 students scored x marks. If the mean of their scores is 57 marks, then the value of x (approx.) is

a 30 b 60
c 35 d 55

4. Let $\bar{x}$ be the mean of $x_1, x_2, \ldots, x_n$ and $\bar{y}$ be the mean of $y_1, y_2, \ldots, y_n$. If $\bar{z}$ is the mean of $x_1, x_2, \ldots, x_n, y_1, y_2, \ldots, y_n$. Then, $\bar{z}$ is equal to

a $(\bar{x}+\bar{y})$ b $\frac{\bar{x}+\bar{y}}{2}$
c $\frac{1}{n}(\bar{x}+\bar{y})$ d $\frac{\bar{x}+\bar{y}}{2n}$

5. The value of p, if the mean of the following distribution is 20, is

x	15	17	19	$20+p$	23
f	2	3	4	$5p$	6

a 2 b 1
c 3 d 4

6. The median of the observations 11, 12, 14, 18, $x+2$, $x+4$, 30, 32, 35 and 41 arranged in ascending order is 24. The value of x is

a 20 b 21
c 22 d 23

7. The mean, median and mode of the numbers 7, 4, 3, 5, 6, 3, 3, 2, 4, 3, 4, 3, 3, 4, 4, 3, 2, 2, 4, 3, 5, 4, 3, 4, 3, 4, 3, 1, 2 and 3, are respectively

a 3.4, 3 and 3
b 3, 3 and 3
c 4, 3 and 3
d 5, 4 and 3

8. Match the following:

	List I		List II
A.	Mean of first 10 odd prime numbers is	i.	0
B.	Median of the values 37, 31, 42, 43, 46, 25, 39, 45 and 32 is	ii.	15.8
C.	If mean of 2, 4, 6, 8, x, y is 5, then $x+y$ is	iii.	39
D.	If M is mean of $x_1, x_2, \ldots, x_6$, then $(x_1-M)+(x_2-M)+\cdots+(x_6-M)$ is	iv.	10

Codes

	A	B	C	D		A	B	C	D
a	(i)	(ii)	(iii)	(iv)	b	(ii)	(iii)	(iv)	(i)
c	(ii)	(iii)	(i)	(iv)	d	(i)	(iii)	(iv)	(ii)

9. Find the odd one from the given data.

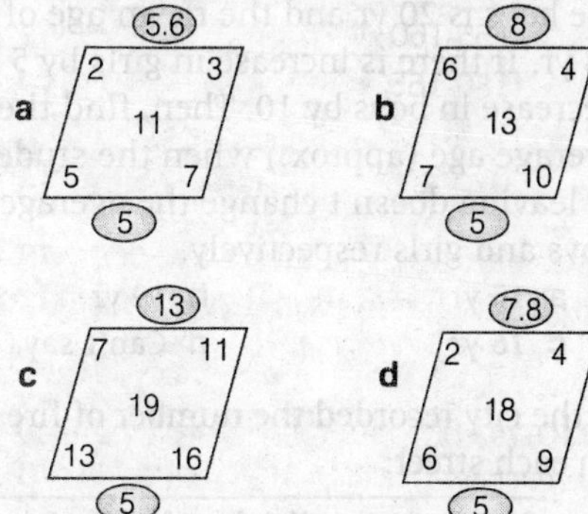

10. The value of p, if the mean of the following distribution is 7.5, is

x	3	5	7	9	11	13
f	6	8	15	p	8	4

a 4 b 3 c 5 d 8

11. If the number 66 replaced 30 in the following data, then the range will

93	50	78	46	63	30	91

a increase b decrease
c no change d Can't say

12. If $x_1, x_2, \ldots, x_n$ are n values of a variable X such that $\sum_{i=1}^{n}(x_i-2)=110$ and $\sum_{i=1}^{n}(x_i-5)=20$. Then, the value of n is

a 25 b 30
c 20 d 22

Directions (Q. Nos. 13-14) *The statements are given below. There are two supporting Statements* I *and* II *are also given. Select the correct option to solve the single* (*main*) *statement.*

Give answer

- **a** if only I required to answer the question
- **b** if only II required to answer the question
- **c** if both I and II together are needed to answer the question
- **d** if both I and II together are not sufficient to answer the question

13. Find the age of the teacher.

I. The mean age of all students and a teacher is 25 yr.

II. The number of students is 15.

a 25 yr **b** 20 yr
c 18 yr **d** Data insufficient

14. Find the 7th observation.

I. The mean of first 7 observations is 18 and that of last 7 observations is 20.

II. The mean of all 13 observations is 19.

15. In a school, there are 40 students in which boys and girls are in the ratio 3 : 1. The mean age of the boys is 20 yr and the mean age of the girls is 18 yr. If there is increase in girls by 5 and decrease in boys by 10. Then, find the new average age (approx.) when the students joining or leaving doesn't change the average age of boys and girls respectively.

a 15 yr **b** 19 yr
c 16 yr **d** Can't say

16. If the city recorded the number of fire hydrants on each street:

Street	Number of hydrants
Rose street	1
Maple street	2
Cherry street	3
Pine street	3
Aspen street	6
Oak street	3

Then, the street corresponding to the mean of the above will be

a Maple street **b** Aspen street
c Oak street **d** All of these

17. In a group, going for picnic, there are 15 students and there is 1 teacher for the 3 students. The median of age of all the persons (students and teachers together), when their ages are written in ascending order is 20 yr. Also, if the students change their age, youngest to eldest, second youngest to second eldest and so on. The median of their ages becomes

a 25 yr **b** 20 yr
c 18 yr **d** Data insufficient

18. State 'T' for true or 'F' for false.

I. If each entry of a data is increased by 5, then the arithmetic mean remains same.

II. If the number of observations is even, then the median is mean of $\frac{n}{2}$th and $\left(\frac{n}{2}+1\right)$th terms.

III. Mean may or may not be the appropriate measure of central tendency.

IV. Median does not depend on the extreme values.

V. The mean and median of $(a-2)$, a and $(a+2)$ are same.

Codes

	I	II	III	IV	V
a	T	F	T	F	T
b	F	T	F	T	T
c	F	T	T	T	F
d	F	T	T	T	T

19. Fill in the blanks with the help of options, given in the box.

(i) 64, (ii) 0, (iii) 13, (iv) 14, (v) $p+1$, (vi) $3p+1$, (vii) $\bar{x}$, (viii) $a\bar{x}$, (ix) $\frac{\bar{x}}{a}$, (x) 66

I. In a data of 10 numbers arranged in ascending order, if the 7th entry is increased by 4. Then, the median increases by ____ .

II. If the mean of 6, y, 7, 14 and x is 8. Then, the value of $x+y$ is ____ .

III. The mean of a data is p. If each observation is multiplied by 3 and then 1 is added to each result. Then, the new mean of data is ____ .

IV. If $\bar{x}$ is the mean of $x_1, x_2, \ldots, x_n$, then for $a \neq 0$, the mean $ax_1, ax_2, \ldots, ax_n$ and $\frac{x_1}{a}, \frac{x_2}{a}, \ldots, \frac{x_n}{a}$ are respectively ____ and ____ .

V. If the values of mode and mean are 60 and 66, respectively. Then, the value of median is ____ .

Codes

	I	II	III	IV	V
a	(iii)	(iv)	(vii)	(ix), (x)	(i)
b	(i)	(ii)	(iii)	(iv), (v)	(vi)
c	(ii)	(iii)	(vi)	(viii), (ix)	(i)
d	(ii)	(iii)	(iv)	(ix), (vii)	(viii)

Probability

1. In a lot of 100 bulbs, 15 bulbs are found to be defective. The probability that one bulb selected at random is a non-defective bulb, is

a 0.15 **b** 0.75
c 0.85 **d** 0

2. Cards marked with 2 to 101 are placed in a box and mixed thoroughly. One card is drawn from the box. The probability that the number on the card drawn is an even prime number less than 20, is

a $\frac{5}{28}$ **b** $\frac{3}{50}$
c $\frac{1}{100}$ **d** $\frac{3}{25}$

3. Pick the odd one out.

a Probability of getting atmost 2 heads in tossing two coins.
b Probability of a red or a black card from a pack of 52 cards.
c Probability of choosing an even or odd number from 1 to 20.
d Probability of choosing a consonant from the set of vowels.

4. Two coins are tossed simultaneously. The probability of getting atleast one head is

a $\frac{1}{4}$ **b** $\frac{1}{2}$
c $\frac{3}{4}$ **d** 0

5. The probability that it will rain today, is 0.84. What is the probability that it will rain tomorrow?

a 0.84 **b** 0.16
c 0 **d** 0.75

6. Two numbers are chosen from 1 to 6. The probability for the two numbers to be consecutive out of the set {(1,2), (1,3), (1,4), (1,5), (1,6), (2,1), (2,3), (2,4), (2,5), (2,6), (3,1), (3,2), (3,3), (3,4)} is

a $\frac{1}{3}$ **b** $\frac{2}{3}$
c $\frac{4}{3}$ **d** None of these

7. There are 25 cards numbered from 1 to 25. One card is drawn at random. What is the probability that the number on this card is not divisible by 3?

a $\frac{6}{25}$ **b** $\frac{17}{25}$ **c** $\frac{25}{6}$ **d** $\frac{25}{17}$

8. A carton contains 145 bulbs out of which 25 are defective and others are good. Sonu will buy a bulb, if it is good and will not buy it, if it is defective. The shopkeeper draws one bulb at random and gives it to him. The probability that he will buy it, is

a $\frac{29}{25}$ **b** $\frac{5}{29}$ **c** $\frac{24}{29}$ **d** $\frac{29}{5}$

9. Three coins are tossed simultaneously 300 times with the following frequencies of different outcomes. The probability that there is atmost 3 heads, is

Outcomes	3 heads	2 heads	1 head	No head
Frequency	45	90	80	85

a $\frac{41}{60}$ **b** 1
c $\frac{9}{60}$ **d** $\frac{34}{60}$

10. The following table gives the ages of teachers working in a primary school:

Age (in years)	**Number of teachers**
20-25	70
25-30	110
30-35	165
35-40	320
40-45	200
45-50	135

A teacher is selected at random from the group.

Match the following based on the above table:

	List A		**List B**
A.	Probability of a teacher having age less than 35, is	i.	$\frac{131}{200}$
B.	Probability of a teacher having age more than 35 and less than 45, is	ii.	$\frac{69}{200}$
C.	Probability of a teacher selected is of age not less than 35, is	iii.	$\frac{26}{50}$
D.	Probability of a teacher selected from the youngest group, is	iv.	$\frac{14}{200}$

Codes

	A	B	C	D
a	(i)	(ii)	(iii)	(iv)
b	(ii)	(iii)	(i)	(iv)
c	(ii)	(i)	(iv)	(iii)
d	(iv)	(iii)	(ii)	(i)

11. In an event of prize distribution ceremony among 200 children of a school, the number of boys and girls are in the ratio of 3 : 2. If a student is given first prize, the probability that it is not boy, is 0.4. Then, the probability that a student selected for first prize is not a girl, is

a 0.4 **b** 0.6
c 0.5 **d** 1

12. A bag contains 54 balls, each of them is either red, grey or pink. The probability of selecting a red ball from the bag is $\frac{1}{3}$ and that of selecting a grey ball is $\frac{4}{9}$. Then, the number of pink balls are

a 10 **b** 18
c 12 **d** 24

13. **Assertion** (A) A die is thrown. If E is the event that number appears on the upper face is less than 1, then $P(E) = \frac{1}{6}$.

Reason (R) Probability of an impossible event is 0.

Which of the following is true?

a Both (A) and (R) are true and (R) is the correct explanation of (A)
b Both (A) and (R) are true and (R) is not the correct explanation of (A)
c (A) is true but (R) is false
d (A) is false but (R) is true

14. State 'T' for true or 'F' for false.

I. If the probability of occurrence of an event is $\frac{1}{3}$, then the probability of not occurrence is $\frac{2}{3}$.

II. From numbers 1 to 100, the probability of occurrence of a doublet is $\frac{1}{10}$.

III. The range of probability of any event lies between −1 to 1.

IV. When a die is rolled, the number of outcomes for getting a prime number is 2.

V. The probability of not getting a prime number in a single throw of a die is $\frac{1}{2}$.

Codes

	I	II	III	IV	V
a	T	F	F	T	F
b	T	T	F	F	T
c	T	F	F	F	T
d	T	F	T	F	T

15. Fill in the blanks with the help of options, given in the box.

(i) 0.037, (ii) 0.37, (iii) 1, (iv) 0, (v) 4, (vi) $\frac{10}{49}$, (vii) $\frac{23}{49}$, (viii) $\frac{1}{10}$, (ix) $\frac{9}{100}$, (x) $\frac{3}{4}$

I. The probability of happening of an event is 37%. Then, probability of the event is ___ .

II. The probability of an impossible event is ___ .

III. Probability of an event A + Probability of event 'not A' is ___ .

IV. The king, queen and jack of clubs are removed from a pack of 52 cards. Then, reshuffled and a card is drawn. The probability of card being club is ___ .

V. Probability of getting a perfect square from numbers 2 to 101 is ___ .

Codes

	I	II	III	IV	V
a	(ii)	(iv)	(iii)	(vi)	(ix)
b	(ii)	(iii)	(iv)	(vi)	(ix)
c	(iii)	(ii)	(iv)	(vi)	(ix)
d	(iii)	(iv)	(ii)	(ix)	(vi)

Practice Sets

ractice Set 1

Vhole Content Based Test for Class 9th Mathematics Olympiad

Which one of the following is divisible by $(1+a+a^5)$ and $(1+a^4+a^5)$ individually?

a $(a^2+a+1)(a^3-a^2+1)(a^3-a+1)$

b $(a^4+a+1)(-a^3-a^2+1)(a^3+a+1)$

c $(a^2+a+1)(a^3+a^2+1)(a^3+a+1)$

d $(a^4-a+1)(a^3+a^2+1)(a^3+a-1)$

The line passing through the points $(-2,8)$ and $(5,7)$

a cuts Y-axis only

b cuts both the axes

c does not cut any axis

d cuts X-axis only

In a ΔABC, if AB is the longest side, then for any point P in the interior of the triangle, which of the following is correct?

a $PA+PB<PC$

b $PA+PB=PC$

c $PA+PB>PC$

d Can't say

f parallel sides of a trapezium are a and b, espectively. Then, the line joining the nid points of its non-parallel sides will be

a $\sqrt{ab}$

b $\frac{2ab}{a+b}$

c $\frac{a+b}{2}$

d $\frac{1}{2}(a-b)$

n the following figure, the value of x is

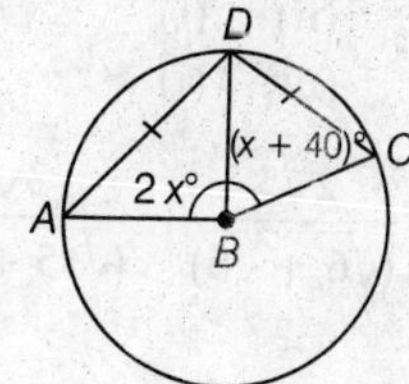

a 60°

b 40°

c 20°

d None of the above

6. Area of an isosceles triangle is given by

$$A=\frac{1}{4}b\sqrt{4a^2-b^2}$$

Here, a refers to the

a equal side

b unequal side

c any side

d None of the above

7. A race car driver kept track of the number of laps he drove in the past 5 days. If median of the numbers is x, then the day corresponding to $x+3$ is

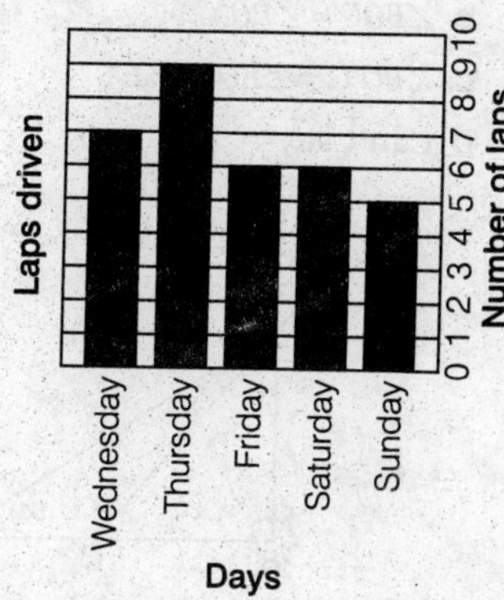

a Sunday

b Friday

c Saturday

d Thursday

8. 70 tickets of a lucky draw were sold. If the probability of Krish winning the draw is $\frac{1}{14}$, then the number of tickets bought by Krish is

a 5

b 10

c 15

d 20

9. The value of

$$\left(\frac{x^{1/a}}{x^{1/b}}\right)^{\frac{a^2b^2}{b-a}}\cdot\left(\frac{x^{1/b}}{x^{1/c}}\right)^{\frac{b^2c^2}{c-b}}\cdot\left(\frac{x^{1/c}}{x^{1/a}}\right)^{\frac{a^2c^2}{a-c}}$$ is

a 0

b 1

c $x^{1/a+1/b+1/c}$

d $x^{ab+bc+ca}$

10. Write the equivalent polynomial. A cosmetic company needs a storage box that has twice the volume of its largest box. Let its largest box measures 4 inch by 5 inch by 3 inch. If the larger box needs to be made larger by adding the same amount to each dimension. Then, the new expression will be

a $x^3 + 12x^2 + 47x - 60 = 0$

b $x^4 + 12x^3 + 47x^2 - 60x + 120 = 0$

c $x^3 + 12x^2 + 47x + 60 = 0$

d None of the above

11.

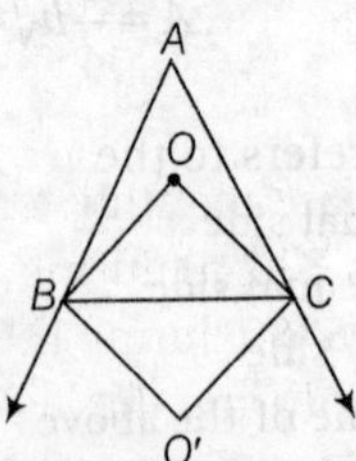

In the above figure, OB and $O'B$ are internal and external bisectors respectively, then which of the following is true?

a $\angle BOC = \angle BO'C + \angle A$

b $\angle BOC = \angle BO'C$

c $\angle BO'C = \angle BOC + \angle A$

d Can't say

12.

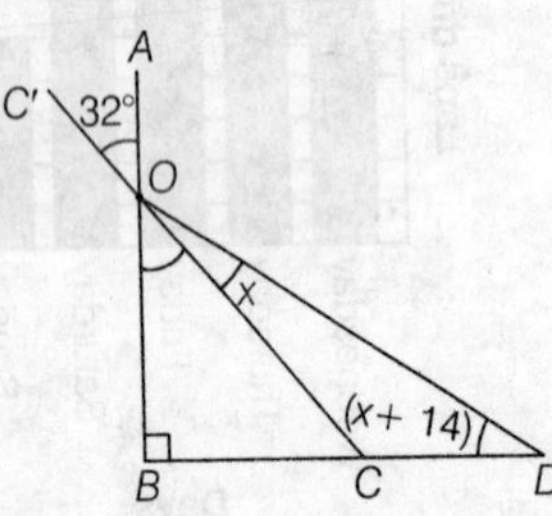

In the above figure, if $AB \perp BC$, then x is equal to

a 18° **b** 22° **c** 25° **d** 32°

13. Assertion (A) If $ABCD$ is a rhombus in which $\angle C = 60°$, then $AC : BD = \sqrt{3} : 1$.

Reason (R) All sides of rhombus are equal and diagonals of rhombus are perpendicular to each other.

Which of the following is true?

a (A) is true and (R) is the correct explanation of (A)

b (A) is true and (R) is not the correct explanation of (A)

c (A) is true and (R) is false

d Both (A) and (R) are false

14. If AB is a line segment, C is a point such that $\angle ACB = 90°$ and D is a point such th $\angle ADB = 90°$. Then, which of the followi can be true?

a $ABCD$ is a rhombus.

b $ABCD$ is a parallelogram.

c $ABCD$ is a cyclic quadrilateral.

d Can't say

15. The minute hand of a clock is $\frac{x}{2}$ cm long. Then, the area of the face of the clock described by the minute hand in 35 min, is

a $\frac{11x^2}{24}$ **b** $\frac{7x^2}{24}$

c $\frac{5x^2}{24}$ **d** $\frac{13x^2}{24}$

16. Match the following :

	List I		List II
A.	A shopkeeper recently sold 15 doughnuts of which 3 were chocolate frosted. What is the probability that the next doughnut will be a chocolate frosted doughnut?	i.	4/5
B.	Kurt is tossing bean bags at a target. He hits the target 7 out of his 14 tries. What is the probability that Kurt's next toss will be a hit?	ii.	1/5
C.	An ice-cream shop, 3 of the last 15 cones sold had vanilla ice-cream. What is the probability that the next sold will not be a vanilla?	iii.	1/2

Codes

	A	B	C
a	(i)	(ii)	(iii)
b	(iii)	(i)	(ii)
c	(iii)	(ii)	(i)
d	(ii)	(iii)	(i)

17. $\frac{7\sqrt{2}}{(3+\sqrt{2})} - \frac{2\sqrt{5}}{(\sqrt{6}+\sqrt{5})} - \frac{3\sqrt{2}}{(\sqrt{15}+3\sqrt{2})}$ is equal to

a 0

b 1

c 2

d None of the above

The given values of x and y are thought to satisfy a linear equation $y = 4x - 2$. When we draw the graph using the values of x and y as given in the table.

x	1	2
y	2	6

At what point the graph of the linear equation intersects the X-axis?

a $(1, 0)$

b $(2, 0)$

c $\left(\frac{1}{2}, 0\right)$

d $\left(\frac{1}{4}, 0\right)$

In a ΔABC, if $AB = AC$ and the bisectors of angles B and C intersect at point O. Then, which of the following is true?

a $BO = OC$

b AO is bisector of $\angle BAC$

c $OA = OB = OC$

d Both (a) and (b)

In the following figure, if $AD = 12$ cm, $AB = 5$ cm and $BC = CD = 13$ cm. Then, the area of quadrilateral $ABCD$ is

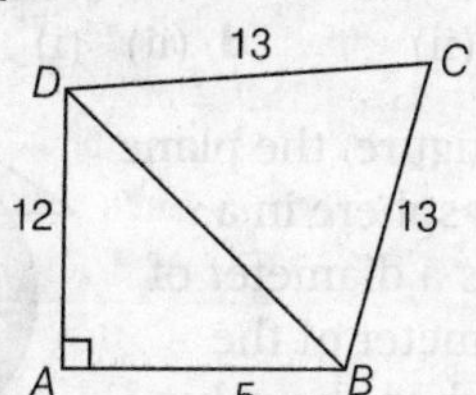

a $\frac{1}{4}(120 + 169\sqrt{3})\text{ cm}^2$

b $\left(120 + \frac{169\sqrt{3}}{4}\right)\text{ cm}^2$

c $(60 + 169\sqrt{3})\text{ cm}^2$

d None of the above

In the following figure, if MK bisects $\angle JKL$ then which of the following is incorrect?

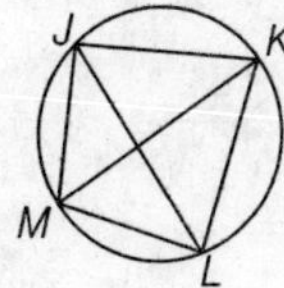

a $JM = ML$

b $\angle JKM = \angle LKM$

c ΔJML is an isosceles

d None of the above

22. Edward walked around two edges of a square field from A to B. Misha walked diagonally from A to B.

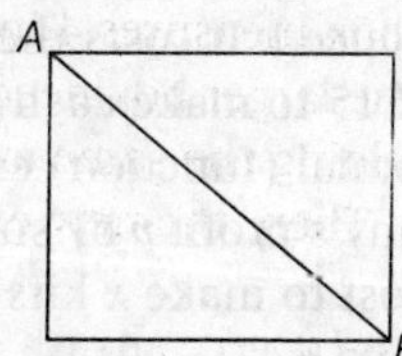

Approximately, what percentage of the distance Edward walked was the distance Misha walked?

a 50% b 71%

c 100% d 141%

23. The aggregate monthly expenditure of a family was ₹ 6240 during the first 3 months, ₹ 6780 during the next 4 months and ₹ 7236 during the last 5 months of a year. If the total savings during the year is ₹ 7080, then the average monthly income of the family is

a ₹ 7425

b ₹ 7500

c ₹ 8425

d ₹ 8500

24. $\sqrt[5]{\sqrt[4]{(2^4)^3}} - 5\sqrt[5]{8} + 2\sqrt[5]{\sqrt[4]{(2^3)^4}}$ is equal to

a $2(\sqrt[5]{8})$ b $-2(\sqrt[5]{8})$

c $3(\sqrt[5]{8})$ d $-3(\sqrt[5]{8})$

25.

17.8 cm 11.6 cm 10.9 cm 0 cm 19.7 cm

Josh planted five seeds which grew into plants. He recorded the height of each plant one month later. If he decides to water some plants twice a day. Then, what is the probability that he doesn't water the plant, having height more than 15 cm, twice a day?

a $\frac{2}{5}$ b $\frac{3}{5}$

c $\frac{1}{5}$ d $\frac{4}{5}$

26. The price p that a make up company can charge for a certain kit is $p = 40 - 4x^2$, where x is the number of kits produced. It costs the make up company ₹ 15 to make each kit. Then, the polynomial (function) expressing the company's profit p by subtracting the total cost to make x kits from the total revenue is

a $-4x^3 + 4x$
b $-4x^3 + 25x$
c $-4x^2 + 5x$
d $-4x^2 + 25x$

27. The value of α for which of the equation $2\alpha x + (\alpha + 8)y = 32$ has a solution $(1, 2)$ is

a 4
b 6
c 8
d 10

28.

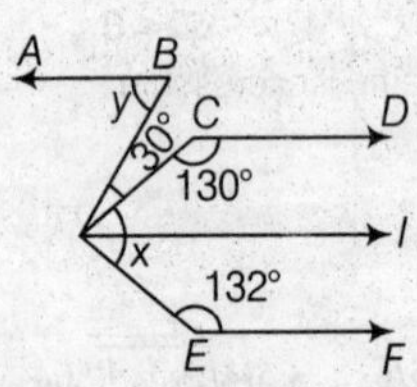

In the above figure, if $AB \parallel CD \parallel EF$ and $EF \parallel l_1$, then the values of x and y are respectively

a 90° and 80°
b 98° and 88°
c 98° and 80°
d 90° and 88°

29. Match the following :

List I	List II
A. 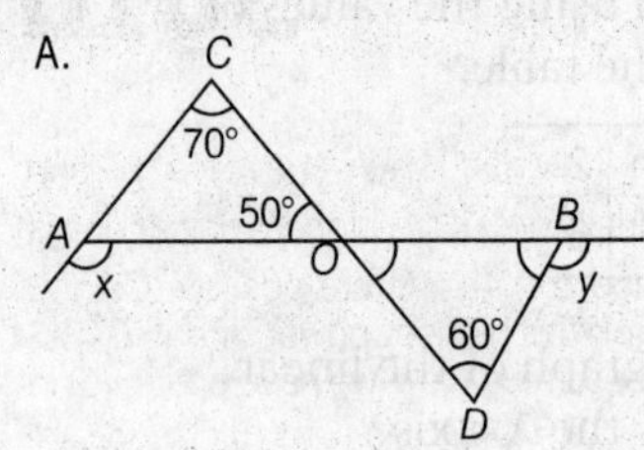	i. $x = 23°$, $y = 67°$
B. 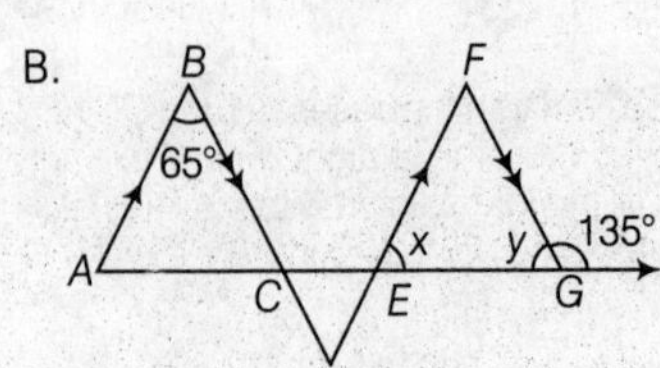	ii. $x = 120°$, $y = 110°$
C. 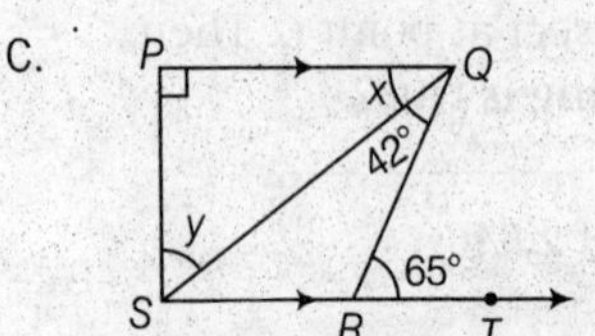	iii. $x = 70°$, $y = 45°$

Codes

	A	B	C
a	(i)	(ii)	(iii)
b	(ii)	(iii)	(i)
c	(i)	(iii)	(ii)
d	(ii)	(i)	(iii)

30. In adjoining figure, the plane intersects the sphere in a circle that has a diameter of 12. If the diameter of the sphere is 20, then the value of x is

a 9 cm
b 8 cm
c 10 cm
d 16 cm

Practice Set 1

Solutions

1. (d) Linear expression divided by $(1+a+a^5)$ and $(1+a^4+a^5)$ individually only if the highest power of a is 10 (i.e. 5 + 5) and 9 (i.e. 5 + 4) both are positive. Clearly, in options (a) and (c), the highest power of a is 8. So, these options are not correct. Now, we have option (d) in which both a^{10} and a^9 are positive.

2. (b)

3. (c)

4. (c) Let $ABCD$ be a trapezium with the bases AB and DC and the mid line EF. Let us draw the straight line DF through the points D and F till the intersection with the extension of the straight line AB at the point G. Compare the ΔDFC and ΔFBG.

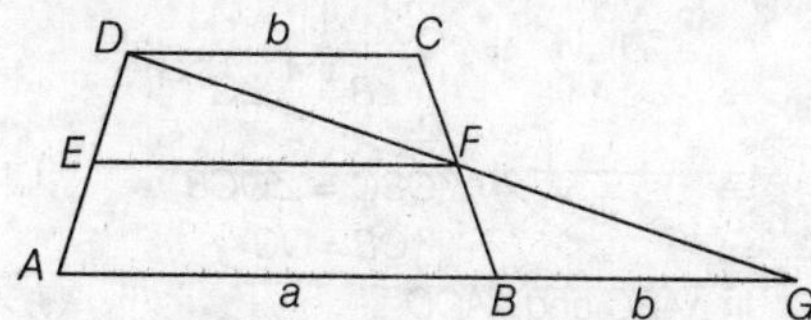

The segments FC and BF are congruent, since the point F is the mid point of the side BC.

$\therefore \quad \angle DFC = \angle BFG$ [vectically opposite angles]

The $\angle DCF$ and $\angle FBG$ are congruent as the alternate exterior angles at the parallel lines AB and DC and the transverse BC.

$\therefore \quad \Delta DFC \cong \Delta FBG$ [by ASA]

$\Rightarrow \quad DF = GF$ [by CPCT]

Thus, the mid line EF of the trapezium $ABCD$ is the straight line segment connecting the mid-points of the ΔAGD. We know that the straight line segment connecting the mid points of the ΔAGD is parallel to the triangle base AG and its length is half of the length of the triangle base. In this case, the length of the segment EF is half of the length AG: $|EF| = 1/2 \times |AG| = 1/2 \times (|AB| + |BG|)$. Since, $|BG| = |DC|$ from the triangles congruency, we have

$|EF| = 1/2 \times (|AB| + |DC|)$ or $|EF| = 1/2 \times (a+b)$,

where a and b are the lengths of the trapezium bases.

(b) Given, $AD = CD$

$\Rightarrow \quad \angle ABD = \angle CBD$

$\Rightarrow \quad 2x = x + 40$

$\Rightarrow \quad x = 40°$

(a)

(d) We have, 5, 6, 6, 7, 9

Here, $n = 5$ [odd]

$\therefore \quad M = \dfrac{n+1}{2}$th term

$= \dfrac{5+1}{2} = \dfrac{6}{2} = 3$rd term

$x = \text{Median} = 6$

Hence, $x + 3 = 6 + 3 = 9$, which corresponds to Thursday.

(a) Given, $P(E) = \dfrac{1}{14}$

Let x be the number of tickets bought.

$\Rightarrow \quad \dfrac{x}{70} = \dfrac{1}{14}$

$\Rightarrow \quad x = 5$

9. (d) $\left(\dfrac{x^{1/a}}{x^{1/b}}\right)^{\frac{a^2b^2}{b-a}} \cdot \left(\dfrac{x^{1/b}}{x^{1/c}}\right)^{\frac{b^2c^2}{c-b}} \cdot \left(\dfrac{x^{1/c}}{x^{1/a}}\right)^{\frac{a^2c^2}{a-c}}$

$= \left(x^{\frac{1}{a}-\frac{1}{b}}\right)^{\frac{a^2b^2}{b-a}} \cdot \left(x^{\frac{1}{b}-\frac{1}{c}}\right)^{\frac{b^2c^2}{c-b}} \cdot \left(x^{\frac{1}{c}-\frac{1}{a}}\right)^{\frac{a^2c^2}{a-c}}$

$\left[\because \dfrac{a^m}{a^n} = a^{m-n}\right]$

$= \left(x^{\frac{b-a}{ab}}\right)^{\frac{a^2b^2}{b-a}} \cdot \left(x^{\frac{c-b}{bc}}\right)^{\frac{b^2c^2}{c-b}} \cdot \left(x^{\frac{a-c}{ac}}\right)^{\frac{a^2c^2}{a-c}}$

$= x^{ab} \cdot x^{bc} \cdot x^{ca}$

$= x^{ab+bc+ca}$ $[\because a^m \cdot a^n = a^{m+n}]$

10. (a) Volume of largest box $= 4 \times 5 \times 3 = 60$

According to the question,

$(4+x)(5+x)(3+x) = 120$

$\Rightarrow x^3 + 12x^2 + 47x + 60 = 120$

$\Rightarrow x^3 + 12x^2 + 47x - 60 = 0$

which is the new expression.

11. (a) We know that,

$\angle BOC = 90° + \dfrac{1}{2}\angle A$

and $\angle BO'C = 90° - \dfrac{1}{2}\angle A$

$\Rightarrow \angle BOC - \angle BO'C = \angle A$

$\therefore \angle BOC = \angle BO'C + \angle A$

12. (b) Since, $\angle AOC' = \angle BOC$ [vertically opposite]

In ΔOBD,

$\angle BOD + \angle BDO + \angle OBD = 180°$

$\Rightarrow \quad x + 32° + x + 14° + 90° = 180°$

$[\because \angle BOD = \angle BOC + \angle COD]$

$\Rightarrow \quad 2x + 136° = 180°$

$\Rightarrow \quad 2x = 44°$

$\therefore \quad x = 22°$

13. (a) Since, $ABCD$ is a rhombus, so its all sides are equal.

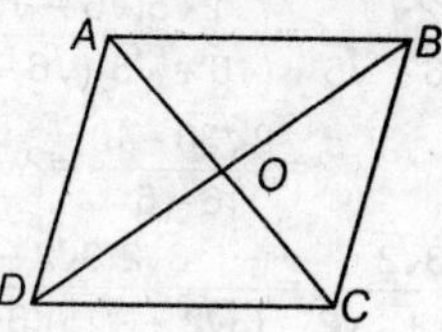

Now, $BC = DC$

In ΔBDC,

$\angle BDC = \angle DBC = x°$

Also, $\angle BCD = 60°$ [given]

$\therefore \quad x + x + 60° = 180°$

$\Rightarrow \quad x = 60°$

$\therefore \quad \angle BDC = \angle DBC = \angle BCD = 60°$

So, ΔBCD is an equilateral triangle.

$\therefore \quad BD = BC = a$

$AB^2 = OA^2 + OB^2$

[$\because$ diagonals of rhombus intersect each other at 90°]

$$\Rightarrow \quad OA^2 = AB^2 - OB^2$$

$$\Rightarrow \quad OA^2 = a^2 - \left(\frac{a}{2}\right)^2 = a^2 - \frac{a^2}{4} = \frac{3a^2}{4}$$

$$\therefore \quad OA = \frac{\sqrt{3}}{2}a$$

Now, $AC = \left(2 \times \frac{\sqrt{3}}{2}a\right) = \sqrt{3}\,a$

$$\therefore \quad AC : BD = \sqrt{3}\,a : a = \sqrt{3} : 1$$

14. (c)

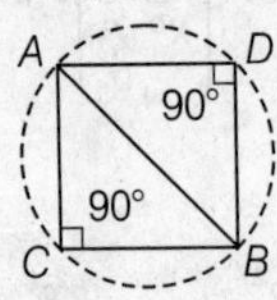

15. (a) Area swept by the minute hand

$$= \pi r^2 \times \frac{35}{60}$$

$$= \frac{22}{7} \times \frac{x}{2} \times \frac{x}{2} \times \frac{35}{60} = \frac{11}{24}x^2$$

16. (d) A. Sample space = 15

Number of favourable outcomes = 3

$\therefore P$ (having a chocolate doughnut) $= \frac{3}{15} = \frac{1}{5}$

B. Sample space = 14

Number of favourable outcomes = 7

$\therefore P$ (target is hit) $= \frac{7}{14} = \frac{1}{2}$

C. Sample space = 15

$\therefore P$ (not having vanilla) $= 1 - \frac{3}{15} = \frac{4}{5}$

17. (d) Consider $\frac{7\sqrt{2}}{3+\sqrt{2}} = \frac{7\sqrt{2}(3-\sqrt{2})}{(3+\sqrt{2})(3-\sqrt{2})} = \frac{7\sqrt{2}\,(3-\sqrt{2})}{(3^2-2)}$

$$= \frac{21\sqrt{2}-14}{9-2}$$

$$= \frac{21\sqrt{2}-14}{7}$$

$$= 3\sqrt{2} - 2$$

Now,

$$\frac{2\sqrt{5}}{\sqrt{6}+\sqrt{5}} = \frac{2\sqrt{5}(\sqrt{6}-\sqrt{5})}{(\sqrt{6}+\sqrt{5})(\sqrt{6}-\sqrt{5})} = \frac{2\sqrt{5}\,(\sqrt{6}-\sqrt{5})}{(\sqrt{6})^2-(\sqrt{5})^2}$$

$$= \frac{2\sqrt{30}-10}{6-5} = 2\sqrt{30} - 10$$

$$\Rightarrow \frac{3\sqrt{2}}{\sqrt{15}+3\sqrt{2}} = \frac{3\sqrt{2}(3\sqrt{2}-\sqrt{15})}{(3\sqrt{2}+\sqrt{15})(3\sqrt{2}-\sqrt{15})}$$

$$= \frac{3\sqrt{2}\,(3\sqrt{2}-\sqrt{15})}{(3\sqrt{2})^2-(\sqrt{15})^2}$$

$$= \frac{3\sqrt{2}(3\sqrt{2}-\sqrt{15})}{18-15} = \frac{3\sqrt{2}\,(3\sqrt{2}-\sqrt{15})}{3}$$

$$= \frac{18-3\sqrt{30}}{3} = 6 - \sqrt{30}$$

$$\therefore \frac{7\sqrt{2}}{3+\sqrt{2}} - \frac{2\sqrt{5}}{\sqrt{6}+\sqrt{5}} - \frac{3\sqrt{2}}{\sqrt{15}+3\sqrt{2}}$$

$$= 3\sqrt{2} - 2 - 2\sqrt{30} + 10 - 6 + \sqrt{30}$$

$$= 3\sqrt{2} - \sqrt{30} + 2$$

18. (c) Since, the equation intersect X-axis.

$\therefore \quad y = 0$

$\Rightarrow \quad 0 = 4x - 2 \Rightarrow 2 = 4x$

$\Rightarrow \quad x = \frac{1}{2}$

Hence, the required point is $\left(\frac{1}{2}, 0\right)$.

19. (d) In ΔABC,

$AB = AC$

$\Rightarrow \angle B = \angle C$

[since, angle opposite to equal sides are eq

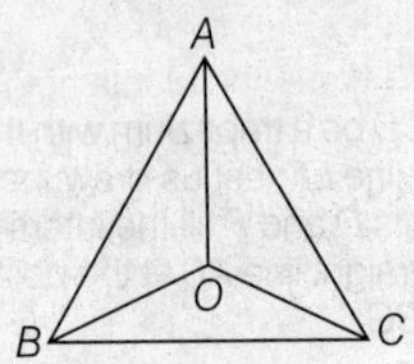

$\Rightarrow \quad \frac{1}{2}\angle B = \frac{1}{2}\angle C$

$\Rightarrow \quad \angle OBC = \angle OCB$

$\Rightarrow \quad OB = OC$

In ΔABO and ΔACO,

$AB = AC$

$\angle OBC = \angle OCB$

and $OB = OC$

By SAS,

$\Delta ABO \cong \Delta ACO$

$\Rightarrow \angle BAO = \angle CAO$ [by CP

Hence, AO is the bisector of $\angle BAC$.

20. (a) **Hint** $BD = \sqrt{AB^2 + AD^2}$

So, ΔABD is a right angled triangle and ΔBDC equilateral triangle.

21. (d) Given,

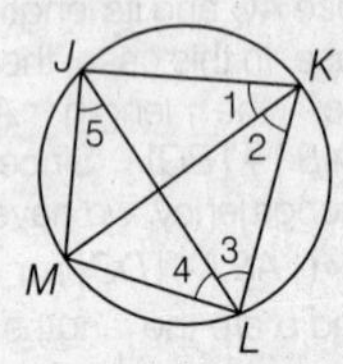

$\angle 1 = \angle 2$ [since, MK bisects $\angle JKL$]

Also, $\angle 1 = \angle 4$

[angles in same segment are e

and $\angle 2 = \angle 5$ [angle in same segments are equal]

From Eqs. (i), (ii) and (iii),

$\angle 4 = \angle 5$

$\Rightarrow \quad JM = ML$

[$\because$ sides opposite to equal angle are e

Hence, $\Delta\, JML$ is an isosceles triangle.

22. (d) Let edge of square field be a.

Area covered by Edward $= a + a = 2a$

Area covered by Misha $= \sqrt{a^2 + a^2} = \sqrt{2}a$

$\therefore$ Required percentage $= \frac{2a}{\sqrt{2}a} \times 100$

$= \sqrt{2} \times 100$

$= 141\%$

23. (a) $\because$ Total expenditure $= 6240 \times 3 + 6780 \times 4 + 7236 \times 5$
$= 18720 + 27120 + 36180$
$= 82020$

and savings = ₹ 7080

Total income = ₹ (82020 + 7080) = ₹ 89100

$\therefore$ Average monthly income $= \frac{89100}{12} =$ ₹ 7425

24. (b) Given, $\sqrt[5]{\sqrt[4]{(2^4)^3}} - 5\sqrt[5]{8} + 2\sqrt[5]{\sqrt[4]{(2^3)^4}}$
$= \sqrt[5]{(2^4)^{3/4}} - 5\sqrt[5]{8} + 2\sqrt[5]{2^3}$
$= \sqrt[5]{8} - 5\sqrt[5]{8} + 2\sqrt[5]{8}$
$= -2(\sqrt[5]{8})$

25. (b) $\because E$ = Water the plants height more than 15 cm
$\bar{E}$ = Doesn't water the plants having height more than 15 cm

$\therefore \quad P(\bar{E}) = 1 - P(E) = 1 - \frac{2}{5} = \frac{3}{5}$

26. (b) $p(x) = (40 - 4x^2)(x) - 15x$
$= 40x - 4x^3 - 15x = -4x^3 + 25x$

27. (a) According to the question,
$2\alpha(1) + (\alpha + 8) \times 2 = 32$
$\Rightarrow \quad 2\alpha + 2\alpha + 16 = 32 \Rightarrow 4\alpha = 16$
$\therefore \quad \alpha = 4$

28. (c) $\because \quad CD \,||\, EF \,||\, l$ [given]

Now, $\angle x = (180° - 130°) + (180° - 132°)$
$= 50° + 48° = 98°$
$\therefore \quad \angle y = (180° - 130°) + 30°$
$= 50° + 30° = 80°$

29. (b) A.

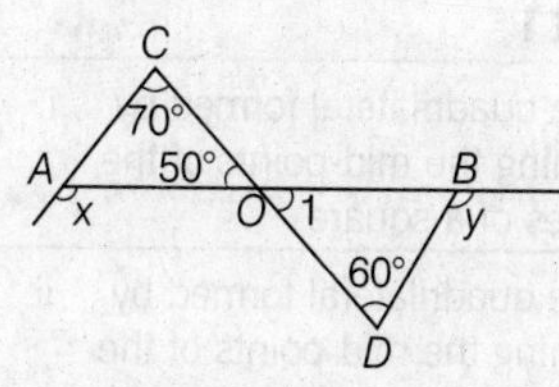

Now, $\angle 1 = \angle CA = 50°$ [vectically opposite angle]
$\therefore \quad y = 50° + 60° = 110°$
Also, $\angle x = 70° + 50° = 120°$

B.

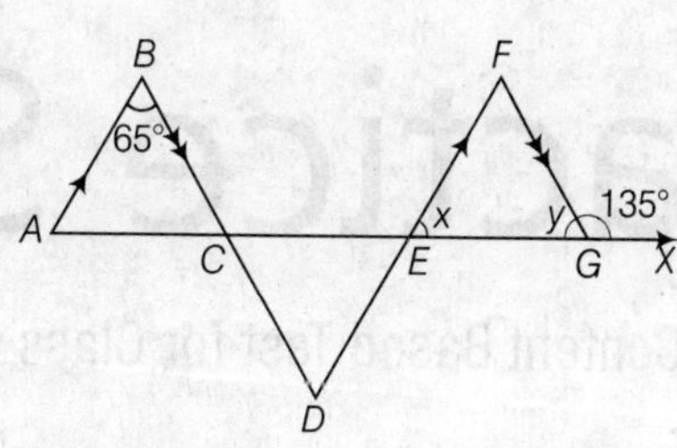

$\angle y = 180° - 135°$ [linear pair]
$= 45°$

Now, $FG \,||\, BC$

$\therefore \angle BCE = FGX = 135°$ [corresponding angle]

$\therefore \angle BAC = \angle BCE - \angle ABC$
$= 135° - 65°$
$= 70°$

Now, $x = \angle BAC = 70°$ [corresponding angle]

C. Similarly, we solve and get
$x = 23°$
and $y = 67°$

30. (b) We have, $AB = \frac{1}{2}$ diameter of circle = 6 cm

and $OA = \frac{1}{2}$ diameter of sphere = 10 cm

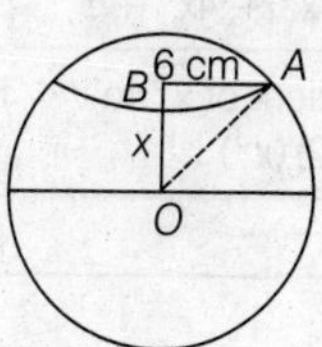

In ΔOBA,
$OA^2 = OB^2 + AB^2$
$\Rightarrow \quad 10^2 = OB^2 + 6^2$
$\Rightarrow \quad OB = 8$ cm
$\therefore \quad x = 8$ cm

Practice Set 2

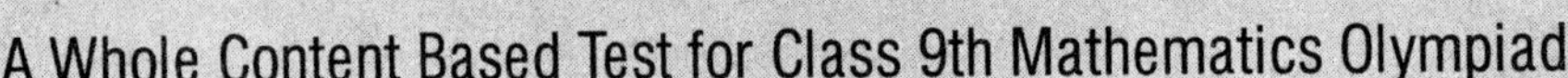

A Whole Content Based Test for Class 9th Mathematics Olympiad

1. $(\sqrt{2}+\sqrt{3})(\sqrt{3}-\sqrt{2})$ is

a a rational number
b an irrational number
c zero
d None of the above

2. Match the following:

	List I		List II
A.	Coefficient of x^3 in $2x^2+4x+1$	i.	4
B.	Coefficient of x^4 in $x^6+7x^5+4x^4+1$	ii.	0
C.	Coefficient of x^3 in $(x^3+2)(x^3)$	iii.	2
		iv.	1

Codes

	A	B	C		A	B	C
a	(ii)	(i)	(iii)	**b**	(i)	(ii)	(iii)
c	(ii)	(iii)	(iv)	**d**	(iii)	(i)	(iv)

3. John and Jack contributed some part of their pocket money towards a child development fund, such that the amount collected was 25% of the square of the difference of their amount, then the equation so formed is

a linear equation with two variables
b linear equation with one variable
c pair of linear equation with two variables
d None of the above

4. If $p+q=10$ and $pq=5$, then the value of $\frac{p}{q}+\frac{q}{p}$ will be

a 22 **b** 18
c 20 **d** 21

5. Pick the odd one out.

a $7x^2+4y^4-7x^3y+7y+8x$
b $3x^3+7y^3-7x^2y+4y^2x+4x+1$
c $4x^2+7y^2-7x^2y^2+2xy+4$
d $9x+2y+7x^3y+7y^3x+2y^3$

6. The percentage increase in the area of an equilateral triangle, if its each side is tripled, is

a 200% increase
b 400% increase
c 600% increase
d 800% increase

7. Marie recorded a certain data as follows:

19	13	20	14	K

If the mode is 14, then K will be

a 19 **b** 13
c 20 **d** 14

8. Match the following:

	List I		List II
A.	The quadrilateral formed by joining the mid-points of the sides of a square.	i.	Rhombus
B.	The quadrilateral formed by joining the mid-points of the consecutive sides of a rectangle.	ii.	Parallelogram
C.	Quadrilateral formed by joining the mid-points of the pair of consecutive sides of a quadrilateral.	iii.	Square

Codes

	A	B	C
a	(i)	(ii)	(iii)
b	(ii)	(iii)	(i)
c	(iii)	(i)	(ii)
d	(i)	(iii)	(ii)

9. A bag contains 7 red square boxes, 8 green rectangular boxes and 9 blue circular boxes. If Seera wants to buy a red colour box, then what is the probability of her choosing the box?

a 7/24
b 8/24
c 9/24
d None of the above

10.

In the above figure, if EG is parallel to HJ and $\angle JIK = 111°$, then $\angle HIF$ is equal to

a 111° b 69°
c 79° d None of these

11. Choose the incorrect statement.
In a parallelogram,

a diagonals divide it into congruent triangles
b opposite sides are equal
c opposite angles are equal
d the diagonals bisect each other at 90°

12. Monisha has a piece of wood in shape of a rectangular box 4 cm × 4 cm × 3 cm. She cuts the wood into small blocks each of 2 cm × 1 cm × 4 cm. How many small blocks can she cut from the piece of wood?

a 4 b 6
c 8 d 12

13. A cricketer has a mean score of 58 runs in 9 innings. If the mean score of 10 innings is raised to 61, then how many runs he scored in 10th innings?

a 68
b 78
c 88
d 98

14. If

$$\frac{(7+4\sqrt{5})+(4-2\sqrt{5})-(10+5\sqrt{5})}{6}=p+q\sqrt{5},$$

then $\sqrt{p-q}$ is equal to

a $\sqrt{6}$ b $\frac{\sqrt{6}}{2}$
c $\frac{\sqrt{6}}{3}$ d $\frac{1}{\sqrt{6}}$

15. The following table represents the number of skirts and jeans bought by persons A and B, respectively with the amount spend by each:

	A	**B**
Number of skirts	3	4
Number of jeans	2	1
Total expenditure	200	350

Which of the following represent the correct linear equation of the above?

a $3x+4y=200,$
$2x+y=350$
b $3x+2y=200,$
$4x+y=350$
c $3x+2y=200,$
$2x+4y=350$
d $2x+3y=200,$
$2y+x=350$

16. If l_1 is parallel to l_2, m_1 is parallel to m_2 and l_1 is perpendicular to m_1, then which of the following is true?

a l_1 is parallel to m_1.
b l_2 is perpendicular to m_2.
c m_2 is not perpendicular to l_2.
d None of the above.

17. Choose the correct statement.

a The sum of the three altitudes of a triangle is less than the sum of three sides of the triangle.
b The perimeter of a triangle is greater than the sum of its three medians.
c Any two sides of a triangle are together greater than twice the median drawn to the third side.
d All of the above

18. $ABCD$ is a cyclic quadrilateral whose diagonals AC and BD intersect at P. If $AB = DC$, then which of the following is/are correct?

a $AD \parallel BC$
b $\Delta PAB \cong \Delta PDC$
c $PA = PB$ and $PC = PD$
d All of the above

19. A school teacher was asked to prepare a table representing the number of students studying different number of hours in a week.

Number of hours studying	Number of students
0-10	8
10-20	7
20-30	1
30-40	1
40-50	5

The probability of number of students studying atleast 20 h in a week is

a 2/22 b 5/22
c 7/22 d 9/22

20. In isosceles ΔABC, BA and BC are congruent. If M and N are points on AC such that MA is congruent to MB and NB is congruent to NC. Then, which of the following is true?

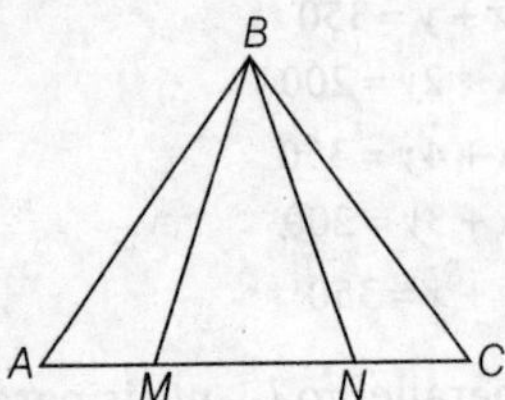

a $\Delta ABN \cong \Delta CNB$

b $\Delta AMB \cong \Delta CNB$

c $\Delta AMB \cong \Delta MNB$

d $\Delta CNB \cong \Delta MBN$

21. $ABCD$ is a parallelogram. If AB is produced to E such that ED bisects BC at O. Then, which of the following is correct?

a $AB = OE$

b $AB = BE$

c $OE = OC$

d None of the above

22. Assertion (A) If the bisector of any angle of a triangle and the perpendicular bisector of its opposite side intersect, then they will intersect on the circumcircle of the triangle.

Reason (R) In a cyclic quadrilateral, the sum of opposite angles is 180°.

Which of the following is correct?

a (A) is true and (R) is correct explanation of (A)

b (A) is false and (R) is correct explanation of (A)

c (A) is true but (R) is not a correct explanation of (A)

d Both (A) and (R) are false

23. If $x = \dfrac{1}{\sqrt{7}+\sqrt{8}}$, then $\dfrac{1}{2}\left[\left(x+\dfrac{1}{x}\right)-\left(x-\dfrac{1}{x}\right)\right]$ is equal to

a $\sqrt{8}+\sqrt{7}$

b $\sqrt{8}-\sqrt{7}$

c $\dfrac{\sqrt{8}+\sqrt{7}}{\sqrt{8}-\sqrt{7}}$

d $\dfrac{\sqrt{8}-\sqrt{7}}{\sqrt{8}+\sqrt{7}}$

24. ABC is a triangle and M is the mid-point of AC. If I and J are points on BM such that AI and CJ are perpendicular to BM. Then, which of the following is incorrect?

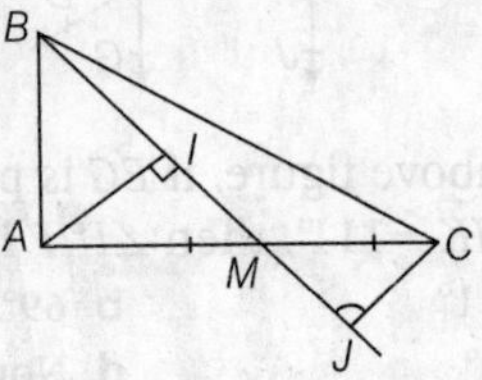

a $\angle AMI = \angle CMJ$

b $\angle IAM = \angle JCM$

c $\Delta AIM \cong \Delta CJM$

d $\angle ABM = \angle CBM$

25. Megha has a piece of land which is in the shape of a trapezium. She wants her one daughter and one son to work on the land and produce different crops and therefore divided the land in such a way that each of them gets equal share of land. If the two parallel sides of the land are 18 m and 10 m in length, one of the non-parallel sides is 1 more than the other and the perimeter of the land is 62 m with height 14 m. Then, the share of land each one gets, is

a 196 m^2

b 98 m^2

c 150 m^2

d 100 m^2

26.

Jack found some lost cards of his pack of cards. To pass his time, he started playing with them by picking any random card. Then, what is the probability that he picks an ace of diamond?

a $\dfrac{0}{10}$

b $\dfrac{1}{10}$

c $\dfrac{2}{10}$

d 1

27. The value of question mark (?) in the expression $x^4 - 7x^2 + 1 = ?$, if $x = \frac{\sqrt{3}+2}{\sqrt{2}}$, is

a $\frac{1}{4}$
b $\frac{3}{4}$
c 1
d 3

28. Consider the following statements below:

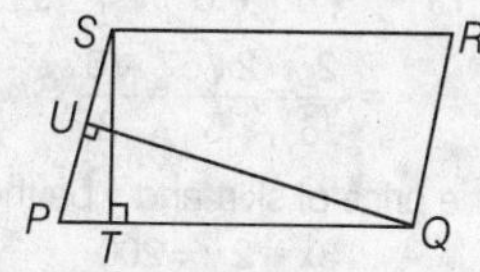

I. A parallelogram and a rectangle on the same base and between the same parallels are equal in area.

II. Area of parallelogram
$$= \frac{1}{2} \times \text{Base} \times \text{Altitude}.$$

III. In the above parallelogram *PQRS*, it is given that $PQ = 20$ cm. If the altitudes *ST* and *QU* being 12 cm and 16 cm respectively, then $PS = 15$ cm.

Which of the following is/are true?

a Only I
b I and III
c Only II
d II and III

29. In a state, Government recruited average of 800 teachers for teaching 5 subjects *viz.* Science, Mathematics, Hindi, Social Science and English. If the average of teachers teaching Science, Mathematics and Social Science is 656 and the number of teachers teaching Hindi is 20% of the total number of teachers. Then, the number of teachers teaching English is

a 1200
b 600
c 168
d 1232

30. Assertion (A) *ABCD* is a square. If *C′* is a point on *BA* and *B′* is a point on *AD* such that *BB′* and *CC′* are equal. Then, $\Delta AB'B$ and $\Delta BC'C$ are congruent.

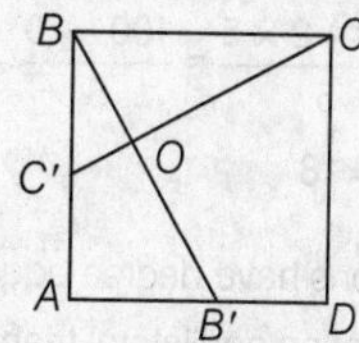

Reason (R) Two triangles are congruent, if two angles of a triangle and side included between them are equal to the corresponding two angles of other triangle and side included between them by ASA rule.

a (A) is true but (R) is not the correct explanation of (A)
b (A) is false and (R) is the correct explanation of (A)
c (A) is true and (R) is false
d Both (A) and (R) are false

Solutions

1. (a) $(\sqrt{2}+\sqrt{3})(\sqrt{3}-\sqrt{2})$
$=(\sqrt{3}+\sqrt{2})(\sqrt{3}-\sqrt{2})$
$=(\sqrt{3})^2-(\sqrt{2})^2$
$=3-2$
$=1=$ Rational number

2. (a)
3. (d)
4. (b) $\frac{p}{q}+\frac{q}{p}=\frac{p^2+q^2}{pq}$
$=\frac{p^2+q^2+2pq-2pq}{pq}=\frac{(p+q)^2-2pq}{pq}$
$=\frac{(10)^2-2\times5}{5}=\frac{100-10}{5}$
$=\frac{90}{5}=18$
5. (b) Other equations have degree equal to 4.
6. (d) Let the side of an equilateral triangle be a cm.
Then, area of triangle $=\frac{\sqrt{3}}{4}a^2$
Again, let new side of the triangle be $3a$.
Then, area $=\frac{\sqrt{3}}{4}\times(3a)(3a)=\frac{9\sqrt{3}}{4}a^2$
Increase in area $=\frac{9\sqrt{3}}{4}a^2-\frac{\sqrt{3}}{4}a^2=2\sqrt{3}a^2$
$\therefore$ Percentage increase in area
$=\frac{2\sqrt{3}a^2}{\frac{\sqrt{3}}{4}a^2}\times100=800\%$
7. (d) $K=14$, because mode is the value occurring the maximum number of times.
[$\because$ 19, 13, 20 occur 1 time and mode = 14]
8. (c)
9. (a) $E=$ Number of red colour boxes $=7$
Total number of boxes $=24$
$\therefore \quad P(E)=\frac{7}{24}$
10. (a) **Hint** Vertically opposite angles
11. (d)
12. (b) Number of small blocks
$=\frac{\text{Volume of bigger box}}{\text{Volume of small blocks}}$
$=\frac{4\times4\times3}{2\times1\times4}=6$
13. (c) Mean score of 9 innings = 58
$\therefore$ Total score $=9\times58=522$
Let the score of 10th innings be x.
$\therefore \quad \frac{x+522}{10}=61$
$\Rightarrow \quad x=88$
14. (c) $\frac{7+4\sqrt{5}+4-2\sqrt{5}-10-5\sqrt{5}}{6}$
$=\frac{1-3\sqrt{5}}{6}=p+q\sqrt{5}=\frac{1}{6}-\frac{3}{6}\sqrt{5}$
$\Rightarrow \quad p=\frac{1}{6}$ and $q=\frac{-3}{6}$ [on comparing]
$\therefore \quad \sqrt{p-q}=\sqrt{\frac{1}{6}-\left(\frac{-3}{6}\right)}=\sqrt{\frac{1+3}{6}}$
$=\frac{2}{\sqrt{6}}=\frac{2\sqrt{6}}{6}=\frac{\sqrt{6}}{3}$
15. (b) Let x be the price of skirt and y be the price of jeans.
Then, $3x+2y=200$
and $4x+y=350$
16. (b)

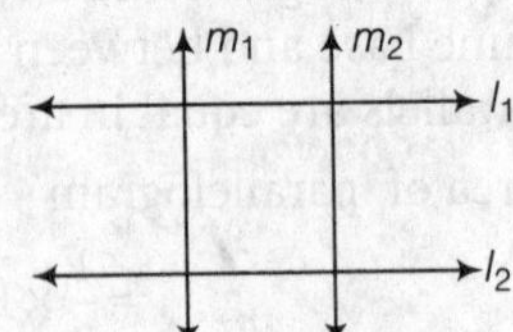

17. (d)
18. (b)

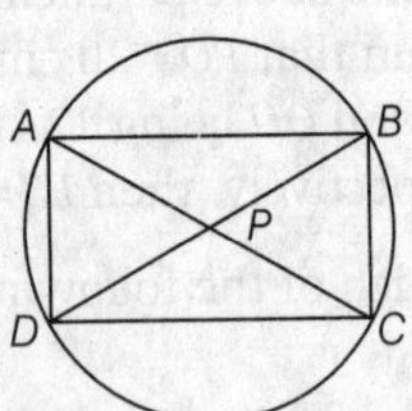

In the given figure, consider ΔPAB and ΔPDC,
$AB=CD$ [given]
$\angle PAB=\angle PDC$ [angle in same segment]
and $\angle PBA=\angle PCD$ [angle in same segment]
$\therefore \quad \Delta PAB\cong\Delta PDC$ [by ASA rule]
19. (c) $E=$ Students studying atleast 20 h in a week
$=1+1+5$ [20-30, 30-40, 40-50]
$=7$
$\therefore P(E)=\frac{7}{22}$
20. (b) Since, ΔABC is isosceles triangle.
and $BA=BC$
Then, $\angle BAM=\angle BCN$
Now, $MA=MB$
Then, ΔAMB is an isosceles triangle.
and $\angle BAM=\angle ABM$
Similarly, $NB=NC$
$\Rightarrow \quad \angle CBN=\angle BCN$
In ΔBAN and ΔCNB,
$AB=BC$
$\angle BAM=\angle BCN$
and $\angle ABM=\angle CBN$
$\therefore \quad \Delta AMB\cong\Delta CNB$

21. (b)

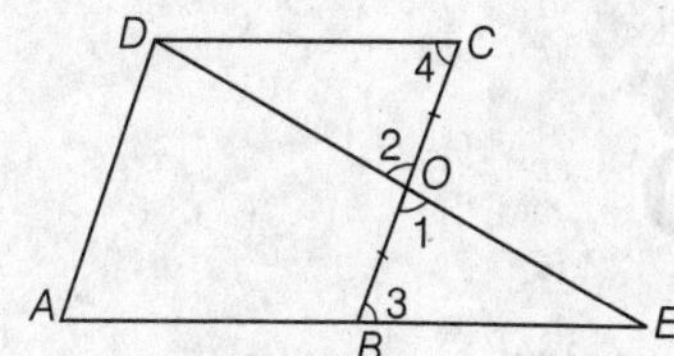

In the above figure, $ABCD$ is a parallelogram, where AB is produced to E such that

$$OC = OB.$$

Consider ΔOBE and ΔOCD,

$\angle 1 = \angle 2$ [vertically opposite angles]

$\angle 3 = \angle 4$ [alternate angles]

$OB = OC$ [given]

$\therefore \quad \Delta OBE \cong \Delta OCD$ [by ASA rule]

$\Rightarrow \quad BE = CD$ [by CPCT]

Also, $\quad AB = CD$ [since, $ABCD$ is a parallelogram]

$\therefore \quad AB = BE$

22. (c)

23. (a) Given, $x = \dfrac{1}{\sqrt{7}+\sqrt{8}} = \dfrac{\sqrt{8}-\sqrt{7}}{(\sqrt{8}+\sqrt{7})(\sqrt{8}-\sqrt{7})}$

$$= \frac{\sqrt{8}-\sqrt{7}}{1}$$

$$= \sqrt{8}-\sqrt{7}$$

$$\therefore \quad \frac{1}{x} = \sqrt{8}+\sqrt{7}$$

Now, $\quad x + \dfrac{1}{x} = \sqrt{8}-\sqrt{7}+\sqrt{8}+\sqrt{7}$

$$= 2\sqrt{8}$$

and $\quad x - \dfrac{1}{x} = \sqrt{8}-\sqrt{7}-\sqrt{8}-\sqrt{7}$

$$= -2\sqrt{7}$$

$$\therefore \frac{1}{2}\left[\left(x+\frac{1}{x}\right)-\left(x-\frac{1}{x}\right)\right] = \frac{1}{2}[2\sqrt{8}+2\sqrt{7}]$$

$$= \frac{2}{2}(\sqrt{8}+\sqrt{7})$$

$$= \sqrt{8}+\sqrt{7}$$

24. (c) $\Delta AIM \cong \Delta CJM$

So, (a) and (b) part also follow.

Since, M is the mid point of AC, then $AM = MC$.

Also, AI and CJ are perpendicular to BM.

So, AI is parallel to CJ with CA as the transversal.

$\therefore \quad \angle MAI = \angle MCJ$ [alternate angles]

$\angle AMI = \angle JMC$ [vertically opposite angles]

$\therefore \quad \Delta AIM \cong \Delta CJM$ [by ASA rule]

25. (b)

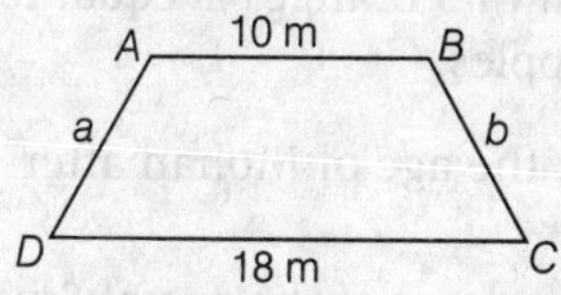

Area of trapezium $= \dfrac{1}{2}(10+18)\times 14$

$$= \frac{1}{2}\times 28 \times 14 = 14 \times 14$$

$$= 196\,\text{m}^2$$

$\therefore$ Share of land each one gets $= \dfrac{196}{2} = 98\,\text{m}^2$

26. (a) Since, there is no ace of diamond in the given cards.

27. (b) Given, $\quad x = \dfrac{\sqrt{3}+2}{\sqrt{2}}$

$$\Rightarrow \quad \sqrt{2}x = \sqrt{3}+2$$

$$\Rightarrow \quad \sqrt{2}x - 2 = \sqrt{3}$$

On squaring both sides, we get

$$(\sqrt{2}x-2)^2 = (\sqrt{3})^2$$

$$\Rightarrow \quad 2x^2 + 4 - 4\sqrt{2}\,x = 3$$

$$\Rightarrow \quad 2x^2 + 1 = 4\sqrt{2}x$$

Again, squaring both sides, we get

$$(2x^2+1)^2 = (4\sqrt{2}x)^2$$

$$\Rightarrow \quad 4x^4 + 1 + 4x^2 = 32x^2$$

$$\Rightarrow \quad 4x^4 - 28x^2 + 1 = 0$$

$$\Rightarrow \quad 4x^4 - 28x^2 + 4 = 3$$

$$\Rightarrow \quad x^4 - 7x^2 + 1 = 3/4$$

28. (b) $\because$ Area of parallelogram = Base $\times$ Height

Hence, Statement II is not true.

29. (d) Given,

Average number of teachers = 800

and total subjects = 5

$\therefore$ Total teachers $= 800 \times 5 = 4000$

Also,

$$\frac{\text{Science + Mathematics + Social science}}{3} = 656$$

$\Rightarrow$ Science + Mathematics + Social Science = 1968

$\Rightarrow \quad$ Hindi + English $= 4000 - 1968 = 2032$

Now, the number of teachers teaching Hindi

$$= \frac{20}{100}\times 4000 = 800$$

$\therefore$ Number of teachers teaching English

$$= 2032 - 800 = 1232$$

30. (a)

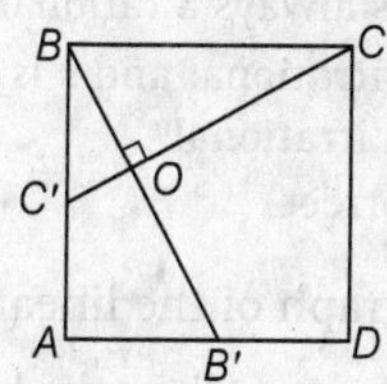

Consider $\Delta AB'B$ and $BC'C$,

$\angle BAB' = \angle CBC'$ [90°]

$AB = BC$ [side of square]

and $\quad BB' = CC'$ [given]

$\therefore \quad \Delta AB'B \cong \Delta BC'C$ [by RHS]

Practice Set 3

A Whole Content Based Test for Class 9th Mathematics Olympiad

1. The ratio of the numbers of sides of two regular polygons is 1 : 2. If each interior angle of the first polygon is 120; then the measure of each interior angle of the second polygon is

a 140° **b** 135°
c 150° **d** 160°

2. In the following parallelogram *ABCD*, if the line segments bisecting $\angle C$ and $\angle D$ meet at *E*. Then, choose the correct statement.

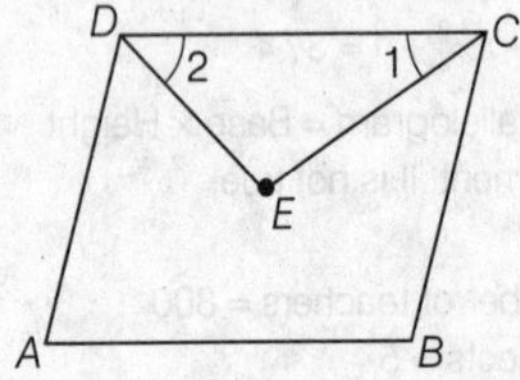

a $\angle A + \angle B = \angle CED$
b $\angle A + \angle B = 2\angle CED$
c $\angle A + \angle B = 3\angle CED$
d None of the above

3. Choose the correct statement.

a If a and b are integers, then $\frac{a}{b}$ is always an integer
b The multiplication of an irrational and a rational is always a rational
c If a is an irrational and b is a rational, then $a - b$ is an irrational
d All are correct

4. The point on graph of the linear equation $2x + 5y = 19$ whose ordinate is $1\frac{1}{2}$ times of abscissa, is

a $\left(-3, \frac{1}{2}\right)$
b $\left(3, 4\frac{1}{2}\right)$
c $(2, 3)$
d $(6, -9)$

5. In the following figure, the area of parallelogram *ABCD* is

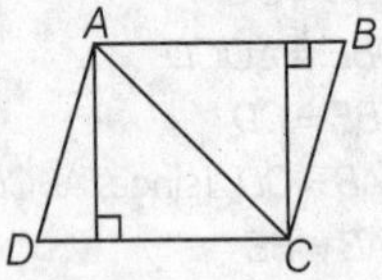

a 2 ar (ΔADC)
b 2 ar (ΔABC)
c Both (a) and (b)
d None of the above

6. Alex has the following data :

8	s	3	5

If the range is 7, then the value of *s* is equal to

a 1 **b** 18
c 20 **d** 2

Directions (Q. Nos. 7-8) Given, two Statements A and B. Study the statements carefully and answer the questions according to the options.

a If both the Statements A and B are required to answer the question
b If any of the two statements is sufficient to answer the question
c If both the statements together are not sufficient to answer the question
d None of the above

7. What will be the cost of 4 oranges and 5 apples?

A. Cost of 5 oranges and 3 apples is ₹ 42.
B. Cost of 5 oranges is equal to the cost of 4 apples.

8. What is the age of Mohan after 10 yr from now?

A. Difference of the age of Swati and Mohan is 10 yr.
B. Roma is as many years younger to Swati as Swati is younger than Mohan.

9. Choose the correct statements.

I. If the sum of interior angles of a polygon is 1080°, then the number of sides is 8.

II. The sum of all interior angles of a hexagon is 720°.

III. The sum of all exterior angles of a polygon is 540°.

IV. The ratio of the measure of an angle of regular octagon to the measure of its exterior angle is 3 : 1.

Which of the following is true?

a I, II and III

b II, III and IV

c I, II and IV

d All of the above

10. Assertion (A) P is a point on the side BC of a ΔABC such that $AB = AP$. Through A and C lines are drawn parallel to BC and PA, respectively, so as to intersect at D. Then, $ABCD$ is a cyclic quadrilateral.

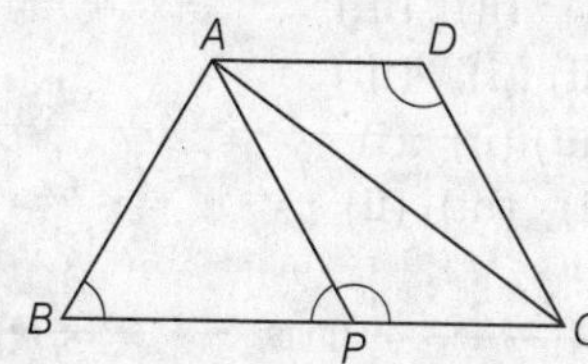

Reason (R) The sum of either pair of opposite angles of a cyclic quadrilateral is 180°.

Which of the following is true?

a (A) is true and (R) is correct explanation of (A)

b (A) is false and (R) is correct explanation of (A)

c (A) is true and (R) is false

d Both (A) and (R) are false

11. The length of a rectangle is decreased by 50% and its width is increased by 50%.

What impact does this have on the area of the rectangle?

a The area does not change

b The area increases by $\frac{3}{4}$

c The area decreases by 25%

d None of the above

12. The tally table below shows the birds that were in John's backyard one day and total birds were 91:

Birds	Tally marks	Numbers
Cardinal	卌 III	8
House wren	卌 IIII	9
Song sparrow	—	12
Humming bird	卌 卌 卌 —	20
Finch	卌 卌 II	—
Woodpecker	—	0
Chickadee	—	—

Which bird is seen the most?

a Finch

b Chickadee

c Song sparrow

d Humming bird

13. Assertion (A) If $a + b + c = 0$, then $x^{a^2 b^{-1} c^{-1}} \cdot x^{a^{-1} b^2 c^{-1}} \cdot x^{a^{-1} b^{-1} c^2}$ is equal to 1.

Reason (R) If $a + b + c = 0$, then $a^3 + b^3 + c^3 = 3abc$.

Which of the following is true?

a (A) is true and (R) is correct explanation of (A)

b (A) is false and (R) is correct explanation of (A)

c (A) is true and (R) is fa se

d (A) is false and (R) is true

14. A point X inside a rectangle $PQRS$ is joined to the vertices, then which of the following is true?

a ar (ΔPSX) = ar (ΔRXQ)

b ar (ΔPSX) + ar (ΔPXQ) = ar (ΔRSX) + ar (ΔRQX)

c ar (ΔPXS) + ar (ΔRQX) = ar (ΔSRX) + ar (ΔPXQ)

d None of the above

15. Assertion (A) A rectangle and an equilateral triangle have equal perimeters. If length of the rectangle is 7 cm more than its breadth and diagonal equal to 13 cm. Then, area of equilateral triangle is 289 cm^2.

Reason (R) If a, b and c denote the lengths of sides of a triangle, then

$$\text{Area} = \frac{1}{2} \times a \times b \times c$$

Which of the following is true?

a If (A) is true and (R) is the correct explanation of (A)

b If (A) is false and (R) is the correct explanation of (A)

c If (A) is true and (R) is false

d If both (A) and (R) are false

16. Fill in the box correctly.

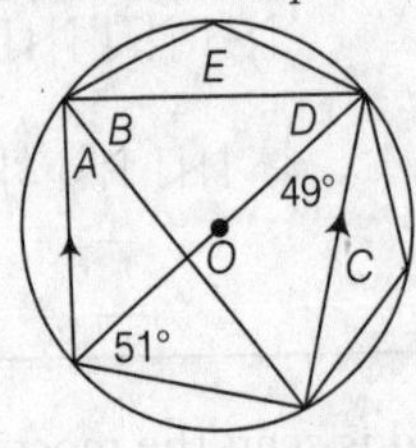

	A	B	C	D	E
a	49°	51°	109°	41°	129°
b	59°	59°	111°	59°	131°
c	49°	51°	129°	51°	131°
d	59°	59°	121°	49°	139°

17. Linda's mother recorded what colour shirt Linda wore on each day. The record is as follows:

Shirts	Days
Blue	3
Red	4
White	2
Black	6

Considering this data, how many times would Linda be expected to wear a black shirt in the next 20 days?

a 6 days **b** 8 days

c 10 days **d** Can't say

18. If $r = \dfrac{na+nb}{ny}$, then an increase in which of the following will decrease the value of r?

a a **b** b **c** n **d** y

19. Two bent poles AD and BC are supported by the rope AC and BD, respectively such that the mid point of the ropes are joined to support the structure. If the distances between the base points and top points of the poles are 15 units and 7 units, respectively as shown in the following figure, then the length of linkage FE is

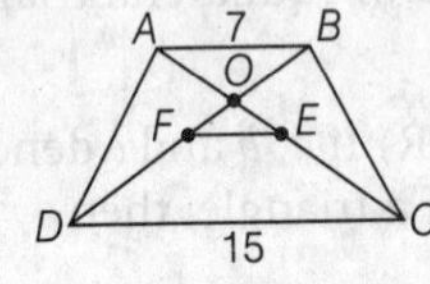

a 8 units **b** 6 units

c 4 units **d** 2 units

20. In the following figure, $ABCD$ is a quadrilateral inscribed in a circle with centre O. If CD is produced to E such that $\angle ADE = 95°$ and $\angle OBA = 30°$. Then, $\angle BAC$ is equal to

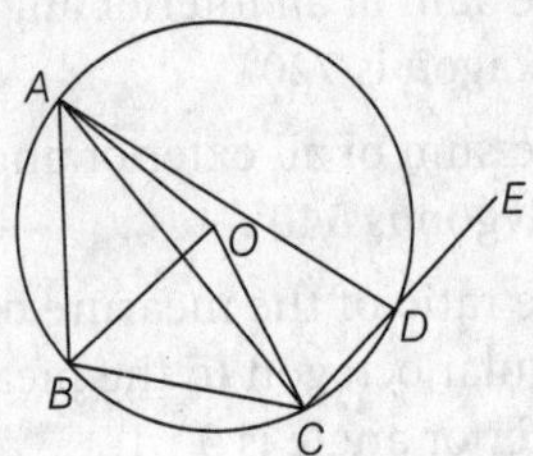

a 10° **b** 15°

c 20° **d** 25°

21. Match the following:

List I	List II
A. $16^{3/4}$	i. 3
B. $81^{0.25}$	ii. $(8^{1/3})^3$
C. $\sqrt[3]{625^{0.75}}$	iii. 5

Codes

	A	B	C
a	(i)	(ii)	(iii)
b	(ii)	(i)	(iii)
c	(iii)	(ii)	(i)
d	(i)	(iii)	(ii)

22.

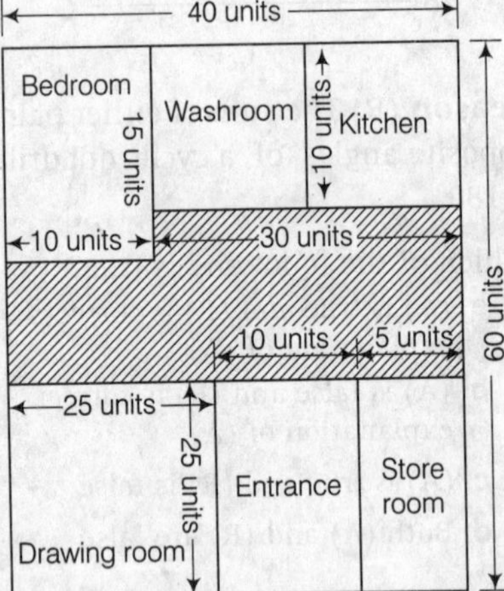

Aleena wanted to reconstruct his house and make a new plan for her 1 bhk flat. She asked his architect friend to prepare a plan for her house. Her friend made the above plan according to the space. Find the area not perfectly utilised (shaded) by her friend.

a 1075 sq units **b** 950 sq units

c 900 sq units **d** None of these

Directions (Q. Nos. 23-25) *Consider the data given below and answer the following questions.*

A company selected 4000 households at random and surveyed them to find out a relationship between income level and the number of AC sets in their home. The information so obtained, is listed.

Monthly income (in ₹)	Number of AC/households			
	0	1	2	Above 2
< 10000	20	80	10	0
10000-14999	10	240	60	0
15000-19999	0	380	120	30
20000-24999	0	520	370	80
25000 and above	0	1100	760	220

23. The probability of a household earning ₹ 10000-₹14999 per year and having exactly one AC, is

a 0.005 b 0.02
c 0.0025 d 0.06

24. The probability of a household earning ₹ 25000 and more per year and owning 2 ACs, is

a 0.15 b 0.19
c 0.24 d 0.28

25. The probability of household not having any AC, is

a 0.0005 b 0.0025
c 0.0050 d 0.0075

26. In the figure given below, if BA is the diameter of the circle. Then, value of x and $\angle DEB$ is

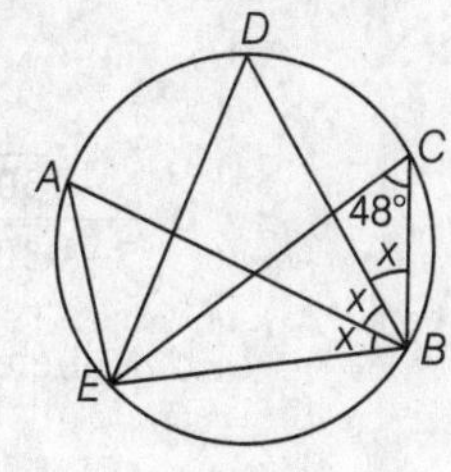

a 48° and 42° b 42° and 48°
c 46° and 44° d 44° and 46°

27. The value of the expression $\sqrt{(x+y+z)(x+y-z)+(z^2-x^2-y^2)-2xy}$ is

a 0 b $2x$
c $2y$ d $x+y+z$

28. Consider the following figure :

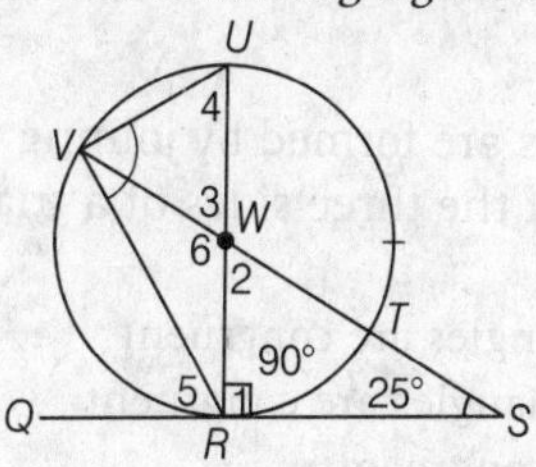

I. $\angle 2 = 65°$ II. $\angle 3 = 75°$
III. $\angle 4 = 57.5$ IV. $\angle 5 = 60°$
V. $\angle UVR = 90°$ VI. $\angle 6 = 115°$

Mark the incorrect matched option.

a II and III b I and III
c III and VI d II and IV

29. If the arithmetic mean of the observations $x_1, x_2, x_3, \ldots, x_n$ is 1, then the arithmetic mean of $\frac{x_1}{p}, \frac{x_2}{p}, \ldots, \frac{x_3}{p}, (p > 0)$ is

a greater than 1
b less than 1
c equal to 1
d None of the above

30. In the given figure, what is the sum in term of n_1, of the degree measures of the four angles marked with arrows?

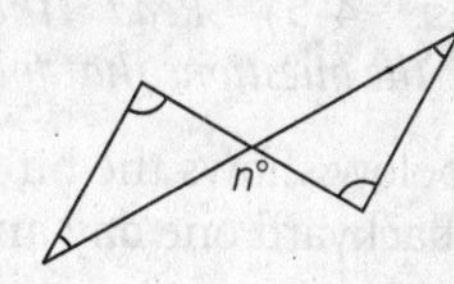

a n b $2n$
c $180n$ d $180-2n$

Answers

1. c	2. b	3. c	4. c	5. c	6. a	7. a	8. c	9. c	10. a
11. c	12. d	13. d	14. c	15. d	16. c	17. b	18. d	19. c	20. d
21. b	22. b	23. d	24. b	25. d	26. b	27. a	28. d	29. d	30. b

Practice Set 4

A Whole Content Based Test for Class 9th Mathematics Olympiad

1. Four triangles are formed by joining the mid-points of the three sides of a triangle, then

a two triangles are congruent
b three triangles are congruent
c All are congruent
d None is congruent

2. The sum of the squares of two consecutive even numbers is two more than two times the squares of their mean. This statement is

a never true
b always true
c true when the numbers are more than 100
d true when the numbers are less than or equal to 100

3. In the given figure, the sum of all the angles is equal to K right angles. K is equal to

a 10 b 12
c 14 d 16

Directions (Q.Nos. 4-5) *Read the following information and answer the questions that follow.*

The tally table below shows the birds that were in John's backyard one day and total birds were 91.

Birds	Tally marks	Numbers
Cardinal	𝍸 III	8
House wren	𝍸 IIII	9
Song sparrow	—	12
Humming bird	𝍸 𝍸 𝍸 —	20
Finch	𝍸 𝍸 II	—
Woodpecker	—	0
Chickadee	—	—

4. How many more times chickadees visited the yard than finch?

a 10 b 18 c 6 d 16

5. Which birds came the same number of times?

a Cardinal and house wren
b Cardinal and song sparrow
c Song sparrow and house wren
d Song sparrow and finch

6. $\log\left(\frac{169}{9}\right) - 2\log 13 + 2\log 3$ is equal to

a 1 b 0
c $\log\left(\frac{13}{3}\right)$ d $\log\left(\frac{3}{13}\right)$

7. In the given figure, if $AB \parallel CD$, then x is equal to

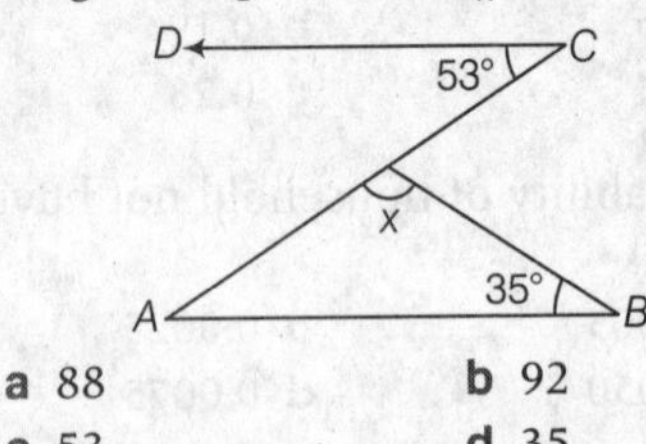

a 88 b 92
c 53 d 35

8. If $x = \frac{\sqrt{6}+\sqrt{5}}{\sqrt{6}-\sqrt{5}}$ and $y = 1$, then the value of $\frac{x+y}{x-y}$ is

a $\frac{6}{5}$ b $\frac{6-\sqrt{30}}{5-\sqrt{30}}$
c $\frac{6+\sqrt{30}}{5}$ d None of these

9. Find the value of x in the given figure.

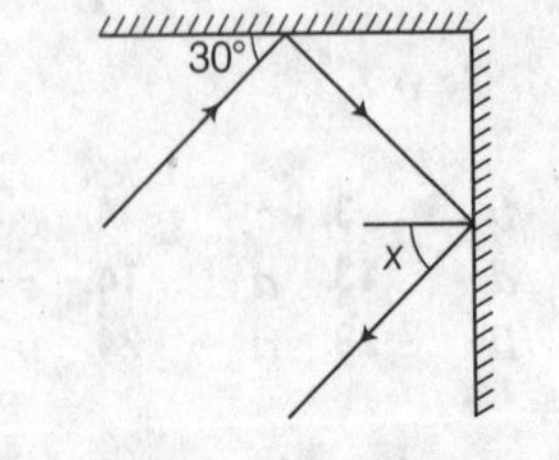

a 30° b 35° c 40° d 45°

10. If $2^{-m} \times \frac{1}{2^m} = \frac{1}{4}$, then $\frac{1}{14}\left[(4^m)^{\frac{1}{2}} + \left(\frac{1}{5^m}\right)^{-1}\right]$ is equal to

a $\frac{1}{2}$ b 2

c 4 d $\frac{-1}{4}$

Directions (Q. Nos. 11-12) *Read the following information and answer the questions that follow.*

The JM Gus trucking company purchases a new truck for \$ 65000. The truck will be depreciated at \$ 13000 per year. If y represents the value of the truck in dollars and x is the age of the truck in years.

11. The equation that describes the depreciation line is

a $x = y - 65000$

b $y = 65000 - 13000x$

c $x = 65000 - 13000y$

d Can't be determined

12. Find the y-intercept of the above data.

a (5, 0) b (0, 5)

c (0, 65000) d (65000, 5)

13.

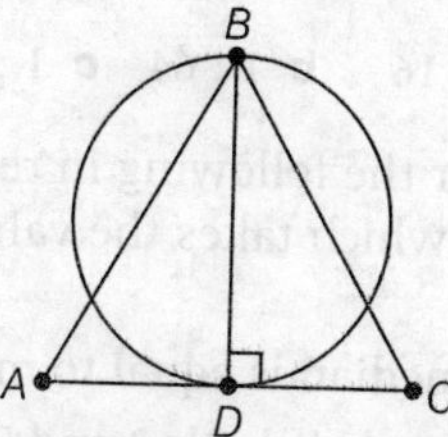

In the figure given above, ABC is an equilateral triangle. D is the mid-point of AC and BD is a diameter of the circle. If $AD = 4$, what is the area of the circle?

a 12π b 16π

c $16\sqrt{3}\pi$ d 48π

14. Which of the following is a homogenous expression?

a $5x^2 - 4xy + 6x^2y + 9y^2$

b $4x + 5y + 100$

c $15x^3 + 14x^2y + 17y^2x + 12y^3$

d $y^2 + x^2 + x + y + 1$

15. A bag contains 7 red, 5 blue, 4 white and 4 black balls. Find the probability that a ball drawn at random is red or white.

a 11/20 b 19/20

c 1/17 d 12/20

16. $x^3 + 6x^2 + 11x + 6$ is divisible by

a $x+1$

b $x+2$

c Both (a) and (b)

d None of the above

17. ABC is an equilateral triangle inscribed in a circle. D is any point on the arc BC. What is $\angle ADB$ equal to?

a 90°

b 60°

c 45°

d None of the above

18. Simplify $\frac{\sqrt{5} + \sqrt{3}}{\sqrt{80} + \sqrt{48} - \sqrt{45} - \sqrt{27}}$.

a 0 b 1

c $\sqrt{5}$ d $\sqrt{3}$

19. In solving a problem, one student makes a mistake in the coefficient of the first degree term and obtains −9 and −1 for the roots. Another student makes a mistake in the constant term of the equation and obtains 8 and 2 for the roots. The correct equation was

a $x^2 + 10x + 9 = 0$

b $x^2 - 10x + 16 = 0$

c $x^2 - 10x + 9 = 0$

d None of the above

20. The median of the values 11, 7, 6, 9, 12, 15, 19 is

a 9 b 11

c 12 d 15

21. ABC is an isosceles triangle with BA and BC congruent. Point K is on AB and point L is on BC. Both KK' and LL' are perpendicular to AC. If the segments KK' and LL' are congruent. Then, $\Delta KK'M \cong \Delta LL'M$ is

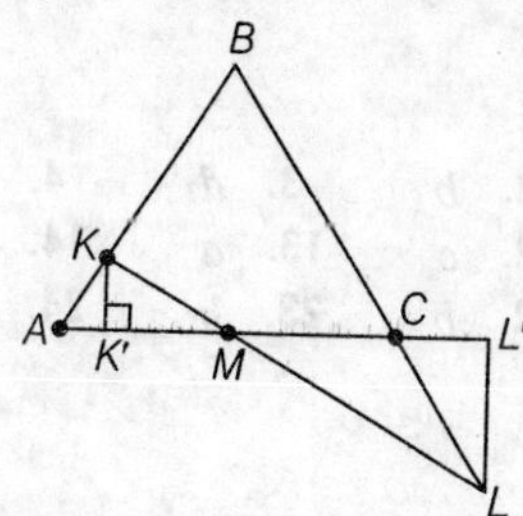

a true

b false

c Can't say

d None of the above

22. The length of a rectangle is increased by 40% and its width is decreased by 40%. What is the impact on the area of rectangle?

a Increase by 40% **b** Decrease by 16%
c Decrease by 40% **d** Increase by 16%

23. *ABCD* is a parallelogram. *G* is the point on *AB* such that $AG = 2GB$, *E* is point on *DC* such that $CE = 2DE$ and *F* is the point on *BC* such that $BF = 2FC$. Then, match the following:

List I	List II
A. ar (*ADEG*)	i. $\frac{1}{6}$ar(*ABCD*)
B. ar (Δ*EGB*)	ii. ar (Δ*EDG*)
C. ar (Δ*EFC*)	iii. ar (*GBCE*)
D. ar (Δ*EBG*)	iv. $\frac{1}{2}$ar(Δ*EBF*)

Codes

	A	B	C	D
a	(i)	(ii)	(iii)	(iv)
b	(iii)	(i)	(iv)	(ii)
c	(iii)	(ii)	(iv)	(i)
d	(ii)	(i)	(iii)	(iv)

24. The area of a sector of a circle of radius 36 cm is $72\pi\,\text{cm}^2$. The length of the corresponding arc of the sector is

a π cm **b** 2π cm **c** 3π cm **d** 4π cm

25.

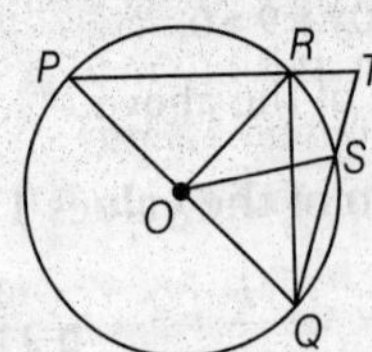

In the figure given above, *PQ* is a diameter of the circle whose centre is at *O*. If $\angle ROS = 44°$, then what is the value of $\angle RTS$?

a 46° **b** 64°
c 69° **d** None of these

26. A single card is chosen at random from a deck of 52 playing cards. What is the probability of choosing a card that is not a king?

a $\frac{11}{13}$ **b** $\frac{12}{13}$
c $\frac{1}{13}$ **d** None of these

27. If area of a square is '*a*' sq units, then the area of the circle formed by the same perimeter is given by

a $\frac{4\pi}{a}$ **b** $\frac{4a^2}{\pi}$
c $4a\pi$ **d** $\frac{a\pi}{4}$

28. An urn contains 6 red, 4 blue, 2 green and 3 yellow marbles. If one marble is picked at random, what is the probability that marble is red or yellow?

a $\frac{1}{6}$ **b** $\frac{1}{3}$
c $\frac{2}{15}$ **d** $\frac{3}{5}$

29. Diameter of the Moon is approximately one-fourth of the diameter of the Earth. What is the ratio (approximate) of their areas?

a 1 : 16 **b** 1 : 64 **c** 1 : 4 **d** 1 : 128

30. Consider the following in respect of the variate, which takes the values 2, 2, 2, 7, 7, 2, 7, 7:

I. The median is equal to mean.

II. The mode is both 2 and 7.

Which of the above statements is/are correct?

a Only I **b** Only II
c Both I and II **d** Neither I nor II

Answers

1. *c*	2. *b*	3. *d*	4. *b*	5. *d*	6. *b*	7. *b*	8. *d*	9. *a*	10. *a*
11. *b*	12. *c*	13. *a*	14. *c*	15. *a*	16. *c*	17. *b*	18. *b*	19. *c*	20. *b*
21. *a*	22. *b*	23. *b*	24. *d*	25. *a*	26. *b*	27. *b*	28. *d*	29. *a*	30. *c*

Practice Set 5

A Whole Content Based Test for Class 9th Mathematics Olympiad

1. If $25x^2 - 30x + K$ is a perfect square, then K is equal to

a 25 b 9
c 16 d 10

2. The side AC of a ΔABC is produced to D such that $BC = CD$. If $\angle ACB$ is 70°, then what is $\angle ADB$ equal to?

a 35° b 45°
c 70° d 110°

3. Consider the following statements:

I. The perpendicular bisector of a chord of a circle does not pass through the centre of the circle.

II. The angle in a semicircle is a right angle.

Which of the statements given above is/are correct?

a Only I
b Only II
c Both I and II
d Neither I nor II

4. Rationalising $\dfrac{x^2}{\sqrt{x^2+y^2}+y}$

a $\sqrt{x^2+y^2}-x$
b $\sqrt{x^2+y^2}-y$
c $x-\sqrt{x^2+y^2}$
d $y-\sqrt{x^2+y^2}$

5. The sides of a right angled triangle are equal to three consecutive numbers expressed in centimetres. What can be the area of such a triangle?

a 6 cm^2
b 8 cm^2
c 10 cm^2
d 12 cm^2

6. The equivalent form of

$$8x^3 - \frac{4x^2}{y} + \frac{2x}{3y^2} - \frac{1}{27y^3} \text{ is}$$

a $2x^2 - \dfrac{1}{3y^2}$

b $2x^3 - \dfrac{1}{3y^3}$

c $\left(2x - \dfrac{1}{3y}\right)^3$

d $8x^3 - \dfrac{1}{3y^3}$

7. The area of a rectangle lies between 40 cm^2 and 45 cm^2. If one of the sides is 5 cm, then its diagonal lies between

a 8 cm and 10 cm
b 9 cm and 11 cm
c 10 cm and 12 cm
d 11 cm and 13 cm

8. $\dfrac{1}{\sqrt{9}-\sqrt{8}} - \dfrac{1}{\sqrt{8}-\sqrt{7}} + \dfrac{1}{\sqrt{7}-\sqrt{6}} - \dfrac{1}{\sqrt{6}-\sqrt{5}} + \dfrac{1}{\sqrt{5}-\sqrt{4}}$ is equal to

a 0 b 1
c 5 d $\frac{1}{3}$

9. ABC is a triangle right angled at B. If $AB = 6$ cm and $BC = 8$ cm, then what is the length of the circumradius of the ΔABC?

a 10 cm b 7 cm
c 6 cm d 5 cm

10. If K is any even positive integer, then $(K^2 + 2K)$ is

a divisible by 24
b divisible by 8, but may not be divisible by 24
c divisible by 4, but may not be divisible by 8
d divisible by 2, but may not be divisible by 4

11. If the expression $(px^3 + x^2 - 2x - q)$ is divisible by $(x - 1)$ and $(x + 1)$, what are the values of p and q, respectively?

a 2 and −1 b −2 and 1
c −2 and −1 d 2 and 1

12. If $a + b + c = 0$, then what is the value of $\frac{a^2}{bc} + \frac{b^2}{ca} + \frac{c^2}{ab}$?

a −3 b 0
c 1 d 3

13. A circle and a square have the same perimeter. Which one of the following is correct?

a The area of the circle is equal to that of square
b The area of the circle is larger than that of square
c The area of the circle is less than that of square
d No conclusion can be drawn

14. What is the radius of the circle inscribed in a triangle having side lengths 35 cm, 44 cm and 75 cm?

a 3 cm b 4 cm
c 5 cm d 6 cm

15. x, y and z are consecutive positive integers such that $x < y < z$; which of the following must be true?

I. xyz is divisible by 6.
II. $(z - x)(y - x + 1) = 4$
III. xy is odd.

a Only I b Only II
c Only III d I and II

16. What is $\frac{(x^2 + y^2)(x - y) - (x - y)^3}{x^2y - xy^2}$ equal to?

a 1 b 2
c 4 d −2

17. Let $ABCD$ be a parallelogram and P, Q, R, S be the mid-points of sides AB, BC, CD, DA respectively. Consider the following statements:

I. Area of $\Delta APS <$ Area of ΔDSR, if $BD < AC$.
II. Area of $\Delta ABC = 4$(Area of ΔBPQ).

Select the correct answer using the codes given below.

a Only I b Only II
c Both I and II d Neither I nor II

18. What are the factors of $x^2 + 4y^2 + 4y - 4xy - 2x - 8$?

a $(x - 2y - 4)$ and $(x - 2y + 2)$
b $(x - y + 2)$ and $(x - 4y + 4)$
c $(x - y + 2)$ and $(x - 4y - 4)$
d $(x + 2y - 4)$ and $(x + 2y + 2)$

19. What is the total area of three equilateral triangles inscribed in a semi-circle of radiu[s] 2 cm?

a $12\ cm^2$ b $\frac{3\sqrt{3}}{4}\ cm^2$
c $\frac{9\sqrt{3}}{4}\ cm^2$ d $3\sqrt{3}\ cm^2$

20. $ABCD$ is a parallelogram. E is a point on B[C] such that $BE : EC = m : n$. If AE and DB intersect in F, then what is the ratio of th[e] area of ΔFEB to the area of ΔAFD?

a $\frac{m}{n}$ b $\left(\frac{m}{n}\right)^2$
c $\left(\frac{n}{m}\right)^2$ d $\left(\frac{m}{m+n}\right)^2$

21. The pair of rational numbers that lies between $\frac{1}{4}$ and $\frac{3}{4}$ is

a $\frac{262}{1000}, \frac{752}{1000}$
b $\frac{24}{100}, \frac{74}{100}$
c $\frac{9}{40}, \frac{31}{40}$
d $\frac{252}{1000}, \frac{748}{1000}$

22. The area of an isosceles ΔABC with $AB =$ [...] and altitude $AD = 3$ cm is 12 sq cm. Wha[t is] its perimeter?

a 18 cm b 16 cm
c 14 cm d 12 cm

23. Which one of the following is a non-terminating and repeating decima[l]?

a $\frac{13}{8}$ b $\frac{3}{16}$
c $\frac{3}{11}$ d $\frac{137}{25}$

24. The perimeter of a rectangle having are[a] equal to $144\ cm^2$ and sides in the ratio [...] is

a 52 cm b 56 cm
c 60 cm d 64 cm

25. The coffee spot has 12 pastries for sale, including 6 bran muffins. What is the probability that a randomly selected pastry will be bran muffin?

a $\frac{1}{2}$ **b** $\frac{2}{3}$

c $\frac{1}{4}$ **d** 1

26. The length of a rectangle is 3 cm more than its width. If its perimeter is 18 cm, then its width is

a 2 cm **b** 3 cm **c** 4 cm **d** 6 cm

27. The blood group of 200 people is distributed as follows: 50 have type A blood, 65 have B blood type, 70 have O blood type and 15 have type AB blood. If a person from this group is selected at random, what is the probability that this person has O blood type?

a 0.4 **b** 0.35

c 0.75 **d** 0.7

28. In a triangle, if sum of two angles is equal to the third angle (considering the interior angles only), then the triangle is

a right angled **b** acute angled

c equilateral **d** obtuse angled

29. The side BC of the ΔABC is extended to D. If $\angle ACD = 120°$, $\angle ABC = \frac{2}{3} \angle CAB$, then what is the value of $\angle BAC$?

a 60°

b 45°

c 30°

d 72°

30. A dice was rolled 20 times. On each roll the dice shows a value from 1 to 6. The results have been recorded in the table below:

Value	Frequency
1	3
2	5
3	2
4	4
5	3
6	3

The mode of the above data is

a 6

b 3

c 4

d 2

Answers

1. *b*	**2.** *a*	**3.** *b*	**4.** *b*	**5.** *a*	**6.** *c*	**7.** *b*	**8.** *b*	**9.** *d*	**10.** *c*
11. *d*	**12.** *d*	**13.** *b*	**14.** *d*	**15.** *d*	**16.** *b*	**17.** *c*	**18.** *a*	**19.** *d*	**20.** *d*
21. *d*	**22.** *a*	**23.** *c*	**24.** *a*	**25.** *a*	**26.** *b*	**27.** *b*	**28.** *a*	**29.** *d*	**30.** *d*

Answer & Explanations

1 Number System

A. Types of Numbers, Rational and Irrational Numbers

1. *a* 2. *b* 3. *b* 4. *b* 5. *c* 6. *b* 7. *b* 8. *b* 9. *b*

B. Properties of Rational and Irrational Numbers

1. *b* 2. *d* 3. *a* 4. *b* 5. *b* 6. *c* 7. *b* 8. *b* 9. *b* 10. *d*
11. *c* 12. *b* 13. *b* 14. *c* 15. *a* 16. *a* 17. *c* 18. *c* 19. *b* 20. *b*
21. *d* 22. *b* 23. *c* 24. *b*

C. *n*th Root of a Real Number and Laws of Exponents with Integral Powers

1. *b* 2. *a* 3. *b* 4. *b* 5. *a* 6. *b* 7. *b* 8. *b* 9. *b* 10. *b*
11. *b* 12. *b* 13. *a* 14. *b* 15. *a* 16. *c*

D. Rationalisation

1. *c* 2. *a* 3. *c* 4. *c* 5. *b* 6. *b* 7. *c* 8. *a* 9. *b* 10. *d*
11. *b* 12. *d* 13. *c* 14. *a* 15. *b* 16. *a* 17. *c* 18. *b* 19. *b* 20. *b*

2 Polynomials

A. Introduction to Polynomials, Degree and Types of Polynomial

1. *c* 2. *b* 3. *c* 4. *c* 5. *b* 6. *c* 7. *b* 8. *b* 9. *c* 10. *c*
11. *b* 12. *a*

B. Zeroes of a Polynomial, Factorisation and Remainder Theorem

1. *c* 2. *d* 3. *b* 4. *c* 5. *a* 6. *b* 7. *a* 8. *a* 9. *b* 10. *b*
11. *a* 12. *b* 13. *c* 14. *c* 15. *b* 16. *b* 17. *a* 18. *b* 19. *a* 20. *a*
21. *a* 22. *d* 23. *b* 24. *c* 25. *a* 26. *d* 27. *b*

C. Factorisation and Algebraic Identities

1. *c* 2. *d* 3. *a* 4. *c* 5. *d* 6. *b* 7. *c* 8. *c* 9. *b* 10. *a*
11. *d* 12. *b* 13. *b* 14. *a* 15. *b* 16. *b* 17. *d* 18. *a* 19. *c* 20. *a*
21. *a* 22. *a* 23. *a* 24. *a* 25. *b* 26. *a* 27. *a* 28. *c* 29. *b*

3 Linear Equations in Two Variables

A. Introduction to Linear Equations in Two Variables and Their Solutions using Algebraic Methods

1. *c* 2. *c* 3. *c* 4. *d* 5. *b* 6. *b* 7. *d* 8. *c* 9. *b* 10. *c*
11. *b* 12. *c* 13. *a* 14. *b* 15. *b* 16. *d* 17. *b* 18. *b* 19. *c* 20. *b*
21. *b*

B. Graphical Representation of Linear Equations in Two Variables and Their Solutions

1. *a* 2. *b* 3. *b* 4. *d* 5. *b* 6. *d* 7. *b* 8. *c* 9. *b* 10. *b*
11. *a* 12. *b* 13. *c*

C. Application Based Problems on Linear Equations in Two Variables

1. *b* 2. *d* 3. *b* 4. *c* 5. *c* 6. *c* 7. *b* 8. *b* 9. *b* 10. *b*
11. *b* 12. *b* 13. *b* 14. *a* 15. *c* 16. *a* 17. *c* 18. *b* 19. *d*

4 Lines and Angles

A. Angles, Types of Angles and Angle on a Straight Line

1. *b* 2. *b* 3. *a* 4. *b* 5. *a* 6. *b* 7. *d* 8. *d* 9. *b* 10. *b*
11. *b* 12. *d* 13. *a* 14. *d* 15. *b* 16. *b* 17. *a* 18. *b* 19. *b*

B. Perpendicular and Parallel Lines, Collinear and Non-collinear Points, Angles of a Triangle

1. *a* 2. *c* 3. *d* 4. *b* 5. *b* 6. *d* 7. *a* 8. *c* 9. *c* 10. *c*
11. *b* 12. *b* 13. *c* 14. *b* 15. *c* 16. *a* 17. *c* 18. *d*

C. Intersection of Two Lines, Intersection of Two Parallel Lines by a Transversal, Angles Formed and Their Properties

1. *b* 2. *d* 3. *b* 4. *b* 5. *b* 6. *b* 7. *d* 8. *b* 9. *b* 10. *d*
11. *b* 12. *c* 13. *b* 14. *b* 15. *a*

5 Triangles

A. Triangles, Its Properties and Types of Triangles

1. *a* 2. *d* 3. *c* 4. *c* 5. *c* 6. *b* 7. *d* 8. *b* 9. *b* 10. *a*
11. *d* 12. *a* 13. *a* 14. *b* 15. *a* 16. *b*

B. Congruency of Triangles, Various Criterion of Congruencies like SSS, SAS, ASA and RHS

1. *a* 2. *d* 3. *d* 4. *b* 5. *d* 6. *b* 7. *c* 8. *b* 9. *c* 10. *d*
11. *d* 12. *c* 13. *c* 14. *a* 15. *d*

C. Triangle Inequalities

1. *d* 2. *a* 3. *c* 4. *c* 5. *d* 6. *b* 7. *b* 8. *a* 9. *c* 10. *b*
11. *d* 12. *b* 13. *b* 14. *c* 15. *a*

6 Quadrilaterals

A. Introduction to Quadrilaterals and Their Types

1. *c* 2. *a* 3. *b* 4. *b* 5. *d* 6. *b* 7. *b* 8. *a* 9. *b* 10. *d*
11. *c* 12. *b* 13. *a* 14. *c* 15. *d* 16. *c* 17. *b*

B. Properties of Parallelogram and Mid-point Theorem

1. *c* 2. *a* 3. *a* 4. *c* 5. *d* 6. *b* 7. *b* 8. *c* 9. *a* 10. *d*
11. *b* 12. *a* 13. *d* 14. *c*

7 Circle

A. Introduction to Circle and Basic Terminology

1. *c* 2. *b* 3. *b* 4. *b* 5. *b* 6. *b* 7. *a* 8. *a* 9. *a* 10. *c*
11. *d* 12. *c* 13. *b* 14. *b* 15. *c* 16. *c* 17. *a* 18. *c* 19. *a* 20. *b*

B. Arc Properties of a Circle and Cyclic Quadrilateral

1. *b* 2. *c* 3. *c* 4. *c* 5. *d* 6. *a* 7. *b* 8. *b* 9. *c* 10. *d*
11. *c* 12. *a* 13. *c* 14. *b* 15. *b* 16. *d* 17. *d* 18. *c* 19. *d* 20. *b*
21. *c*

8 Area of Parallelograms and Triangles

A. Area of Triangle using Heron's Formula (Various Types of Triangles and Perimeter of Plane Figures)

1. *a* **2.** *a* **3.** *c* **4.** *c* **5.** *b* **6.** *d* **7.** *c* **8.** *b* **9.** *b* **10.** *a*
11. *c* **12.** *a* **13.** *d*

B. Area of Circle and Parallelogram (Using Area of Triangle and Its Properties)

1. *b* **2.** *b* **3.** *b* **4.** *c* **5.** *c* **6.** *d* **7.** *c* **8.** *c* **9.** *c* **10.** *d*
11. *b* **12.** *b* **13.** *c* **14.** *a* **15.** *a*

9 Statistics

A. Introduction to Statistics–Different Terminology, Bar Graphs Representation and Frequency Distribution

1. *a* **2.** *d* **3.** *d* **4.** *a* **5.** *b* **6.** *c* **7.** *d* **8.** *b* **9.** *b*
10. *d* **11.** *d* **12.** *b* **13.** *c* **14.** *c* **15.** *b* **16.** *b* **17.** *a* **18.** *c*

B. Measure of Central Tendencies–Mean, Median, Mode and Relation among Them

1. *c* **2.** *c* **3.** *a* **4.** *b* **5.** *b* **6.** *b* **7.** *b* **8.** *b* **9.** *c*
10. *b* **11.** *b* **12.** *b* **13.** *d* **14.** *c* **15.** *b* **16.** *c* **17.** *b* **18.** *d*
19. *c*

10 Probability

1. *c* **2.** *c* **3.** *d* **4.** *c* **5.** *c* **6.** *d* **7.** *b* **8.** *c* **9.** *b* **10.** *b* **11.** *b*
12. *c* **13.** *d* **14.** *c* **15.** *a*

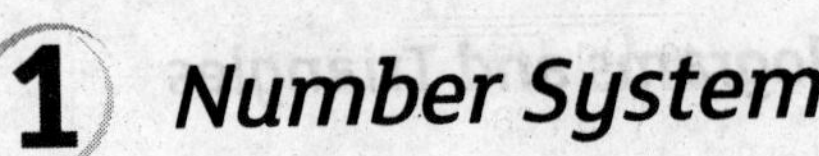

1 Number System

A. Types of Numbers, Rational and Irrational Numbers

1. On solving, we get 1 which is a rational number.

$$\left[\begin{array}{l}\because (2+\sqrt{3})(2-\sqrt{3}) \\ = 4-2\sqrt{3}+2\sqrt{3}-3=1\end{array}\right]$$

3. Statements I and II are correct, while Statement III, if $n = 2$, then

$\sqrt{n-1} = \sqrt{2-1} = \sqrt{1} = 1$ and 1 is not irrational.

5. Between two rational numbers, there are infinite rational numbers.

6. e.g. $(2+\sqrt{3})+(2-\sqrt{3}) = 4$ which is not an irrational number.

7. $x > y \Rightarrow -x < -y$

8. $5\pi + 3\pi = 8\pi$

$\Rightarrow \quad 9\pi - 8\pi = \pi$

which is an irrational number.

9. $\frac{1}{0}$ is not defined.

B. Properties of Rational and Irrational Numbers

1. We know that, product of any number with its reciprocal is always 1. This is called multiplicative inverse.

i.e. $\quad a \times \frac{1}{a} = 1$

2. For any two rational numbers,

$x \geq y$ or $x < y$

i.e. $x > y$, $x = y$ or $x < y$ anyone of these three is valid at a time.

3. $\because A + B = B + A = 0$

i.e. A and B are called additive inverse.

4. A. $\frac{1}{0}$ i.e. multiplicative inverse of 0 is not defined.

B. Additive inverse of $\frac{2}{5} = -\frac{2}{5}$

C. $A + B = B + A = 0$ i.e. additive inverse of each other.

D. $A \times \frac{1}{A} = 1$ i.e. multiplicative inverse.

5. $2\sqrt{3}+3\sqrt{3}-4\sqrt{3} = \sqrt{3}$

6. $\frac{2-\sqrt{5}+3+2\sqrt{5}-4-\sqrt{5}}{4} = p + q\sqrt{5}$

$\Rightarrow \quad \frac{1+0}{4} = p + q\sqrt{5}$

i.e. $p = \frac{1}{4}, q = 0 \quad$ [on comparing]

7. $\because$ Additive inverse of $\frac{2}{3} = -\frac{2}{3}$

and multiplicative inverse of $\frac{2}{3} = \frac{3}{2}$

According to the question,

$$-\frac{2}{3} + \frac{3}{2} = \frac{-4+9}{6} = \frac{5}{6}$$

8. Since, $\sqrt[7]{a^4b^3c^5} \times \sqrt[7]{a^3b^4c^2}$

$= \sqrt[7]{a^{4+3}b^{3+4}c^{5+2}}$

$= \sqrt[7]{a^7b^7c^7} = abc$

9. $\because \quad x = 1.242424... \quad ...(i)$

$\Rightarrow \quad 100x = 124.24 \quad ...(ii)$

On subtracting Eq. (i) from Eq. (ii), we get

$99x = 123$

$\Rightarrow \quad x = \frac{123}{99}$

$\Rightarrow \quad x = \frac{41}{33} = \frac{p}{q}$

$\therefore \quad p = 41$

and $\quad q = 33$

Now, $p + q = 41 + 33 = 74$

10. $\because$ Product of two rational numbers $= -\frac{9}{16}$

and one of the numbers $= -\frac{4}{3}$

$\therefore \quad$ Other number $= -\frac{9}{16} \div \frac{-4}{3}$

$= -\frac{9}{16} \times \frac{3}{-4} = \frac{27}{64}$

11. Let x be the number.

So, $-\frac{4}{39} \times x = 25$

$\Rightarrow \quad x = \frac{25}{-\frac{4}{39}}$

$\Rightarrow \quad x = 25 \times \frac{(-39)}{4} = -\frac{975}{4}$

12. $\because \frac{p}{q} = \frac{r}{s} \Rightarrow ps = rq$

13. $\sqrt{18} \times \sqrt{27} \div \sqrt{12} + \sqrt{\frac{81}{2}}$ of $\sqrt{36} - \sqrt{8}$

$= \sqrt{\frac{18 \times 27}{12}} + \frac{9}{\sqrt{2}} \times 6 - 2\sqrt{2}$

$= \frac{9}{\sqrt{2}} + \frac{54}{\sqrt{2}} - 2\sqrt{2}$

$= \frac{63}{\sqrt{2}} - 2\sqrt{2} = \frac{63-4}{\sqrt{2}} = \frac{59}{\sqrt{2}}$

Now, $\quad \frac{59}{\sqrt{2}} = a + \frac{b}{\sqrt{2}}$

$\Rightarrow \quad a = 0, b = 59$

$\therefore \quad \frac{a-b}{a+b} = \frac{-59}{59} = -1$

15. Given, $x = \frac{\sqrt{3}-\sqrt{2}}{\sqrt{3}+\sqrt{2}}, y = \frac{\sqrt{3}+\sqrt{2}}{\sqrt{3}-\sqrt{2}}$

$\Rightarrow \quad \frac{1}{x} = \frac{\sqrt{3}+\sqrt{2}}{\sqrt{3}-\sqrt{2}}$

and $\quad \frac{1}{y} = \frac{\sqrt{3}-\sqrt{2}}{\sqrt{3}+\sqrt{2}}$

According to the question,

$$\left(x + \frac{1}{y}\right) + \left(y + \frac{1}{x}\right) - 2y = \frac{1}{P + \sqrt{q}}$$

$$\Rightarrow \left(\frac{\sqrt{3}-\sqrt{2}}{\sqrt{3}+\sqrt{2}} + \frac{\sqrt{3}-\sqrt{2}}{\sqrt{3}+\sqrt{2}}\right) + \left(\frac{\sqrt{3}+\sqrt{2}}{\sqrt{3}-\sqrt{2}} + \frac{\sqrt{3}+\sqrt{2}}{\sqrt{3}-\sqrt{2}}\right) - 2\left(\frac{\sqrt{3}+\sqrt{2}}{\sqrt{3}-\sqrt{2}}\right) = \frac{1}{P+\sqrt{q}}$$

$$\Rightarrow \frac{2\sqrt{3}-2\sqrt{2}}{\sqrt{3}+\sqrt{2}} + 2\left(\frac{\sqrt{3}+\sqrt{2}}{\sqrt{3}-\sqrt{2}}\right) - 2\left(\frac{\sqrt{3}+\sqrt{2}}{\sqrt{3}-\sqrt{2}}\right) = \frac{1}{p+\sqrt{q}}$$

$$\Rightarrow \frac{2\sqrt{3}-2\sqrt{2}}{\sqrt{3}+\sqrt{2}} = \frac{1}{p+\sqrt{q}}$$

$$\Rightarrow \quad p+\sqrt{q} = \frac{\sqrt{3}+\sqrt{2}}{2\sqrt{3}-2\sqrt{2}}$$

$$\Rightarrow \quad p+\sqrt{q} = \frac{\sqrt{3}+\sqrt{2}}{2(\sqrt{3}-\sqrt{2})}$$

$$\Rightarrow \quad p+\sqrt{q} = \frac{(\sqrt{3}+\sqrt{2})(\sqrt{3}+\sqrt{2})}{2(\sqrt{3}-\sqrt{2})(\sqrt{3}+\sqrt{2})}$$

$$\Rightarrow \quad p+\sqrt{q} = \frac{(\sqrt{3}+\sqrt{2})(\sqrt{3}+\sqrt{2})}{2(3-2)}$$

$$\Rightarrow \quad p+\sqrt{q} = \frac{3+2+2\sqrt{6}}{2}$$

$$= \frac{5}{2} + \sqrt{6}$$

On comparing both sides, we get

$p = 5/2$

and $\quad \sqrt{q} = \sqrt{6}$

$\Rightarrow \quad q = 6$

$\therefore \quad \frac{p}{q} = \frac{5}{2 \cdot 6} = \frac{5}{12}$

16. Given, $\quad a + b + c = 117 \quad ...(i)$

Such that $b = ap$ and $c = aq \quad [\because b \leq c]$

We have,

$a + ap + aq = 117$

$\Rightarrow \quad a(1 + p + q) = 3 \times 39$

$\Rightarrow \quad a = 3$

Now, from Eq. (i), we have

$$b + c = 114$$

To have greatest value for b and c,

we have $b = c = 57$

$\therefore \quad a \times b \times c = 3 \times 57 \times 57 = 9747$

17. Given, $p = t^{1/2} + t^{-1/2}$

and $q = t^{1/2} - t^{-1/2}$

$\Rightarrow p^2q^2 + 2$

$= [(t^{1/2} + t^{-1/2})(t^{1/2} - t^{-1/2})]^2 + 2$

$= [(t^{1/2})^2 - (t^{-1/2})^2]^2 + 2$

$= (t - t^{-1})^2 + 2$

$= t^2 - 2 + t^{-2} + 2$

$= t^2 + \dfrac{1}{t^2}$

8. Given, $(x^{1/3})^2 - 5(x^{1/3}) + 6 = 0$

Let $y = x^{1/3}$, then

$y^2 - 5y + 6 = 0$

$\Rightarrow \quad y = 2, 3$

When $y = 2$, then $x^{1/3} = 2$

$\Rightarrow \quad x = 2^3 = 8$

When $y = 3$, then $x^{1/3} = 3$

$\Rightarrow \quad x = 3^3 = 27$

Given, $\quad (BE)^2 = MPB$

Since, MPB is a three-digit square number.

$\therefore \quad 10 \le BE \le 31$

Also, we have

$(BE)^2 = MPB$ (equal)

$\therefore$ B can be equal to 1, 2, 3, since 2, 3 never occur as the unit digit of a square number.

$\therefore \quad B = 1$

Now, we have

$(1E)^2 = MP1$

We know,

$(11)^2 = 121$

and $\quad (19)^2 = 361$

$\therefore$ The suitable digit is $(19)^2 = 361$

$\Rightarrow \quad M = 3$

$\sqrt{32 - x\sqrt{15}} = \sqrt{27} + \sqrt{5}$

Squaring both sides, we got

$32 - x\sqrt{15} = (\sqrt{27})^2 + (\sqrt{5})^2 + 2\sqrt{27 \times 5}$

$\Rightarrow \quad 32 - x\sqrt{15} = 27 + 5 + 2\sqrt{3 \times 3 \times 3 \times 5}$

$\Rightarrow \quad 32 - x\sqrt{15} = 32 + 6\sqrt{15}$

$\Rightarrow \quad x = -6$ [on comparing]

21. Let $\sqrt{\dfrac{49}{36}\sqrt{\dfrac{49}{36}\sqrt{\dfrac{49}{36}}}} \ldots \infty = x$

$\Rightarrow \quad \sqrt{\dfrac{49}{36}x} = x$

Squaring both sides, we get

$\Rightarrow \quad \dfrac{49}{36}x = x^2$

$\Rightarrow \quad x = \dfrac{49}{36}$

22. Let $x = \sqrt{5\sqrt{5\sqrt{5\ldots}}}$

$\Rightarrow x = \sqrt{5x}$ [$\because \sqrt{x\sqrt{x\sqrt{x\ldots}}} = x$ and it is infinite series]

$\Rightarrow \quad x^2 = 5x$ [on squaring]

$\Rightarrow \quad x^2 - 5x = 0$

$\Rightarrow \quad x(x - 5) = 0$

$\Rightarrow \quad x = 5$

Similarly, $\sqrt{7\sqrt{7\sqrt{7\ldots}}} = 7$

and $\quad \sqrt{3\sqrt{3\sqrt{3\ldots}}} = 3$

$\therefore \left(\dfrac{\sqrt{5\sqrt{5\sqrt{5\ldots}}} + \sqrt{7\sqrt{7\sqrt{7\ldots}}}}{\sqrt{3\sqrt{3\sqrt{3\ldots}}}}\right) = \dfrac{5 + 7}{3} = \dfrac{12}{3} = 4$

23. We have, $\sqrt{11 + 2\sqrt{30}} + \sqrt{11 - 2\sqrt{30}}$

$= \sqrt{(\sqrt{6})^2 + (\sqrt{5})^2 + 2\sqrt{6} \times \sqrt{5}} + \sqrt{(\sqrt{6})^2 + (\sqrt{5})^2 - 2\sqrt{6} \times \sqrt{5}}$

$= \sqrt{(\sqrt{6} + \sqrt{5})^2} + \sqrt{(\sqrt{6} - \sqrt{5})^2}$

$= \sqrt{6} + \sqrt{5} + \sqrt{6} - \sqrt{5} = 2\sqrt{6}$

24. $(\sqrt[6]{15 - 2\sqrt{56}})(\sqrt[3]{\sqrt{7} + 2\sqrt{2}})$

$= (\sqrt[6]{(\sqrt{8})^2 + (\sqrt{7})^2 - 2\sqrt{7 \times 8}})(\sqrt[3]{\sqrt{7} + 2\sqrt{2}})$

$= (\sqrt[6]{(\sqrt{8} - \sqrt{7})^2})(\sqrt[3]{2\sqrt{2} + \sqrt{7}})$

$= (\sqrt{8} - \sqrt{7})^{2/6}\,(2\sqrt{2} + \sqrt{7})^{1/3}$

$= (2\sqrt{2} - \sqrt{7})^{1/3}\,(2\sqrt{2} + \sqrt{7})^{1/3}$

$= [(2\sqrt{2})^2 - (\sqrt{7})^2]^{1/3}$

$= (8 - 7)^{1/3} = 1$

C. nth Root of a Real Number and Laws of Exponents with Integral Powers

1. $(a^{mn})^{\frac{1}{mn}} = a$

2. $\dfrac{\sqrt[2]{64}}{\sqrt[3]{64}} = \dfrac{8}{4} = 2$

3. $\because \left\{\left(\dfrac{2}{3}\right)^4\right\}^3 = \left(\dfrac{2}{3}\right)^{4 \times 3} = \left(\dfrac{2}{3}\right)^{12}$

Now, $\left(\dfrac{2}{3}\right)^{12} = \left(\dfrac{3}{2}\right)^x$

$\Rightarrow \quad \left(\dfrac{3}{2}\right)^{-12} = \left(\dfrac{3}{2}\right)^x \quad \left[\because a^{-1} = \dfrac{1}{a}\right]$

$\therefore \quad x = -12$ [by comparing]

4. Given, $a = 2$ and $b = 3$

$\therefore \quad a^a + b^b = 2^2 + 3^3 = 4 + 27 = 31$

and $\quad a^b + b^a = 2^3 + 3^2 = 8 + 9 = 17$

5. Given surds are in the form

$2^{1/2}, 3^{1/6}, 4^{1/3}$ and $5^{1/4}$

So, LCM of 2, 6, 3 and 4 is 12.

$\therefore \; 2^{1/2} = (2^6)^{1/12} = (64)^{1/12}$

$3^{1/6} = (3^2)^{1/12} = (9)^{1/12}$

$4^{1/3} = (4^4)^{1/12} = (256)^{1/12}$

$5^{1/4} = (5^3)^{1/12} = (125)^{1/12}$

Clearly, greatest surd $(256)^{1/12} = \sqrt[3]{4}$ i.e. 256 is greatest.

6. A. $\left(\sqrt[m]{\sqrt[n]{\dfrac{1}{a}}}\right)^{mn} = \left(\dfrac{1}{a}\right)^{\frac{mn}{mn}} = \dfrac{1}{a}$

B. $\dfrac{2^{m+n}}{2^{n-m}} = 16$

$\Rightarrow 2^{(m+n-n+m)} = 2^4 \quad \left[\because \dfrac{a^m}{a^n} = a^{m-n}\right]$

$\Rightarrow \quad 2^{2m} = 2^4$

$\Rightarrow \quad 2m = 4$ [$\because a^m = a^n \Rightarrow m = n$]

$\Rightarrow \quad m = 2$

C. $\left(\dfrac{100}{9}\right)^{-3/2} = \left(\left(\dfrac{10}{3}\right)^2\right)^{-3/2}$

$= \left(\dfrac{10}{3}\right)^{2 \times \frac{-3}{2}}$

$\left[\because (a^m)^n = a^{mn}, a^{-n} = \dfrac{1}{a^n}\right]$

$= \left(\dfrac{3}{10}\right)^3 = \dfrac{3}{10} \times \dfrac{3}{10} \times \dfrac{3}{10}$

D. $(x^{-1} + y^{-1})^{-1} = \left(\dfrac{1}{x} + \dfrac{1}{y}\right)^{-1}$

$= \left(\dfrac{y + x}{xy}\right)^{-1} = \dfrac{xy}{x + y}$

7. Given, $x = 2$ and $y = 4$

$\therefore \quad \left(\dfrac{x}{y}\right)^{y-x} + \left(\dfrac{y}{x}\right)^{x-y}$

$= \left(\dfrac{2}{4}\right)^2 + \left(\dfrac{4}{2}\right)^{-2}$

$= \left(\dfrac{2}{4}\right)^2 + \left(\dfrac{2}{4}\right)^2$

$= \dfrac{1}{4} + \dfrac{1}{4} = \dfrac{2}{4} = \dfrac{1}{2}$

8. Let $2^a = 3^b = 6^{-c} = K$

$\Rightarrow \quad 2 = K^{1/a}, 3 = K^{1/b}$ and $6 = K^{-1/c}$

$\therefore \quad 2 \times 3 = 6$

$\Rightarrow \quad K^{1/a} \times K^{1/b} = K^{-1/c}$

$\Rightarrow \quad K^{\left(\frac{1}{a} + \frac{1}{b}\right)} = K^{-1/c}$

$\therefore \quad \dfrac{1}{a} + \dfrac{1}{b} = \dfrac{-1}{c}$

$\Rightarrow \quad \dfrac{1}{a} + \dfrac{1}{b} + \dfrac{1}{c} = 0$

9. $\because \sqrt{2^n} = 1024$ [given]

$\Rightarrow (2^n)^{1/2} = 2^{10} \Rightarrow 2^{n/2} = 2^{10}$

$\Rightarrow \frac{n}{2} = 10$ [by comparing]

$\Rightarrow n = 20$

$\therefore 3^{2\left(\frac{n}{4}-4\right)} = 3^{2\left(\frac{20}{4}-4\right)} = 3^{2(5-4)}$

$= 3^{2(1)} = 3^2 = 9$

10. $\frac{5^{n+2} - 6\times 5^{n+1}}{13\times 5^n - 2\times 5^{n+1}}$

$= \frac{5^n\times 5^2 - 6\times 5\times 5^n}{13\times 5^n - 2\times 5\times 5^n}$

$= \frac{5^n}{5^n}\left(\frac{25-30}{13-10}\right) = \frac{-5}{3}$

11. $25^{x-1} = 5^{2x-1} - 100$

$\Rightarrow 100 = 5^{2x-1} - 25^{x-1}$

$\Rightarrow 100 = 5^{2x-1} - (5^2)^{x-1}$

$\Rightarrow 100 = 5^{2x-1} - 5^{2x-2}$

$\Rightarrow 100 = 5^{2x-2}(5-1)$

$\Rightarrow \frac{100}{4} = 5^{2x-2}$

$\Rightarrow 25 = 5^{2x-2}$

$\Rightarrow 5^2 = 5^{2x-2} \Rightarrow 2x-2 = 2$

$\Rightarrow 2x = 4 \Rightarrow x = 2$

12. $\left(\frac{x^a}{x^b}\right)^{a+b}\cdot\left(\frac{x^b}{x^c}\right)^{b+c}\cdot\left(\frac{x^c}{x^a}\right)^{c+a}$

$= x^{(a-b)(a+b)}\cdot x^{(b-c)(b+c)}\cdot x^{(c-a)(c+a)}$

$= x^{a^2-b^2+b^2-c^2+c^2-a^2} = x^0 = 1$

13. $\frac{(x^{-2}y^2)^{1/2}}{[(\sqrt{x^4+y^4})^2 - (x^2)^2]^{1/4}}$

$= \frac{x^{-1}\cdot y}{(x^4+y^4-x^4)^{1/4}}$

$= \frac{x^{-1}\cdot y}{(y^4)^{1/4}} = \frac{x^{-1}\cdot y}{y} = \frac{1}{x}$

15. Given, $a^x = c^q = b \Rightarrow a^x = b$

$\Rightarrow a = b^{1/x}$ ...(i)

and $c^q = b$

$\Rightarrow c = b^{1/q}$ ...(ii)

Also given, $c^y = a^z = d$

$\Rightarrow c^y = d$

$\Rightarrow c = d^{1/y}$ ...(iii)

and $a^z = d$

$\Rightarrow a = d^{1/z}$ ...(iv)

From Eqs. (i) and (iv), we get

$b^{1/x} = d^{1/z} \Rightarrow b = d^{x/z}$ ...(v)

From Eqs. (ii) and (iii), we get

$b^{1/q} = d^{1/y} \Rightarrow b = d^{q/y}$ ...(vi)

From Eqs. (v) and (vi), we get

$d^{x/z} = d^{q/y}$

$\therefore \frac{x}{z} = \frac{q}{y} \Rightarrow xy = qz$

16. Here, volume of cube = 64 cu units

$\therefore$ Side $= \sqrt[3]{64} = 4$

and area of square = 64 sq units

$\therefore$ Side $= \sqrt{64} = 8$

$\therefore$ Length of rectangular field = 4

and breadth of rectangular field = 8

Now, Perimeter (boundary's length)

$= 2(4+8) = 24$

$\therefore$ Cost $= 24\times 15 =$ ₹ 360

D. Rationalisation

1. Conjugate of $\sqrt{3}-2$ is $\sqrt{3}+2$.

2. $\frac{\sqrt{2}+1}{\sqrt{2}-1} = \frac{\sqrt{2}+1}{\sqrt{2}-1}\times\frac{\sqrt{2}+1}{\sqrt{2}+1}$

$= \frac{(\sqrt{2}+1)^2}{2-1}$

$= \frac{2+1+2\sqrt{2}}{1}$

$= 3+2\sqrt{2}$

$\left[\begin{array}{l}\because (a+b)^2 = a^2+b^2+2ab \\ \text{and } (a+b)(a-b) = a^2-b^2\end{array}\right]$

3. $\frac{3}{5-\sqrt{3}} + \frac{2}{5+\sqrt{3}}$

$= \frac{3(5+\sqrt{3})+2(5-\sqrt{3})}{(5-\sqrt{3})(5+\sqrt{3})}$

$= \frac{15+3\sqrt{3}+10-2\sqrt{3}}{25-3}$

$= \frac{25+\sqrt{3}}{22}$

4. We have,

$\frac{x-\sqrt{6}}{\sqrt{3}+\sqrt{2}} = \frac{3\sqrt{3}-4\sqrt{2}}{1}$

LHS $= \frac{x-\sqrt{6}}{\sqrt{3}+\sqrt{2}}$

On rationalising, we get

LHS $= \frac{(x-\sqrt{6})(\sqrt{3}-\sqrt{2})}{(\sqrt{3}+\sqrt{2})(\sqrt{3}-\sqrt{2})}$

$= \frac{\sqrt{3}x-\sqrt{2}x-3\sqrt{2}+2\sqrt{3}}{3-2}$

$= \frac{\sqrt{3}x+2\sqrt{3}-\sqrt{2}x-3\sqrt{2}}{3-2}$

$= \frac{(x+2)\sqrt{3}-(3+x)\sqrt{2}}{1}$

Comparing it with RHS, we get

$x+2 = 3$

$\therefore x = 1$

5. Denominator

$= (r+\sqrt{r^2-q^2})(r-\sqrt{r^2-q^2})$

$= r^2-r^2+q^2 = q^2$

7. Given, $\frac{\sqrt{3}-1}{\sqrt{3}+1} = a+b\sqrt{3}$

$\Rightarrow \frac{\sqrt{3}-1}{\sqrt{3}+1}\times\frac{\sqrt{3}-1}{\sqrt{3}-1} = a+b\sqrt{3}$

$\Rightarrow \frac{(\sqrt{3}-1)^2}{3-1} = a+b\sqrt{3}$

$\Rightarrow \frac{3+1-2\sqrt{3}}{2} = a+b\sqrt{3}$

$\Rightarrow \frac{4-2\sqrt{3}}{2} = a+b\sqrt{3}$

$\Rightarrow 2-\sqrt{3} = a+b\sqrt{3}$

On comparing both sides, we get

$a = 2$

and $b = -1$

8. Given, $\frac{5-\sqrt{3}}{2+\sqrt{3}} = x+y\sqrt{3}$

$\Rightarrow \frac{5-\sqrt{3}}{2+\sqrt{3}}\times\frac{2-\sqrt{3}}{2-\sqrt{3}} = x+y\sqrt{3}$

$\Rightarrow \frac{10-5\sqrt{3}-2\sqrt{3}+3}{4-3} = x+y\sqrt{3}$

$\Rightarrow 13-7\sqrt{3} = x+y\sqrt{3}$

On comparing both sides, we get

$x = 13$

and $y = -7$

9. A. $\frac{2}{\sqrt{7}} = \frac{a\sqrt{7}}{7}$

$\Rightarrow 2\times 7 = a\sqrt{7}\times\sqrt{7}$

$\Rightarrow a = 2$

B. $\left(\sqrt[6]{27} - \sqrt{6\frac{3}{4}}\right)^2$

$= \left(\sqrt[6]{27} - \sqrt{\frac{27}{4}}\right)^2$

$= \sqrt[3]{27} + \frac{27}{4} - 2\times\sqrt[6]{27}\times\sqrt{\frac{27}{4}}$

$= 3 + \frac{27}{4} - \frac{2}{2}\times(27)^{\frac{1}{6}+\frac{1}{2}}$

$= \frac{39}{4} - (27)^{\frac{2}{3}}$

$= \frac{39}{4} - 9 = \frac{3}{4}$

C. $2+\sqrt{3}$

D. LCM of (9, 6, 3) = 18

We get,

$(4^2)^{\frac{1}{18}}, (3^3)^{\frac{1}{18}}, (2^6)^{\frac{1}{18}}$

i.e. $(16)^{\frac{1}{18}}, (27)^{\frac{1}{18}}, (64)^{\frac{1}{18}}$

$\therefore \sqrt[3]{2}$ is the greatest.

10. Given, $x = \sqrt{6}+\sqrt{5}$

$\therefore \frac{1}{x} = \frac{1}{\sqrt{6}+\sqrt{5}}$

$= \frac{1}{\sqrt{6}+\sqrt{5}}\times\frac{\sqrt{6}-\sqrt{5}}{\sqrt{6}-\sqrt{5}}$

$= \frac{\sqrt{6}-\sqrt{5}}{6-5}$

$= \sqrt{6}-\sqrt{5}$

Now, $x - \frac{1}{x} = \sqrt{6}+\sqrt{5}-\sqrt{6}+\sqrt{5}$

$= 2\sqrt{5}$

$\therefore x^2 + \frac{1}{x^2} - 2 = \left(x-\frac{1}{x}\right)^2$

$\left[\because \left(x-\frac{1}{x}\right)^2 = x^2 + \frac{1}{x^2} - 2\cdot x\cdot\frac{1}{x}\right]$

$= (2\sqrt{5})^2 = 20$

11. $\because a + \frac{1}{a} = \sqrt{3}$ [given]

On squaring both sides, we get

$$\left(a + \frac{1}{a}\right)^2 = (\sqrt{3})^2$$

$$\Rightarrow a^2 + \frac{1}{a^2} + 2 \cdot a \cdot \frac{1}{a} = 3$$

$$\Rightarrow a^2 + \frac{1}{a^2} + 2 = 3$$

$$\therefore a^2 + \frac{1}{a^2} = 3 - 2 = 1$$

12. Given, $x = \frac{\sqrt{5} + \sqrt{3}}{\sqrt{5} - \sqrt{3}}, y = \frac{\sqrt{5} - \sqrt{3}}{\sqrt{5} + \sqrt{3}}$

Now,

$$x + y = \frac{(\sqrt{5} + \sqrt{3})^2 + (\sqrt{5} - \sqrt{3})^2}{(\sqrt{5})^2 - (\sqrt{3})^2}$$

$[\because (a + b)^2 + (a - b)^2 = 2(a^2 + b^2)]$

$$= \frac{2(5 + 3)}{2} = \frac{2 \times 8}{2} = 8$$

and $xy = \left(\frac{\sqrt{5} + \sqrt{3}}{\sqrt{5} - \sqrt{3}}\right)\left(\frac{\sqrt{5} - \sqrt{3}}{\sqrt{5} + \sqrt{3}}\right) = 1$

$\therefore x^2 + y^2 + xy = (x + y)^2 - xy$

$= 8^2 - 1$ $[\because xy = 1]$

$= 63$

13. $\frac{1}{1 + \sqrt{2}} + \frac{1}{\sqrt{2} + \sqrt{3}} + \ldots + \frac{1}{\sqrt{8} + \sqrt{9}}$

Consider $\frac{1}{1 + \sqrt{2}} = \frac{1 - \sqrt{2}}{1 - 2}$

$= \sqrt{2} - 1$ [rationalisation]

Similarly, $\frac{1}{\sqrt{2} + \sqrt{3}} = \sqrt{3} - \sqrt{2}$

[rationalisation]

$\frac{1}{\sqrt{3} + \sqrt{4}} = \sqrt{4} - \sqrt{3}$

[rationalisation]

$\vdots \quad \vdots$

$$\frac{1}{\sqrt{8}} + \frac{1}{\sqrt{9}} = \sqrt{9} - \sqrt{8}$$

$\therefore$ Value of given expression

$= \sqrt{9} - 1 = 3 - 1 = 2$

15. $\because$ Area of square = 12 sq units

$\therefore$ One side $= \sqrt{12} = 2\sqrt{3}$ units

Now, diagonal of square

$= \sqrt{2}a = \sqrt{2} \times 2\sqrt{3}$

$= 2\sqrt{2}\sqrt{3} = 2\sqrt{6}$

$\therefore$ Length of rectangular field $= 2\sqrt{3}$

and breadth of field $= 2\sqrt{6}$

$\therefore$ Required ratio $= \frac{2\sqrt{6} + 2\sqrt{3}}{2\sqrt{6} - 2\sqrt{3}}$

[we take greater – lower]

$$= \frac{\sqrt{6} + \sqrt{3}}{\sqrt{6} - \sqrt{3}}$$

$$= \frac{\sqrt{6} + \sqrt{3}}{\sqrt{6} - \sqrt{3}} \times \frac{\sqrt{6} + \sqrt{3}}{\sqrt{6} + \sqrt{3}}$$

$$= \frac{6 + 3 + 2 \times \sqrt{3} \times \sqrt{6}}{6 - 3}$$

$$= \frac{9 + 2\sqrt{18}}{3} = \frac{9 + 6\sqrt{2}}{3}$$

$$= \frac{3 + 2\sqrt{2}}{1}$$

$= 3 + 2\sqrt{2} : 1$

17. $\frac{1}{\sqrt{9} + \sqrt{10}} + \frac{1}{\sqrt{10} + \sqrt{11}}$

$$+ \frac{1}{\sqrt{11} + \sqrt{12}} + \ldots + \frac{1}{\sqrt{24} + \sqrt{25}}$$

$$= \frac{\sqrt{10} - \sqrt{9}}{1} + \frac{\sqrt{11} - \sqrt{10}}{1}$$

$$+ \frac{\sqrt{12} - \sqrt{11}}{1} + \ldots + \frac{\sqrt{25} - \sqrt{24}}{1}$$

$= \sqrt{25} - \sqrt{9}$

$= 5 - 3 = 2$

18. Given,

$$a * b * c = \sqrt{\sqrt{\frac{(a + 3)(b - 3)}{(c - 1)}}}$$

$$\therefore 6 * 12 * 26 = \sqrt{\sqrt{\frac{(6 + 3)(12 - 3)}{(26 - 1)}}}$$

$$= \sqrt{\sqrt{\frac{9 \times 9}{25}}}$$

$$= \sqrt{\frac{9}{5}} = \frac{3}{\sqrt{5}} = \frac{3\sqrt{5}}{5}$$

19. Consider $\frac{\sqrt{15 + 4\sqrt{11}}}{\sqrt{31 + 8\sqrt{15}}}$

Numerator $= \sqrt{15 + 4\sqrt{11}}$

$= \sqrt{4 + 11 + 2 \times 2 \times \sqrt{11}}$

$= \sqrt{(2 + \sqrt{11})^2}$

$= \sqrt{11} + 2$

Denominator $= \sqrt{31 + 8\sqrt{15}}$

$= \sqrt{15 + 16 + 2 \times 4 \times \sqrt{15}}$

$= \sqrt{(\sqrt{15} + 4)^2}$

$= \sqrt{15} + 4$

$\therefore \frac{\text{Numerator}}{\text{Denominator}} = \frac{\sqrt{11} + 2}{4 + \sqrt{15}}$

On rationalising, we get

$$\frac{\sqrt{11} + 2}{4 + \sqrt{15}} = \left(\frac{\sqrt{11} + 2}{4 + \sqrt{15}}\right)\left(\frac{4 - \sqrt{15}}{4 - \sqrt{15}}\right)$$

$$= \frac{4\sqrt{11} - \sqrt{165} + 8 - 2\sqrt{15}}{1}$$

$= 8 + 4\sqrt{11} - \sqrt{165} - 2\sqrt{15}$

$\therefore 8 + 4\sqrt{11} - \sqrt{165} - 2\sqrt{15}$

$$\times \frac{1}{8 + 4\sqrt{11} - \sqrt{165} - 2\sqrt{15}} = 1$$

2 Polynomials

A. Introduction to Polynomials, Degree and Types of Polynomial

1. Others are not polynomials.

2. $(7x^2 - 14x + 5) + 3x^3 - 2x + 1 - x - 1$

$= 7x^2 - 14x + 5 + 3x^3 - 3x$

$= 3x^3 + 7x^2 - 17x + 5$

$\therefore$ Highest degree = 3

5. Let length and breadth of rectangular field be $3x$ and $5x$, respectively.

Then, area of rectangle $= l \times b$

$= 3x \times 5x$

$= 15x^2$

Since, x^2 term is present.

Hence, the polynomial is of degree 2 i.e. quadratic polynomial.

10. We can write given polynomial as $0x^3 + x^2 + 5x + 6$.

Here, coefficient of x^3 is 0.

12. Required polynomial,

$f(x) = (30 - 2x)(15 - 2x)\,x$

$= (30 - 2x)(15x - 2x^2)$

$= 450x - 60x^2 - 30x^2 + 4x^3$

$= 4x^3 - 90x^2 + 450x$

B. Zeroes of a Polynomial, Factorisation and Remainder Theorem

1. Since, $x^3 - 1 = (x - 1)(x^2 + x + 1)$

2. If $(x - 2)$ is a factor of $x^2 + 3ax - 2a$, then $x = 2$ makes the polynomial $x^2 + 3ax - 2a = 0$.

$\therefore (2)^2 + 3 \cdot a \cdot (2) - 2a = 0$

$\Rightarrow 4 + 6a - 2a = 0$

$\Rightarrow 4a + 4 = 0$

$\therefore a = -1$

4. $2x + 4 = 0$

$\Rightarrow 2x = -4$

$\Rightarrow x = -2$

6. $(x-3)$ is a factor of $x^2 + ax - 4 = 0$ and $x^2 - 4x + b = 0$.

So, $x = 3$, put in polynomials.

$\therefore \quad (3)^2 + a \times 3 - 4 = 0$

$\Rightarrow \quad 9 + 3a - 4 = 0$

$\Rightarrow \quad 3a + 5 = 0$

$\Rightarrow \quad a = -\frac{5}{3}$

and $(3)^2 - 4 \times 3 + b = 0$

$\Rightarrow \quad 9 - 12 + b = 0$

$\Rightarrow \quad -3 + b = 0$

$\Rightarrow \quad b = 3$

So, $2a - b = 2 \times \left(-\frac{5}{3}\right) - 3$

$= \frac{-10}{3} - 3 = \frac{-10-9}{3} = \frac{-19}{3}$

7. Let $f(x) = px^2 + 5x + r$

Now, $f(2) = 0$

$\Rightarrow 4p + 2 \times 5 + r = 0$

$\Rightarrow \quad 4p + r = -10 \quad \ldots(i)$

and $f\left(\frac{1}{2}\right) = 0$

$\Rightarrow \quad \frac{1}{4}p + \frac{5}{2} + r = 0$

$\Rightarrow \quad p + 4r + 10 = 0$

$\Rightarrow \quad p + 4r = -10 \quad \ldots(ii)$

From Eqs. (i) and (ii), we get

$p + 4r = 4p + r$

$\Rightarrow \quad 3p = 3r$

$\Rightarrow \quad p = r$

8. Since, $x + 1$ is a factor.

$\therefore a - b + c - d + e = 0$

$\Rightarrow \quad a + c + e = b + d$

9. $(x-1)$ and $(x-2)$ are factors of given polynomial.

We have,

$1 + 10 + a + b = 0$

$\Rightarrow \quad a + b = -11 \quad \ldots(i)$

and $\quad 8 + 40 + 2a + b = 0$

$\Rightarrow \quad 48 + 2a + b = 0$

$\Rightarrow \quad 2a + b = -48 \quad \ldots(ii)$

From Eqs. (i) and (ii), we get

$a = -37$

$\therefore \quad b = 26$

10. Let $f(x) = ax^3 + 4x^2 + 3x - 4$ is divided by $(x-3)$, then

Remainder $= f(3)$

According to the question,

$a \cdot (3)^3 + 4 \cdot (3)^2 + 3 \cdot 3 - 4$

$= (3)^3 - 4 \times 3 + a$

[since, remainders are same]

$\Rightarrow 27a + 36 + 9 - 4 = 27 - 12 + a$

$\Rightarrow \quad 27a + 41 = 15 + a$

$\Rightarrow \quad 26a = -26 \Rightarrow a = -1$

11. $p(1) = 4 - 3 - 2 + 1 - 7 = 5 - 12 = -7$

$\therefore$ Remainder $= -7$

12. Since, $(x-2)$ is a factor.

Now, dividing $x^3 - 7x + 6$ by $(x-2)$, we get quotient as

$(x^2 + 2x - 3)$

Consider $x^2 + 2x - 3 = 0$

$\Rightarrow \quad x^2 - x + 3x - 3 = 0$

$\Rightarrow x(x-1) + 3(x-1) = 0$

$\Rightarrow \quad (x-1)(x+3) = 0$

$\therefore \quad x = 1, -3$

13. Let $f(x) = x^{40} + 2$

Put $x^4 = -1$ in $f(x)$.

$\therefore$ Remainder $= (-1)^{10} + 2 = 1 + 2 = 3$

14. Since, $(x-1)$ and $(x+1)$ are factors of the given polynomial.

$\therefore \quad a - 3b + 1 = 0 \quad \ldots(i)$

and $\quad a + 3b + 1 = 0 \quad \ldots(ii)$

On adding Eqs. (i) and (ii), we get

$\Rightarrow \quad 2a + 2 = 0$

$\Rightarrow \quad a = -1$ and $b = 0$

15. Since, $(x + a)$ is a factor of $p(x)$, then $p(-a) = 0$.

16. Since, $x^{49} + 49$ is divided by $(x+1)$, then remainder is

$(x^{49} + 49) = (-1)^{49} + 49 \quad [\because x = -1]$

$= 49 - 1 = 48$

17. **Statement I** It is correct for $K = 1$.

$\Rightarrow \quad n = 2 \times 1 + 1 = 3$

$\therefore a^3 + b^3 = (a+b)(a^2 - ab + b^2)$ which is divisible by $(a+b)$.

Statement II It is correct as for

$K = 1, n = 2.$

$\Rightarrow a^2 - b^2 = (a-b)(a+b)$

which is divisible by $(a-b)$.

19. $p(2) = 16 + 16 - 12 + 2 - 1$

$= 32 + 2 - 13 = 21$

21. Given,

$(9x^2 + 3px + 6q)$, when divided by $(3x+1)$ leaves a remainder $\frac{-3}{4}$. Hence, it means $f(x) = 9x^2 + 3px + 6q - \left(\frac{-3}{4}\right)$ will be exactly divisible by $(3x+1)$.

$\therefore \quad 9\left(-\frac{1}{3}\right)^2 + 3p\left(-\frac{1}{3}\right) + 6q + \frac{3}{4} = 0$

$\Rightarrow \quad 6q - p + \frac{7}{4} = 0$

$\Rightarrow \quad 24q - 4p + 7 = 0 \quad \ldots(i)$

Since, $qx^2 + 4px + 7$ is also divisible by $(x+1)$.

$\therefore \quad q - 4p + 7 = 0 \quad \ldots(ii)$

Solving Eqs. (i) and (ii), we get

$p = \frac{7}{4}$ and $q = 0$

22. $\because a^8 - a^8 + a^6 - a^6 + a^4$

$-a^4 + 3a - a + 2 = 0$

$\Rightarrow \quad 3a - a + 2 = 0$

$\Rightarrow \quad 2a = -2$

$\therefore \quad a = -1$

23. Zeroes of $f(x) = x^2 + 2x + 1$

$= (x+1)^2$

So, $x = -1$ is the zeroes of $f(x)$.

$\therefore (px^5 + qx^4 + rx^3 + sx^2 + tx + u) = 0$

$\Rightarrow -p + q - r + s - t + u = 0$

$[\because x = -1]$

$\Rightarrow p + r + t = q + s + u$

24. Given, $\quad f(x) = ax^3 + 3x^2 - 3$

and $\quad g(x) = 3x^3 - 7x + a$

such that $f(1) = m$ and $g(1) = n$

$\therefore \quad a + 3 - 3 = m \quad \ldots(i)$

and $\quad 3 - 7 + a = n \quad \ldots(ii)$

On adding Eqs. (i) and (ii), we get

$m + n = a - 4 + a$

$\Rightarrow \quad 0 = 2a - 4$

$[\because m + n = 0$, given$]$

$\therefore \quad a = 2$

25. Given, $(x-a)$ and $\left(x - \frac{1}{a}\right)$ are factors of

$px^2 + 5x + q = 0.$

Then, $pa^2 + 5a + q = 0 \quad \ldots(i)$

and $\quad \frac{p}{a^2} + \frac{5}{a} + q = 0$

$\Rightarrow \quad p + 5a + qa^2 = 0 \quad \ldots(ii)$

On subtracting Eq. (ii) from Eq. (i), we get

$(a^2 - 1)p + (1 - a^2)q = 0$

$\Rightarrow \quad (a^2 - 1)p - q(a^2 - 1) = 0$

$\therefore \quad p = q$

26. Given, $f(x) = x^2 + px + q$

and $\quad g(x) = x^2 + lx + m$

such that $f(-a) = 0$

and $\quad g(-a) = 0$

$\therefore \quad (-a)^2 + p(-a) + q = 0$

$\Rightarrow \quad a^2 - pa + q = 0 \quad \ldots(i)$

Also, $\quad a^2 - la + m = 0 \quad \ldots(ii)$

On subtracting Eq. (ii) from Eq. (i), we get

$(l - p)a + q - m = 0$

$\Rightarrow \quad (l - p)a = m - q$

$\therefore \quad a = \frac{m - q}{l - p}$

27. Consider

$m^4 + 6m^3 + 11m^2 + 6m + 1$

$= m^2\left(m^2 + \frac{1}{m^2} + 6m + \frac{6}{m} + 11\right)$

$= m^2\left[m^2 + \frac{1}{m^2} + 2 \times \frac{1}{m} \times m + 6\left(m + \frac{1}{m}\right) + 11 - 2\right]$

$= m^2\left[\left(m + \frac{1}{m}\right)^2 + 6\left(m + \frac{1}{m}\right) + 9\right]$

$= m^2\left(m + \frac{1}{m} + 3\right)^2$

$= (m^2 + 3m + 1)^2 \quad \ldots$

Now, square root of Eq.(i) is

$m^2 + 3m + 1.$

C. Factorisation and Algebraic Identities

1. $\because x+y+z=0 \Rightarrow x+y=-z$

$\therefore x^3+y^3+z^3=3xyz$

2. Given, $6x^2+17x+5$

$=6x^2+15x+2x+5$

$=3x(2x+5)+1(2x+5)$

$=(3x+1)(2x+5)$

3. $\because \quad a+b+c=0$

$\therefore \quad a^3+b^3+c^3=3abc$

$\Rightarrow a^3+b^3+c^3-3abc=0$

4. $101\times 99=(100+1)(100-1)$

$[\because (a+b)(a-b)=a^2-b^2]$

6. Given, $x^2-4x+3=x^2-3x-x+3$

$\therefore$ The terms obtained after splitting the middle term are $-3x$ and $-x$.

So, the coefficients of the term obtained are $(-3,-1)$.

7. $\because x+\dfrac{1}{x}=13$

On squaring both sides, we get

$x^2+\dfrac{1}{x^2}+2\cdot x\cdot\dfrac{1}{x}=169$

$\therefore \quad x^2+\dfrac{1}{x^2}=169-2=167$

8. We know that,

$a^3+b^3+c^3-3abc$

$=(a+b+c)\dfrac{1}{2}[(a-b)^2+(b-c)^2+(c-a)^2]$

$=(225+226+227)\dfrac{1}{2}(1+1+4)$

$=678\times 3=2034$

9. Given expression is of the form

$\dfrac{a^2+b^2+2ab}{a+b}=\dfrac{(a+b)(a+b)}{a+b}$

$=a+b$

$\therefore a+b=1.5+4.7=6.2$

10. $p=2-a \Rightarrow p+a=2$

On cubing both sides, we get

$(p+a)^3=2^3$

$\Rightarrow p^3+a^3+3ap(p+a)=8$

$\Rightarrow \quad p^3+a^3+3ap\times 2=8$

$\Rightarrow \quad p^3+a^3+6ap-8=0$

11. Consider

$\sqrt{3}x^2+11x+6\sqrt{3}=0$

$\Rightarrow \sqrt{3}x^2+9x+2x+6\sqrt{3}=0$

$\Rightarrow \sqrt{3}x(x+3\sqrt{3})+2(x+3\sqrt{3})=0$

$\Rightarrow \quad (\sqrt{3}x+2)(x+3\sqrt{3})=0$

These are the factors.

12. Given, $(p-q)^6-27r^3$

$=\{(p-q)^2\}^3-(3r)^3$

$=[\{(p-q)^2-3r\}\{(p-q)^4+9r^2+(p-q)^2 3r\}]$

13. Given,

$(p+q)^3-(p-q)^3-6q(p^2-q^2)$

$=p^3+q^3+3pq(p+q)-p^3+q^3+3pq(p-q)-6p^2q+6q^3$

$=2q^3+3p^2q+3pq^2+3p^2q-3pq^2-6p^2q+6q^3$

$=8q^3$

14. $\because a+b+c=9$

and $ab+bc+ca=23$

$\therefore a^3+b^3+c^3-3abc$

$=(a+b+c)(a^2+b^2+c^2-ab-bc-ca)$

$=(a+b+c)\{(a+b+c)^2-3(ab+bc+ca)\}$

$=9\times(81-3\times 23)=9\times 12=108$

16. $4a^2+4a-3=4a^2+6a-2a-3$

$=2a(2a+3)-1(2a+3)$

$=(2a-1)(2a+3)$

17. $\because \dfrac{a}{b}+\dfrac{b}{a}=1$

$\Rightarrow \quad a^2+b^2=ab$

$\Rightarrow a^2-ab+b^2=0$

$\therefore a^3+b^3=(a+b)(a^2-ab+b^2)$

$=0$

18. $\because x^3+\dfrac{1}{x^3}=110$

$\Rightarrow\left(x+\dfrac{1}{x}\right)^3-3\cdot x\cdot\dfrac{1}{x}\left(x+\dfrac{1}{x}\right)=110$

Let $x+\dfrac{1}{x}=z$, then $z^3-3z-110=0$

We put $z=5$, then $x+\dfrac{1}{x}=5$

[cubic equation can be solved by hit and trial method]

19. $\because a+b+c=0$

$\therefore a^3+b^3+c^3=3abc$

20. Given equation is

$4a^2+8a+3=0$

$\Rightarrow \quad 4a^2+6a+2a+3=0$

$\Rightarrow 2a(2a+3)+1(2a+3)=0$

$\Rightarrow \quad (2a+1)(2a+3)=0$

$\Rightarrow \quad a=\dfrac{-1}{2},\dfrac{-3}{2}$

Let $\alpha=\dfrac{-1}{2}$ and $\beta=\dfrac{-3}{2}$

$\therefore \quad \dfrac{\alpha}{\beta}=\dfrac{1}{3}$ and $\dfrac{\beta}{\alpha}=3$

So, the new polynomial formed will be

$\left(x-\dfrac{1}{3}\right)(x-3)$.

$=x^2-\left(\dfrac{1}{3}+3\right)x+1=x^2-\dfrac{10}{3}x+1$

$\therefore$ The required equation is

$x^2-\dfrac{10}{3}x+1=0$

$\Rightarrow \quad 3x^2-10x+3=0$

21. Given, x^3-3x^2+3x+7

$=(x+1)(ax^2+bx+c)$

$\Rightarrow x^3+x^2-4x^2-4x+7x+7$

$=(x+1)(ax^2+bx+c)$

$\Rightarrow x^2(x+1)-4x(x+1)+7(x+1)$

$=(x+1)(ax^2+bx+c)$

$\Rightarrow (x+1)(x^2-4x+7)$

$=(x+1)(ax^2+bx+c)$

$\therefore \; ax^2+bx+c=x^2-4x+7$

On comparing both sides, we get

$a=1, b=-4, c=7$

$\therefore \; a+b+c=1-4+7=8-4=4$

22. $\because \; 2x^2+4x+1=p(x+1)^2-q$

$\Rightarrow 2(x+1)^2-1=p(x+1)^2-q$

$[\because (x+1)^2=x^2+2x+1]$

$\therefore \; p=2, q=1$ [on comparing]

24. Let number of boys be x

and number of girls be y.

According to the question,

$x^2-y^2=400$ ...(i)

$xy=375$ ...(ii)

and $\quad x-y=10$ ...(iii)

From Eqs. (i) and (iii),

$x^2-y^2=(x+y)(x-y)=400$

$\Rightarrow \quad (x+y)10=400$

$\therefore \quad x+y=40$ ...(iv)

From Eqs. (iii) and (iv),

$x=25$ and $y=15$

$\therefore$ Required ratio $=x:y=25:15$

$=5:3$

25. Let unit's digit be y and digit at ten's place be x.

Then, $x+y=9$ ...(i)

According to the question,

$(10y+x)-(10x+y)=9$

$\Rightarrow \quad y-x=1$ ...(ii)

From Eqs. (i) and (ii),

$y=5, x=4$

$\therefore$ Number $=45$

Now, $y^3-x^3=(y-x)(y^2+xy+x^2)$

$=1\times\{(x+y)^2-xy\}$

$=1\times(81-20)=61$

27. Let $x=\dfrac{1}{a}$, $y=\dfrac{1}{b}$ and $z=\dfrac{1}{c}$

then, $\left(\dfrac{1}{x}+\dfrac{1}{y}+\dfrac{1}{z}\right)^2-\left(\dfrac{2}{xy}+\dfrac{2}{yz}+\dfrac{2}{zx}\right)$

$=(a+b+c)^2-(2ab+2bc+2ca)$

$=a^2+b^2+c^2$

29. Given,

$a^2+b^2+c^2+3=2a-2b+2c$

$\Rightarrow a^2+1-2a+b^2+2b+1+c^2-2c+1=0$

$\Rightarrow (a-1)^2+(b+1)^2+(c-1)^2=0$

$\Rightarrow \quad a=1, b=-1, c=1$

$\therefore (a+b-c)^3=(1-1-1)^3=-1$

3 Linear Equations in Two Variables

A. Introduction to Linear Equations in Two Variables and Their Solutions using Algebraic Methods

1. $ax + by + c = 0$ represents a linear equation in two variables, if $a \neq 0, b \neq 0$, i.e. coefficients of x and y should not be equal to 0.

4. Except (1, 1), all are solutions of equation.

5. By observing the data, we analyse that $y = 2x - 1$.
If $x = -1$, then $y = -2 - 1 = -3$
If $x = 0$, then $y = -1$
If $x = 1$, then $y = 1$
If $x = 2$, then $y = 3$

7. Since, (2, 0) is a solution of $3x + 2y = k/2$.
$\therefore \quad 3 \times 2 + 2 \times 0 = k/2$
$\Rightarrow \quad k = 6 \times 2 = 12$

9. Given, $3y = ax + 7$
Since, (1, 3) lies on the graph of the given equation.
$\therefore \quad 3(3) = a + 7$
$\Rightarrow \quad 9 = a + 7$
$\Rightarrow \quad a = 2$

10. $\because 2(x - y) + 3(y - x) = 5$
$\Rightarrow 2x - 2y + 3y - 3x = 5$
$\Rightarrow \quad y - x = 5$
i.e. linear equation has infinitely many solutions.

11. Consider $ax + by = c$
$2ax + 2by = 2c$
$3ax + 3by = 3c$
i.e. equation remains the same.

12. Let Deepika has a number of bags.
According to the question,
$a + a + x = y$
$\Rightarrow \quad 2a = y - x$
$\Rightarrow \quad a = \dfrac{y - x}{2}$

13. Given, $2x + cy = 8$
and $x = y$
$\Rightarrow \quad 2x + cy = 8$
$\Rightarrow \quad 2x + cx = 8$
$\Rightarrow \quad (2 + c)x = 8$
$\Rightarrow \quad 2 + c = 8 \quad [\because x = 1]$
$\therefore \quad c = 6$

14. Total distance covered = x km
Total taxi fare = ₹ y
Fare for first kilometre = ₹ 8
$\therefore$ Remaining distance = $(x - 1)$km
$\therefore$ Fare for $(x - 1)$km = ₹ $5(x - 1)$
According to the question,
$8 + 5(x - 1) = y$
$\Rightarrow \quad 8 + 5x - 5 = y$
$\Rightarrow \quad 5x + 3 - y = 0$
$\therefore \quad 5x - y + 3 = 0$

15. In right angled isosceles triangle, the angles are 90°, $x°$ and $y°$.

$\because \quad x° = y°$
[since, angles opposite to equal sides are equal]
$\therefore \quad$ Ratio = 90° : 45° : 45°
$[\because x + y + 90° = 180° \therefore x = y = 45°]$
= 45° : 45° : 90° = 1 : 1 : 2

16. Since, α and β are the solutions of linear equation.
$\therefore \quad ax + by + c = 0$
$\Rightarrow \quad a\alpha + b\beta + c = 0$
$\therefore \quad a\alpha + b\beta = -c$

18. $\because 2x + 3y = k$
Here, $x = 1$, $y = 1$ is a solution.
i.e. $k = 2 \times 1 + 3 \times 1 = 5$

19. $\dfrac{p}{x} + \dfrac{q}{y} = m$ ...(i)
and $\dfrac{q}{x} + \dfrac{p}{y} = n$ ...(ii)
On multiplying Eq. (i) by q and Eq. (ii) by p and subtracting, we get
$\Rightarrow \quad \dfrac{q^2}{y} - \dfrac{p^2}{y} = mq - np$
$\Rightarrow \quad q^2 - p^2 = y(mq - np)$
$\Rightarrow \quad y = \dfrac{q^2 - p^2}{mq - np} = \dfrac{p^2 - q^2}{np - mq}$
Again, on multiplying Eq.(i) by p and Eq. (ii) by q and subtracting, we get
$\Rightarrow \quad \dfrac{p^2}{x} - \dfrac{q^2}{x} = mp - nq$
$\Rightarrow \quad p^2 - q^2 = x(mp - nq)$
$\therefore \quad x = \dfrac{p^2 - q^2}{mp - nq}$ and $y = \dfrac{p^2 - q^2}{np - mq}$

20. $\because \left(\dfrac{k + 2}{k - 1}\right) \times 1 - 0 = 3$
$\Rightarrow \quad k + 2 = 3(k - 1)$
$\Rightarrow \quad k + 2 = 3k - 3 \Rightarrow 2k = 5$
$\therefore \quad k = 5/2$

21. We know that, a point (2, 4) can satisfy, many linear equations passing through it and also a linear equation in two variables has infinitely many solutions.

B. Graphical Representation of Linear Equations in Two Variables and Their Solutions

1. A graph of a linear equation in two variables is always a straight line.
e.g. $x + y = 3$

x	1	0	−1
y	2	3	4
(x, y)	(1, 2)	(0, 3)	(−1, 4)

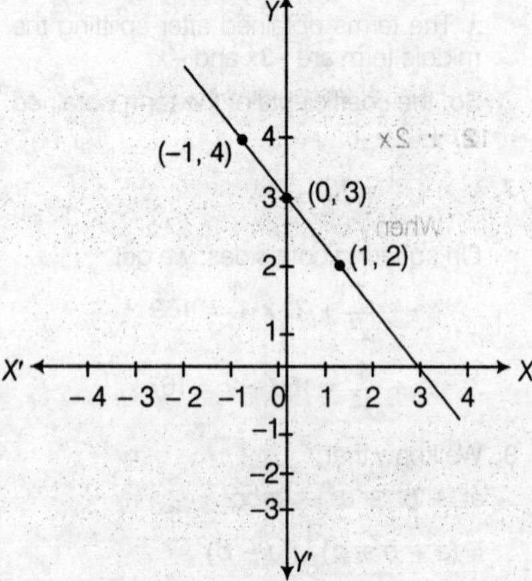

3. We know that, $y = mx + c$
Since, the line passes through the origin.
$\therefore \quad 0 = 0 + c \Rightarrow c = 0$
$\therefore \quad y = mx$

4. Since, $y = x$ passes through the points (0, 0), (1, 1), (2, 2), ...

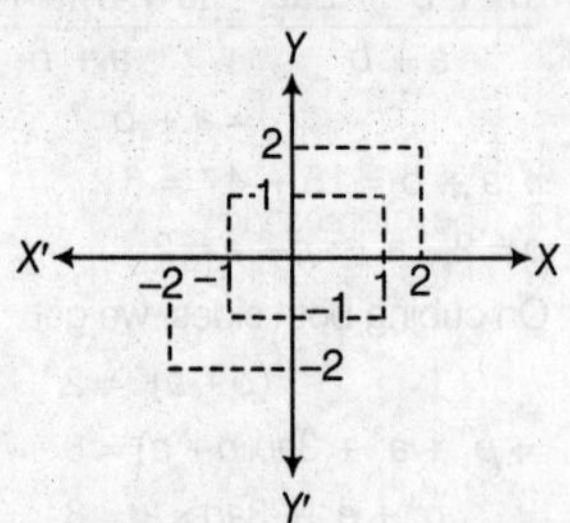

6. $\because \quad 3x - 4y = 8$ [given]
For Y-axis, $x = 0$
$\Rightarrow \quad -4y = 8 \Rightarrow y = -2$
Hence, the required point is (0, − 2).

7. From the given points, we see that
$x = -y$
or $y = -x$
i.e. $x + y = 0$

8. $\because$ Ordinate (y-intercept) = y
and abscissa (x-intercept) = x
$\therefore \quad x + y = 0$

9.

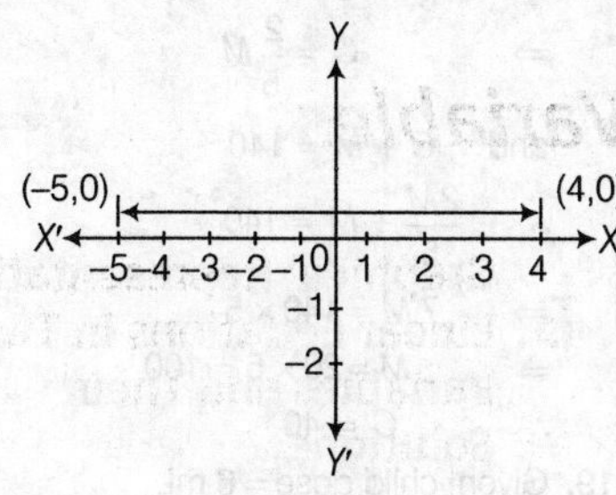

$\therefore$ Required distance $= 4 + 5 = 9$

10. $\because$ $y = 3/2\,x$

Equation of line given is

$$2x + 4y = 8$$

$\Rightarrow$ $2x + 4 \times 3/2\,x = 8$ [put $y = 3/2\,x$]

$\Rightarrow$ $2x + 6x = 8$

$\therefore$ $x = 1$

Hence, the point is (1, 3/2).

12. $\because$ $2x + 3y = 6$ [given]

When $x = 0$, then $y = 2$

When $y = 0$, then $x = 3$

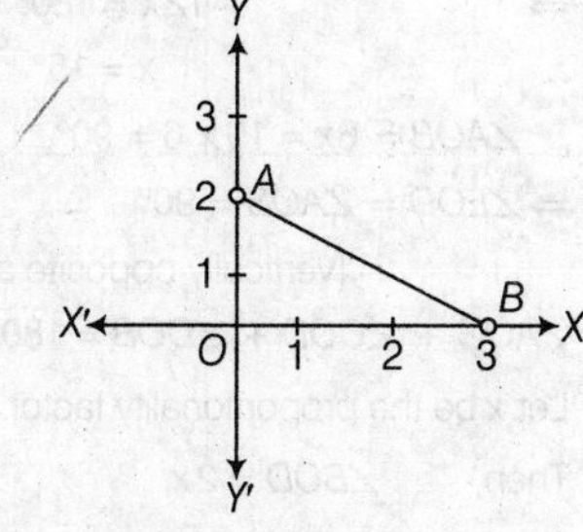

Since, the triangle formed is OAB.

$\therefore$ Area of ΔOAB

$$= \frac{1}{2} \times \text{Base} \times \text{Height}$$

$$= \frac{1}{2} \times 3 \times 2$$

$= 3$ sq units

13. The intersection point of $x = 7$ and $y = 3$ at the line $2x + 3y = 23$ is (7, 3).

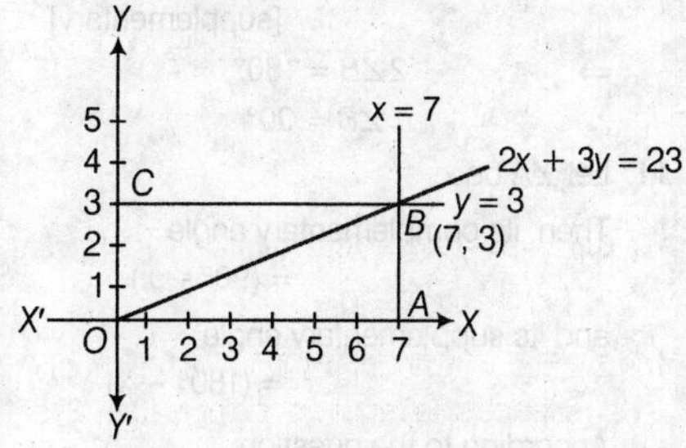

$\therefore$ Area of $\Delta OAB = \frac{1}{2} \times$ Base $\times$ Height

$$= \frac{1}{2} \times 7 \times 3$$

$$= \frac{21}{2} = 10.5 \text{ sq units}$$

C. Application Based Problems on Linear Equations in Two Variables

1. Let the cost of a pen be ₹ x and the cost of a pencil be ₹ y.

$\therefore$ $x = 2y + 3$

3. Let number of red balls be $3x$ and number of blue balls be $2x$.

According to the question,

$$3x + 2x = 50$$

$\Rightarrow$ $5x = 50$

$\Rightarrow$ $x = 10$

$\therefore$ Number of red balls $= 3x = 30$

4. Let present age of Raju be x yr and present age of Rita be y yr.

$\therefore$ 5 yr ago, age of Raju $= (x - 5)$ yr

and age of Rita $= (y - 5)$ yr

According to the question,

$$x - 5 = (y - 5) + 10$$

$\Rightarrow$ $x - 5 = y + 5$

$\Rightarrow$ $x - y - 10 = 0$

$\Rightarrow$ $x - y = 10$

5. Let cost of potato be ₹ x per kg and cost of tomato be ₹ y per kg.

According to the question,

$$3x = 2y$$

$\Rightarrow$ $y = 3x/2$

Also, $3x + 2y = 90$

$\Rightarrow$ $3x + 3x = 90$

$\Rightarrow$ $x = \frac{90}{6}$

$\Rightarrow$ $x = 15$

$\therefore$ Cost of tomato $= y = \frac{3x}{2} = \frac{45}{2}$

= ₹ 22.5per kg

6. Let length of rectangular field be x and breadth of rectangular field be y.

According to the question,

$$x = \frac{3}{4}y$$

Also, $xy = \frac{25}{3}$

$\Rightarrow$ $\frac{3}{4}y \cdot y = \frac{25}{3}$

$\Rightarrow$ $y^2 = \frac{25}{3} \times \frac{4}{3}$

$\Rightarrow$ $y = \frac{10}{3}$

$\therefore$ Length of rectangular field

$$x = \frac{3}{4} \times \frac{10}{3} = \frac{5}{2}$$

8. Let number of one rupee coins be x and number of fifty paisa coins be y.

According to the question,

$$y = x/2$$

$\Rightarrow$ $x = 2y$

Also, $x + \frac{1}{2}y = 25$

$\Rightarrow$ $2y + \frac{1}{2}y = 25$

$\Rightarrow$ $\frac{5}{2}y = 25$

$\Rightarrow$ $y = 10$

$\therefore$ Number of one rupee coins $= x = 2y = 20$

9. $\because$ Speed $= \frac{\text{Distance}}{\text{Time}}$

Let distance (d_1) travelled in time t_1 at a speed of s_1 and distance (d_2) travelled in time t_2 at a speed of s_2.

According to the question,

$$d_2 = \frac{d_1}{2} \text{ and } t_2 = 2t_1$$

$\therefore$ $\frac{s_1}{s_2} = \frac{d_1}{t_1} / \frac{d_2}{t_2} = \frac{d_1}{t_1} \times \frac{t_2}{d_2}$

$\Rightarrow$ $\frac{s_1}{s_2} = \frac{2d_2}{t_1} \times \frac{2t_1}{d_2}$

$\Rightarrow$ $\frac{s_1}{s_2} = \frac{4}{1} \Rightarrow s_1 = 4s_2$

$\therefore$ $s_2 = \frac{s_1}{4} = \frac{40}{4}$ [$\because s_1 = 40$ km/h]

$= 10$ km/h

10. $\because$ Total distance travelled

$= AC + BC + BD$

$= 2 + 2 + 2 = 6$ km

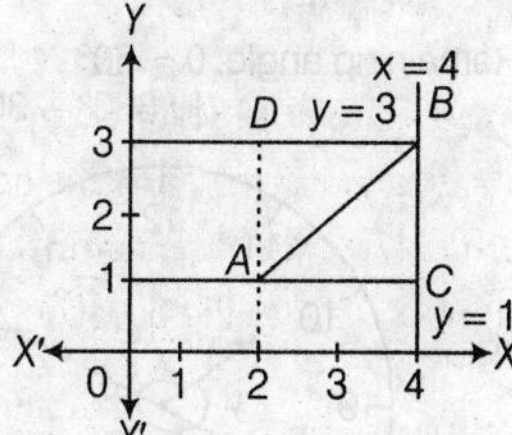

Total time taken $= \frac{10 + 5}{60} = \frac{1}{4}$ h

$\therefore$ Average speed $= \frac{6}{1/4} = 24$ km/h

11. $\because$ $x + 2y = 80$ [given]

$\Rightarrow$ $40 + 2y = 80 \Rightarrow 2y = 40$

$\Rightarrow$ $y = 20$

$\therefore$ Number of girls $= 20$

12. Total number of students in the class $= 40 + 20 = 60$

13. Since, each group has 2 boys and 1 girl.

$\therefore$ Number of groups $= 20$

Since, there are 20 girls i.e. 20 groups.

14. Let cost of a pen be ₹ x and cost of a pencil be ₹ y.

According to the question,

$$5x + 3y = 35$$

Also, $5x = 4y$

$\therefore\quad 4y + 3y = 35$

$\Rightarrow\quad y = 5$

and $\quad x = \frac{4 \times 5}{5} = 4$

$\therefore$ Cost of 4 pens + 5 pencils

$= 4 \times 4 + 5 \times 5 =$ ₹ 41

Hence, both the statements together answer the question.

15. In Statement B, there is no relation between Nisha and Ajay as given.

16. Let number of boys be x and number of girls be y.

According to the question,

$$x + y = 64$$

Also, $\quad x - y = 10$

$\Rightarrow\quad x = 10 + y$

$\therefore\quad y + 10 + y = 64$

$\Rightarrow\quad 2y = 54$

$\Rightarrow\quad y = 27$

$\therefore\ x = 27 + 10 = 37$

Hence, both the statements together answer the question.

17. Let number of cars and motorbikes be C and M respectively.

According to the question,

$$10\,C = 4\,M$$

$\Rightarrow\quad C = \frac{2}{5}M$

and $\quad C + M = 140$

$\therefore\quad \frac{2M}{5} + M = 140$

$\Rightarrow\quad 7\,M = 140 \times 5$

$\Rightarrow\quad M = 20 \times 5 = 100$

$\therefore\quad C = 40$

19. Given, child dose = 6 mL

Age = 4 yr odd

We have,

$6 =$ Adult dose $\times \frac{4}{4 + 12}$

$\Rightarrow$ Adult dose $= 6 \times \frac{16}{4}$

$= 24$ mL

4 Lines and Angles

A. Angles, Types of Angles and Angle on a Straight Line

1.

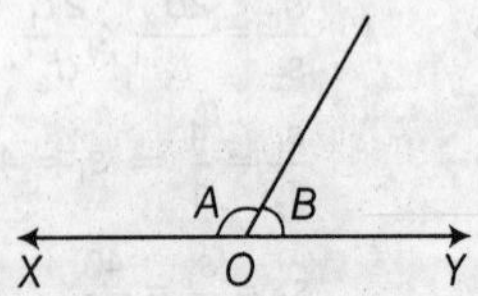

If $\angle A + \angle B = 180°$, then the arms OX and OY make a straight line.

3. An angle which is less than 360° and more than 180° is called a reflex angle.

4. Angle formed by hour hand

$$= \frac{360°}{12} \times 10 = 300°$$

Remaining angle, $\theta = 60°$ $\quad [\because 360° - 300° = 60°]$

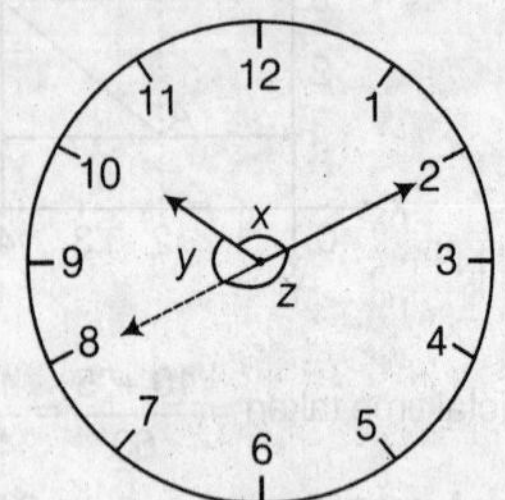

Angle formed by minute hand

$$= \frac{360°}{60°} \times 10 = 60°$$

Angle formed by second hand

$$= \frac{360°}{60°} \times 40 = 240°$$

From the given figure, we see

$\angle x = 60° + 60°$

[remaining angle of hour hand + angle formed by minute hand]

$\Rightarrow\quad \angle x = 120°$

Also, $\quad \angle z = 180°$ [angle formed by minute hand from 2 to 8]

Now, $\angle y = 360° - \angle x - \angle z$

$= 360° - 120° - 180°$

$= 60°$

We have,

$$x = \frac{y + z}{2} = \frac{60° + 180°}{2} = 120°$$

5. Let one angle be x.

$\therefore\quad$ Other angle $= \frac{3}{2}x$

According to the question,

$$x + \frac{3}{2}x = 90°$$

$\Rightarrow\quad \frac{5}{2}x = 90° \quad\Rightarrow\quad x = 36°$

So, the smallest angle is 36°.

6. Let one angle be x.

$\therefore$ Other angle $= (180° - x)$

According to the question,

$(180° - x) - x = 30°$

$\Rightarrow\quad 180° - 2x = 30°$

$\Rightarrow\quad 2x = 150°$

$\Rightarrow\quad x = 75°$

$\therefore$ Other angle $= 180° - 75° = 105°$

7. We know that, angle made on the straight line is 180°.

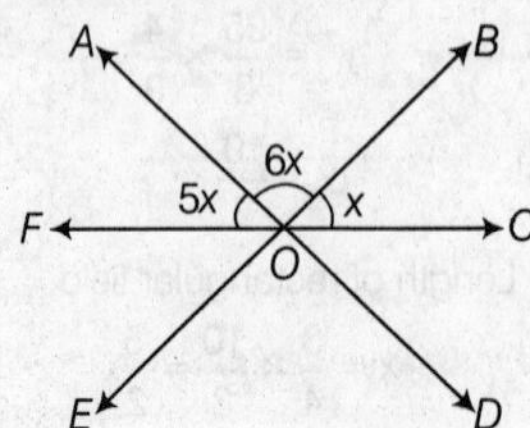

$\therefore\quad 5x + 6x + x = 180°$

$\Rightarrow\quad 12x = 180°$

$\therefore\quad x = 15°$

$\therefore\ \angle AOB = 6x = 15 \times 6 = 90°$

$\Rightarrow \angle EOD = \angle AOB = 90°$

[vertically opposite angles]

8. $\angle AOC + \angle COD + \angle DOB = 180°$

Let x be the proportionality factor.

Then, $\quad \angle BOD = 2x$,

$\angle AOC = 3x$

$\therefore\quad 3x + 2x + 90° = 180°$

$\Rightarrow\quad 5x = 90°$

$\Rightarrow\quad x = 18°$

$\therefore\quad \angle BOD = 2x = 36°$

10. If $\angle A$ is complementary to each other.

Then, $\quad \angle A + \angle A = 90°$

$\Rightarrow\quad 2\angle A = 90°$

$\Rightarrow\quad \angle A = 45°$

Also, given $\quad \angle B + \angle B = 180°$ [supplementary]

$\Rightarrow\quad 2\angle B = 180°$

$\therefore\quad \angle B = 90°$

11. Let $\angle A$ be x.

Then, its complementary angle $= (90° - x)$

and its supplementary angle $= (180° - x)$

According to the question,

$$5(90° - x) = \frac{5}{7}(180° - x)$$

$\Rightarrow 7(450° - 5x) = 900° - 5x$

$\Rightarrow 3150° - 35x = 900° - 5x$

$\Rightarrow\quad 30x = 2250°$

$\therefore\quad x = 75°$

12.

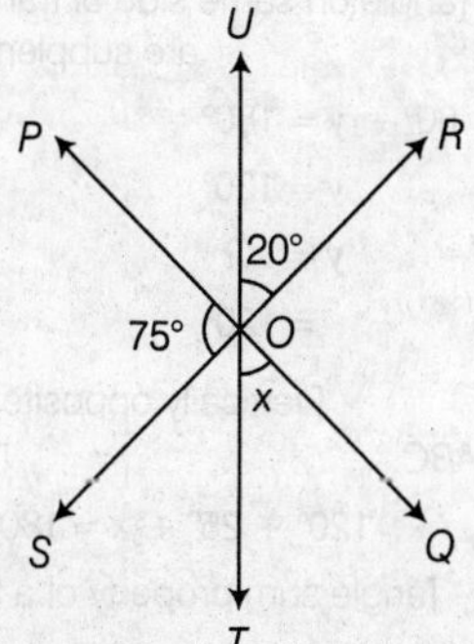

We know,

$$\angle UOR = \angle SOT = 20°$$

[vertically opposite angles]

$\therefore \quad \angle POS + \angle SOT + \angle TOQ = 180°$

[linear pair]

$\Rightarrow \quad 75° + 20° + x = 180°$

$\Rightarrow \quad x = 180° - 95° = 85°$

13. Since, AB is a straight line.

$\therefore \quad \angle AOB = 180°$

$\therefore \quad x + y = 180°$

and $z + w = 180°$

$\therefore \quad x + y = z + w$

15. In the given figure,

OP bisects $\angle BOC$.

$\therefore \quad \angle BOC = 2\angle POC \quad$ ...(i)

Again, OQ bisects $\angle AOC$.

$\therefore \quad \angle AOC = 2\angle QOC \quad$ ...(ii)

Since, the ray OC stands on line AB.

$\therefore \quad \angle AOC + \angle BOC = 180°$

$\Rightarrow \quad 2\angle QOC + 2\angle POC = 180°$

[from Eqs. (i) and (ii)]

$\Rightarrow \angle POC + \angle QOC = 90°$

$\therefore \quad \angle POQ = 90°$

18. Since,

$\angle a + \angle b = 90°$

$\Rightarrow \quad 2x + 3x = 90°$

$\therefore \quad x = 18°$

$\Rightarrow \quad \angle a = 36°$

Now, $\angle c = 180° - (90° - 36°)$

$= 126°$

19. $\because \angle BOD = \angle AOC$ [vertically opposite angles]

$\Rightarrow \quad 2x = y$

$\therefore \angle COE + \angle EOB + \angle BOD = 180°$

$90° + x + 2x = 180°$

$\Rightarrow \quad 3x = 90°$

$\Rightarrow \quad x = 30°$

B. Perpendicular and Parallel Lines, Collinear and Non-collinear Points, Angles of a Triangle

2. Ray '1 point'

Line segment '2 points'

$\therefore$ Required difference = 2 − 1 = 1

4. Since, the angles of triangle are in the ratio 2 : 3 : 4.

We know that, the sum of all angles of a triangle is 180°.

$\therefore \quad 2x + 3x + 4x = 180°$

$\Rightarrow \quad 9x = 180° \Rightarrow x = 20°$

$\therefore$ Difference between greatest and smallest angles $= 4x - 2x = 2x = 40°$

5. A triangle can have maximum 1 obtuse angle.

6. We know that, each angle of an equilateral triangle is 60°.

So, the difference between any two angles is 0°.

7. $x + x + 80° = 180°$

[since, the sum of all angles of a triangle is 180°]

$\Rightarrow \quad 2x + 80° = 180°$

$\Rightarrow \quad 2x = 100°$

$\therefore \quad x = 50°$

8. Angles of a triangle are in the ratio = 3 : 5 : 4

i.e. $3x + 5x + 4x = 180°$

$\Rightarrow \quad 12x = 180°$

$\therefore \quad x = 15°$

$\therefore$ Required angles = 45°, 75°, 60°

So, the triangle formed will be a scalene triangle.

10. Let the greatest angle of triangle be x.

$\therefore$ Least angle of triangle $= x - 30°$

and third angle of triangle $= x - 15°$

Now,

$x + x - 30° + x - 15° = 180°$

$\Rightarrow \quad 3x - 45° = 180°$

$\Rightarrow \quad 3x = 225° \Rightarrow x = 75°$

So, the angles of a triangle are 45°, 75° and 60°, respectively.

11.

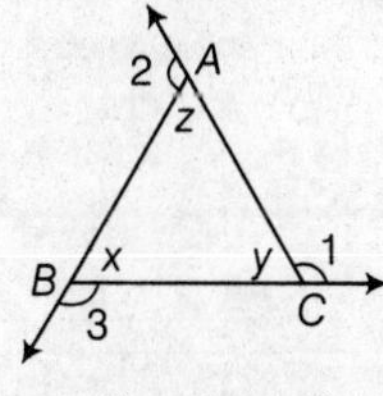

$\angle 1 = \angle z + \angle x \quad$ ...(i)

[exterior angle = sum of two interior angles]

$\angle 2 = \angle x + \angle y \quad$ ...(ii)

$\angle 3 = \angle y + \angle z \quad$ ...(iii)

On adding Eqs. (i), (ii) and (iii), we get

$\angle 1 + \angle 2 + \angle 3 = \angle x + \angle z + \angle x + \angle y + \angle y + \angle z$

$= 2(\angle x + \angle y + \angle z)$

$= 2 \times 180° = 360°$

[since, the sum of all angles of a triangle is 180°]

12. If area of triangle is zero, i.e. triangle is not formed with the three given points.

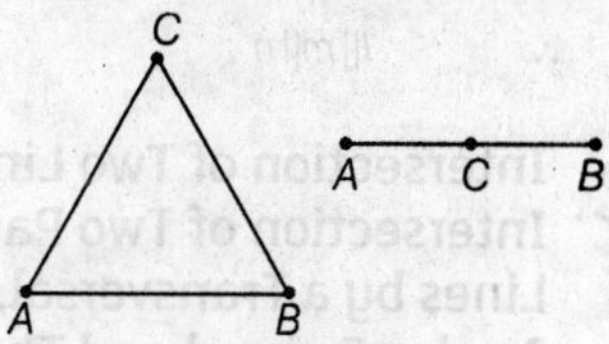

So, the points are collinear.

13. $\because x + x + 10° + x + 20° = 180°$

[angles on a straight line]

$\Rightarrow \quad 3x + 30° = 180°$

$\Rightarrow \quad 3x = 150°$

$\Rightarrow \quad x = 50°$

$\because \quad OD = OC$

i.e. ΔOCD is isosceles triangle.

$\therefore \quad \angle C + \angle D + \angle x = 180°$

$\Rightarrow \quad \angle C + \angle D + 50° = 180°$

$\Rightarrow \quad \angle C + \angle D = 130°$

$\Rightarrow \quad 2\angle C = 2\angle D = 130°$

$\therefore \quad \angle C = \angle D = 65°$

14. Here, $\dfrac{\angle A}{\angle w} = \dfrac{5}{2}$ and $\dfrac{\angle B}{\angle w} = \dfrac{3}{2}$

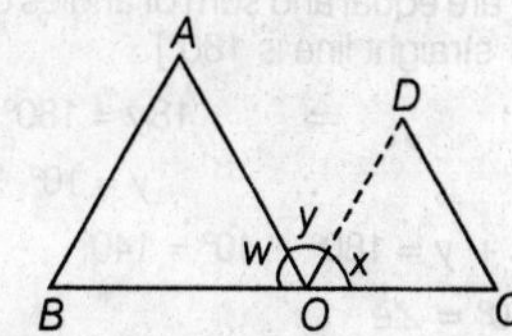

In ΔAOB,

$\angle A + \angle B + \angle w = 180°$

$\dfrac{5}{2}w + \dfrac{3}{2}w + w = 180°$

$\Rightarrow \quad 5w + 3w + 2w = 180° \times 2$

$\Rightarrow \quad w = 36°$

$\therefore \quad \angle A = 90°, \angle B = 54°, \angle w = 36°$

$\therefore$ Exterior angles of ΔAOB

$\angle x + \angle y = \angle A + \angle B = 90° + 54°$

$\Rightarrow \angle x + \angle y = 144°$

$\Rightarrow \quad 2\angle x = 2\angle y = 144°$

[since, OD is angle bisector of exterior angle of ΔAOB, i.e. $\angle x = \angle y$]

$\Rightarrow \quad \angle x = \angle y = 72°$

$\therefore \quad \angle x = 72°$

15. $\because \angle x + \angle y + \angle w = 180°$

[angles on a straight line]

$\Rightarrow \quad 144° + \angle w = 180°$

$\Rightarrow \quad \angle w = 36°$

$\therefore \quad \angle x = 2\angle w$

18. Given, $\angle 1 = 60^\circ$

$\angle 5 = \frac{2}{3} \times 90^\circ = 60^\circ$

$\Rightarrow \quad \angle 1 = \angle 5$

$\Rightarrow \quad l \| n$ [P is the transversal]

Now, $\angle 6 = \frac{4}{3} \times 90^\circ$

$= 120^\circ$

$\Rightarrow \quad \angle 4 = 60^\circ$

$\Rightarrow \quad \angle 4 = \angle 5$

$\Rightarrow \quad m \| n$

$\therefore \quad l \| m \| n$

C. Intersection of Two Lines, Intersection of Two Parallel Lines by a Transversal, Angles Formed and Their Properties

1.

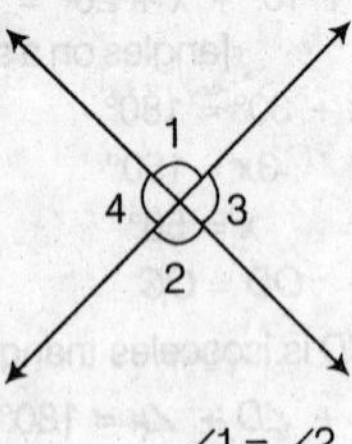

$\angle 1 = \angle 2$

$\angle 3 = \angle 4$

So, the vertically opposite angles are equal.

2. $4y + 5y + 9y = 180^\circ$

[since, vertically opposite angles are equal and sum of angles on a straight line is 180°]

$\Rightarrow \quad 18y = 180^\circ$

$\therefore \quad y = 10^\circ$

3. $x + y = 180^\circ - 40^\circ = 140^\circ$

5. $50^\circ = \angle e$

[since, both are corresponding angles]

Also, $\angle d + \angle e = 180^\circ$ [linear pair]

$\therefore \quad \angle d = 180^\circ - 50^\circ = 130^\circ$

6. Since, $CE \| BA$ and AC is transversal.

$\therefore \angle ACE = \angle BAC = 60^\circ$

[alternate angles]

$\therefore \angle ACD = \angle ACE + \angle ECD$

$= 60^\circ + 65^\circ = 125^\circ$

Now, $\angle ACB = 180^\circ - \angle ACD$

$= 180^\circ - 125^\circ = 55^\circ$

8. Since, PQ, ST are parallel lines and QS is a transversal.

Then, $75^\circ = \angle QST + 38^\circ$

$\Rightarrow \quad \angle QST = \angle x = 37^\circ$

Also, $37^\circ + 90^\circ + y = 180^\circ$

[in ΔPQS, the sum of all angles of a triangle is 180°]

$\Rightarrow \quad y = 180^\circ - 127^\circ = 53^\circ$

$\therefore \quad |x - y| = |37^\circ - 53^\circ| = 16^\circ$

9.

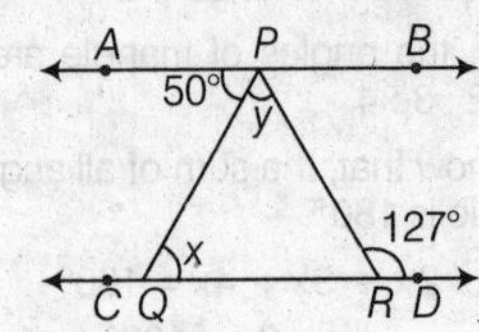

In ΔPQR, an exterior angle is equal to the sum of the two non-adjacent interior angles.

$\angle x + \angle y = 127^\circ$

11. $\because \quad \angle ACD = \angle B + \angle A$

$\therefore \quad \frac{1}{2}\angle ACD = \frac{1}{2}\angle A + \frac{1}{2}\angle B$

[since, BE and CE are bisectors of $\angle B$ and $\angle ACD$]

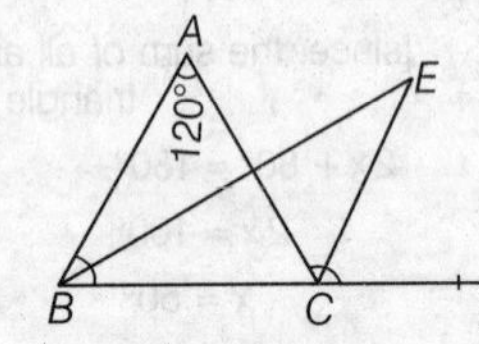

$\Rightarrow \quad \angle ECD = \frac{1}{2}\angle A + \angle EBC$ ...(i)

In ΔBCE,

$\angle ECD = \angle EBC + \angle E$ ...(ii)

From Eqs. (i) and (ii),

$\frac{1}{2}\angle A + \angle EBC = \angle EBC + \angle E$

$\therefore \quad \angle E = \frac{1}{2}\angle A = \frac{1}{2} \times 120^\circ = 60^\circ$

13.

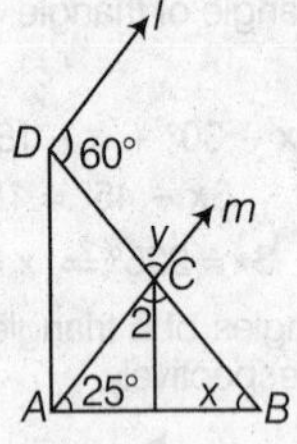

As, $l \| m$ and DC is transversal.

[angle on same side of transversal are supplementary]

$\therefore \quad 60^\circ + y = 180^\circ$

$\Rightarrow \quad y = 120^\circ$

$\therefore \quad y = \angle 2$

$= 120^\circ$

[vertically opposite angles

In ΔABC,

$120^\circ + 25^\circ + x = 180^\circ$

[angle sum property of a triangle

$\Rightarrow \quad x = 35^\circ$

$\therefore \quad \frac{y}{x} = \frac{120^\circ}{35^\circ} = \frac{24}{7}$

14. We know that,

$\angle x + \angle y = 180^\circ$

[since, angle on same side o transversal are supplementary

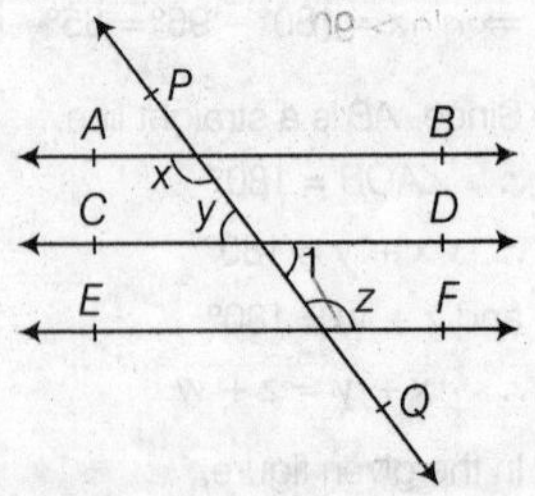

Also, PQ is a transversal

and $AB \| CD \| EF$

Now, $\angle 1 = \angle y$

[vertically opposite angles

Also, $\angle 1 + \angle z = \angle y + \angle z = 180^\circ$

Here, $y : z = 3 : 7$ [given]

$\therefore \quad y = \frac{3}{3+7} \times 180^\circ = 54^\circ$

and $z = \frac{7}{3+7} \times 180^\circ = 126^\circ$

We know that,

$\angle x + \angle y = 180^\circ$

$\therefore \quad \angle x = 180^\circ - 54^\circ = 126^\circ$

$\therefore \angle x + \angle z = 126^\circ + 126^\circ = 252^\circ$

[$\because \angle x = \angle z$, by proper

5 Triangles

A. Triangles, Its Properties and Types of Triangles

1.

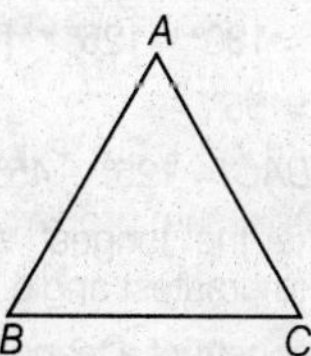

Here, A, B and C are non-collinear.

2. Sum of all angles of a triangle is 180°.

3. There can be three acute angles, a triangle can have

(60°, 60°, 60°), (70°, 50°, 60°), ...

4. There can be only one obtuse angle, i.e. angle > 90°.

5.

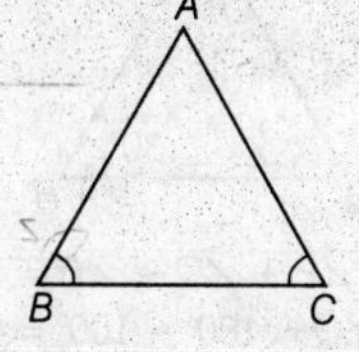

$\because \angle B = \angle C$ and $AC = AB$
[since, sides opposite to equal angles are equal]

7.

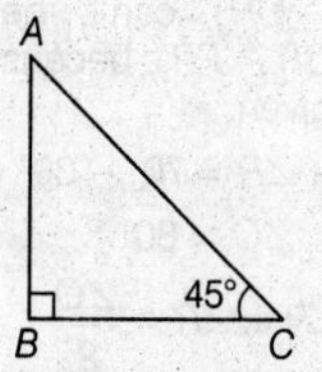

$\therefore \quad \angle A = 180° - (90° + 45°) = 45°$

8.

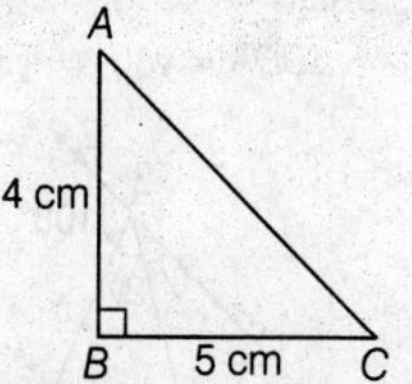

In a right angled triangle, hypotenuse is the largest side.

9. In ΔADB and ΔADC,

$BD = DC$ [since, AD divides BC]

$\angle ADB = \angle ADC$ [each 90°]

$AD = AD$ [common]

$\therefore \Delta ADB \cong \Delta ADC$ [by SAS criterion]

$\Rightarrow AB = AC$ [by CPCT]

$\therefore \Delta ABC$ is an isosceles triangle.

1. Since, angles are in the ratio 5 : 3 : 2.

i.e. $\quad 5x + 3x + 2x = 180°$

$\Rightarrow \quad x = \frac{180°}{10} = 18°$

So, the angles are 90°, 54° and 36°.
In right angled triangle, largest side is hypotenuse.

Here, $\quad 10^2 \neq 4^2 + 6^2$

Hence, triangle can't be constructed.

12. $\because 135° + \theta = 180°$

[angle on a straight line is 180°]

$\therefore \quad \theta = 45°$

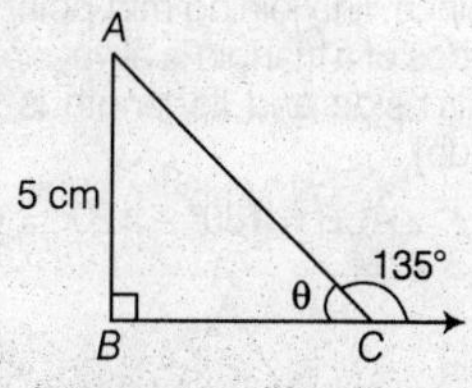

In ΔABC, $90° + 45° + \angle A = 180°$

[angle sum property of a triangle]

$\therefore \quad \angle A = 45°$

i.e. isosceles triangle.

Now, $\quad BC = 5$ cm

$\therefore \quad AC = \sqrt{5^2 + 5^2} = 5\sqrt{2}$ cm

13. We have,

$3x^2 + 2x + 1 = 2x^2 + 1 + 3x + 6$

[$\because$ exterior angle = sum of non-adjacent interior angles]

$\Rightarrow \quad x^2 - x - 6 = 0$

$\Rightarrow (x - 3)(x + 2) = 0$

$\Rightarrow \quad x = 3, -2$

$\therefore$ We take $x = 3$ [+ve value]

$\Rightarrow 3x^2 + 2x + 1 = 3 \times 3^2 + 2 \times 3 + 1$

$= 27 + 6 + 1 = 34°$

$\therefore \quad \angle ABC = 180° - 34° = 146°$

14. $3^2 + 4^2 = 5^2$

i.e. 3, 4, 5 form a right angled triangle and 5, 6, 7 can't form a right angled triangle.

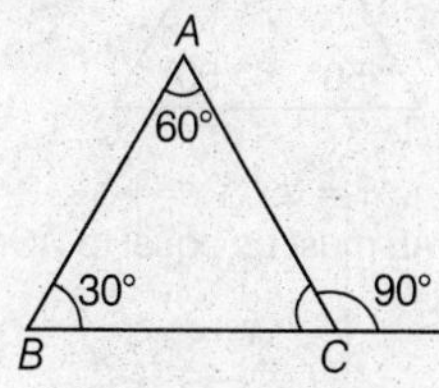

$\therefore \quad \angle C = 180° - (30° + 60°) = 90°$

which forms right angled triangle.

15. Since, BD is angle bisector of $\angle B$.

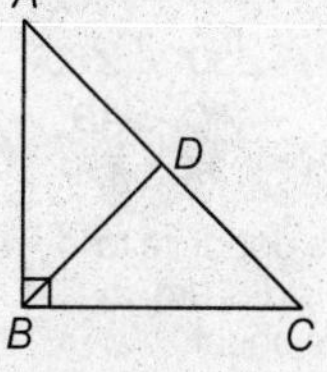

$\therefore \quad \angle ABD = \angle DBC$, $AB = BC$

i.e. $\quad \angle A = \angle C = 45°$

[angles opposite to equal sides are equal]

$\therefore \quad \angle B = 90°$

$\Rightarrow \angle BDC = 180° - (45° + 45°) = 90°$

i.e. ΔBDC is right angled triangle.

Since, side opposite to a greatest angle is larger.

Hence, BC is longest side.

B. Congruency of Triangles, Various Criterion of Congruencies like SSS, SAS, ASA and RHS

1.

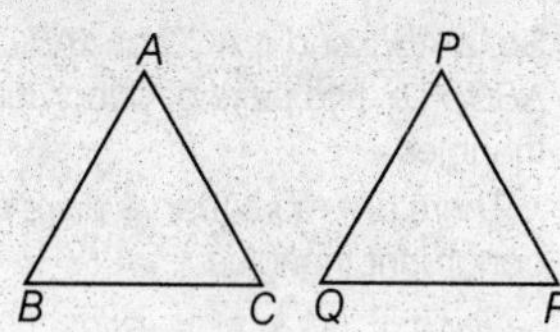

$\because \Delta ABC \cong \Delta PQR$ [given]

Now, $\angle A = \angle P$, $\angle B = \angle Q$

$\therefore \quad \angle C = \angle R$

2. AAA is not a criterion for congruency.

4. In ΔABC and ΔABD, we see that

$AC = AD$

$BC = BD$

$AB = AB$ [common]

$\therefore \quad \Delta ABC \cong \Delta ABD$

[by SSS criterion]

5. We can't calculate DF because other side (either AB or DE) must be given.

6.

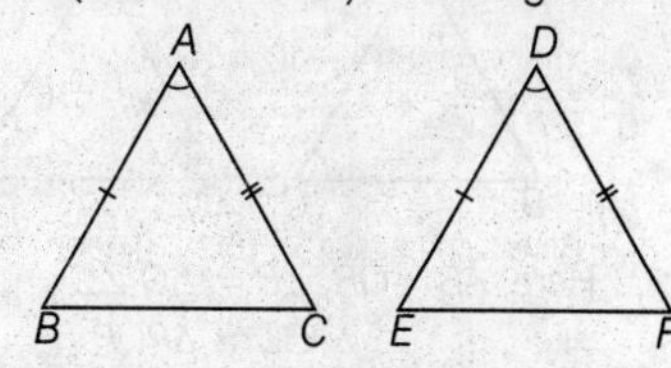

$\therefore \quad AC = DF$ and $AB = AD$

7. Here,

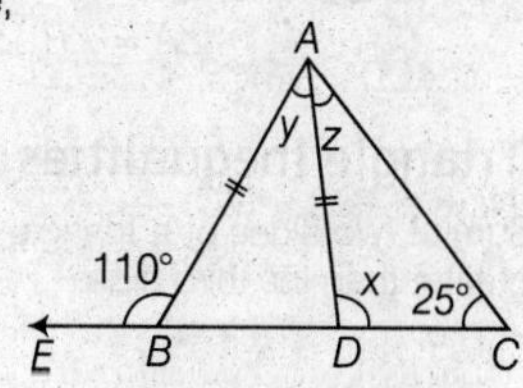

$\Rightarrow \quad \angle ABD = \angle ADB$

Also, $\quad \angle ABD = 180° - 110° = 70°$

$\therefore \quad \angle ADB = 70° = \angle ABD$

Also, $\quad x + \angle ADB = 180°$

[by linear pair]

$\therefore \quad x = 180° - 70° = 110°$

In ΔADC,

$z + x + 25° = 180°$

$\Rightarrow \quad z + 110° + 25° = 180°$

$\therefore \quad z = 45°$

9. In the given figure, ΔABC and ΔADC are right angled triangles.

In ΔACD,

$AC = 5$ cm, $AD = 3$ cm

$\therefore \quad CD = \sqrt{5^2 - 3^2} = \sqrt{16} = 4$ cm

$\because \Delta ABC \cong \Delta ACD$ [by RHS criterion]

Now, $BC = CD = 4$ cm

$\therefore \quad BC + CD = 8$ cm

10. Since, sufficient data is not given to find the value of x.

11. Here, $\angle 1 = \angle 2, \angle 2 = \angle 4$

$\angle 3 = \angle 4, \angle 1 = \angle 3,$

$\angle 2 = \angle 3, \angle 1 = \angle 4$

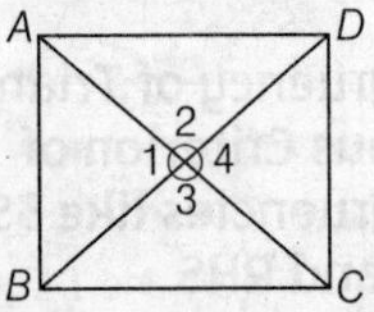

So, ΔABD and ΔACD or ΔABC and ΔBCD i.e. two pairs of congruent triangles.

$\therefore$ There are more than 8 pairs of congruent triangles.

13. $\because \quad AB = \sqrt{5^2 + 5^2} = 5\sqrt{2}$

$QS = 5\sqrt{2}$

$\therefore \quad \Delta OAB \cong \Delta PQS$

and $\quad \Delta OAB \cong \Delta RQS$

14. In ΔAFE and ΔDBC,

$AB = CF$

$\Rightarrow \quad AB + BF = BF + CF$

$\Rightarrow \quad AF = CB$

$EF = BD$ and $\angle AFE = \angle DBC$

$\therefore \Delta AFE \cong \Delta CBD$ [by SAS criterion]

15.

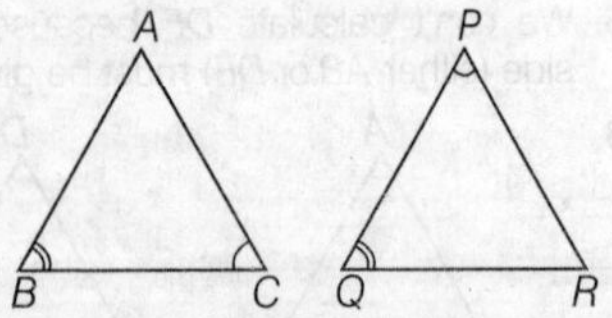

Here, $AB = QR, \angle B = \angle Q, \angle C = \angle P$

$\Rightarrow \quad \Delta ABC \not\equiv \Delta PQR$

and ABC is not isosceles triangle.

[$\Delta ABC \cong \Delta PQR$, if $AB = PQ$, $\angle A = \angle P, \angle B = \angle Q$]

C. Triangle Inequalities

1. Sum of two sides of a triangle is always greater than the third side.

i.e. $\quad a + c > b$

3.

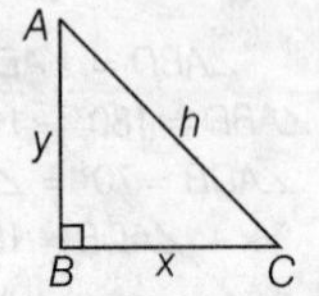

$h^2 = x^2 + y^2$

$\Rightarrow \quad h = \sqrt{x^2 + y^2} < (x + y)$

i.e. hypotenuse is always less than sum of other two sides.

5. According to the property,

$6 - 3 < x \Rightarrow 3 < x$

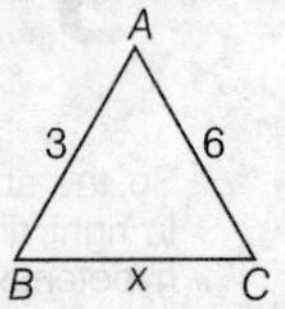

i.e. difference of two sides is always less than the third side.

and $x < 3 + 6$

$\Rightarrow \quad x < 9$

i.e. sum of two sides of a triangle is always greater than its third side.

$\therefore \quad 3 < x < 9$

6. $DE = \frac{1}{2} BC = \frac{6}{2} = 3$ cm

[since, line joining mid-point of any two sides of a triangle is always parallel to the third side and its length is half of third side]

7. $\because \quad \angle ACB = 180° - 120° = 60°$

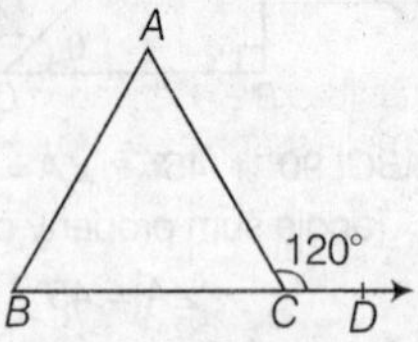

$\because \quad \angle A + \angle B = 120°$

[exterior angle is sum of interior opposite angles]

$\therefore \quad \angle A + \angle B - \angle C = 120° - 60° = 60°$

8. Triangle in option (a) only is constructed correctly.

(a)

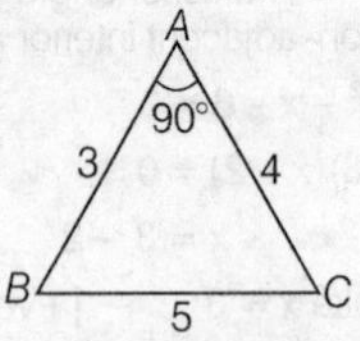

In right angled triangle,

$H = \sqrt{P^2 + B^2} = \sqrt{3^2 + 4^2} = 5$

(b)

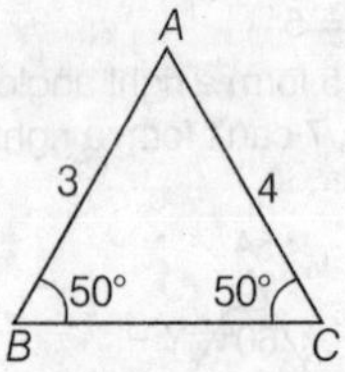

$\because \quad \angle B = \angle C$

$\therefore \quad AB$ must be equal to AC.

(c)

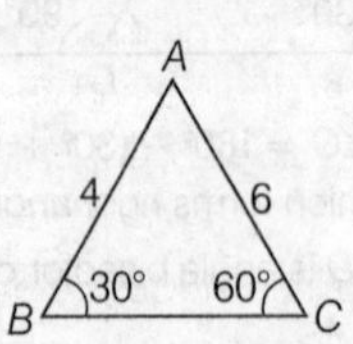

$\angle 30° < \angle 60°$

$\therefore \quad AC < AB$

But $\quad 6 \nless 4$

(d) Angles opposite to equal sides are always equal.

But $\angle B \neq \angle C$

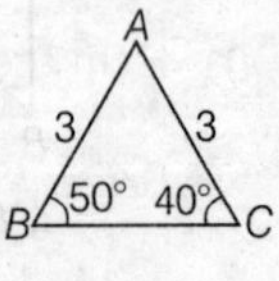

9.

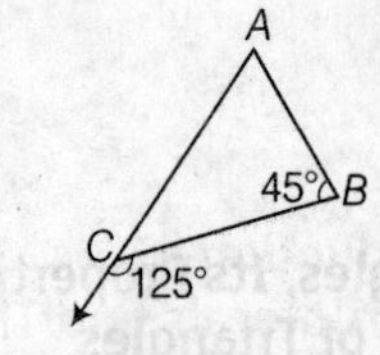

Now, $\quad \angle ABC = 45°$

$\therefore \angle ACB = 180° - 125°$ [by linear pair]

$= 55°$

and $\quad \angle BAC = 125° - 45° = 80°$

So, BC is the longest side as it is opposite to greatest angle.

11. We can't construct a triangle with sides 7 cm, 5 cm and 2 cm.

$\because \quad 7 - 5 < 2$ i.e. $2 \nless 2$

Also, $\Delta ABC \cong \Delta PQR$

$\Delta DEF \cong \Delta ABC$

$\Rightarrow \quad \Delta DEF \cong \Delta PQR$ [condition fail]

12. (a)

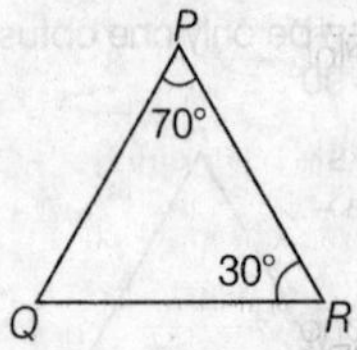

$\because \quad \angle P + \angle Q + \angle R = 180°$

$\therefore \quad \angle Q = 180° - 100° = 80°$

i.e. $\quad \angle 80° > \angle 30°$

$\Rightarrow \quad PR > PQ$

i.e. $\quad PQ < PR$

(b) $(PQ - QR)$ can't be comparec to $(QR - PR)$ because sides are not given.

(c) $\angle P - \angle R = 70° - 30° = 40°$

$\angle Q = 80°$

$\therefore \quad \angle P - \angle R = \frac{\angle Q}{2}$

(d) $PQ + PR > QR$

13. Let $\quad \angle BAD = y$

$\therefore \quad \angle BDA = y \quad$ [$\because AB = DB$

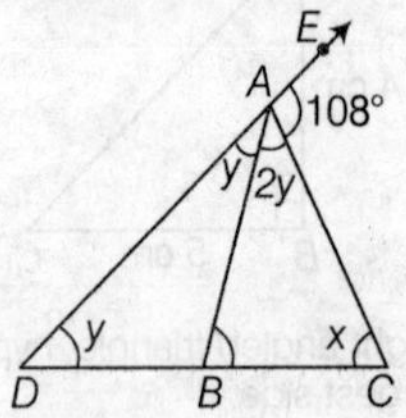

Now, $y + 2y + 108° = 180°$

$\Rightarrow \quad 3y = 72°$

$\Rightarrow \quad y = 24°$

$\therefore \quad \angle BDA = \angle BAD = 24°$

$\therefore \quad \angle BAC = 2y = 48°$

In ΔADC,

$y + 3y + x = 180°$

$\Rightarrow \quad 4y + x = 180°$

$\therefore \quad x = 180° - 4y$

$= 180° - 4 \times 24°$

$= 84°$

6 Quadrilaterals

A. Introduction to Quadrilaterals and Their Types

1. $\because$ Sum of all angles of a quadrilateral $= 360°$

$\therefore \quad x + 2x + 3x + 4x = 360°$

$\Rightarrow \quad 10x = 360°$

$\therefore \quad x = 36°$

So, the angles in ascending order are $36°, 72°, 108°$ and $144°$.

5. $\because$ Difference between greatest and smallest angles $= 2x - (x - 10°)$

$= x + 10°$

Now, $x + x - 10° + x + 30° + 2x = 360°$

$\Rightarrow \quad 5x = 340°$

$\Rightarrow \quad x = 68°$

$\therefore$ Required difference $= 68° + 10° = 78°$

8. $\because \angle C = 90°$

$\therefore \angle D = 180° - 90° = 90° = \angle B$

[adjacent angles]

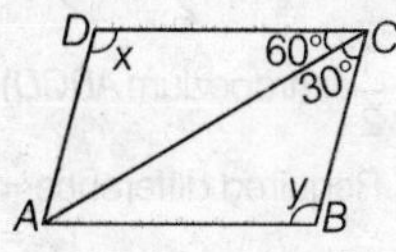

$\therefore \quad \angle B = 90° = \angle A$

$\therefore \quad x = y = 90°$

9. Since, ΔCDE is an equilateral triangle, where $AB = EC = ED = CE$.

So, $\angle DCE = \angle DEC$

$= \angle EDC = 60°$

$\therefore \angle ECB = \angle BAE = \angle 102°$

[$\because$ in rhombus, opposite angles are equal]

$\therefore \angle BCD = \angle BCE + \angle DCE$

$= 102° + 60° = 162°$

[$\because \angle BCE = \angle BAE$]

10. $\because$ Interior angle $= \dfrac{(n-2)\times 180°}{n}$

and exterior angle $= \dfrac{360°}{n}$

Now, $\dfrac{(n-2)\times 180°}{n} - \dfrac{360°}{n} = 120°$

$\Rightarrow (n-2)\times 180° - 360° = 120° n$

$\Rightarrow 180° n - 360° - 360° = 120° n$

$\Rightarrow \quad 60° n = 720°$

$\therefore \quad n = 12$

11. We know that, the sum of the angle made by angle bisector of two angles of a quadrilateral is equal to angle made by intersecting point of a bisector line.

$\therefore \quad \angle AOB = \dfrac{1}{2}(\angle C + \angle D)$

Here, angles are in the ratio $1:2:3:4$.

$\therefore \quad \angle C + \angle D = \dfrac{3+4}{10} \times 360°$

$= 7 \times 36° = 252°$

$\therefore \quad \angle AOB = \dfrac{1}{2} \times 252° = 126°$

12. In a parallelogram, opposite angles are equal.

i.e. $\quad 3x - 10° = 50° - 3x$

$\Rightarrow \quad 6x = 60°$

$\therefore \quad x = 10°$

So, the angles are $20°, 20°, 160°$ and $160°$.

$\therefore$ Difference between greatest and smallest angles $= 160° - 20°$

$= 140°$

15. In ΔABD,

$\angle ABD + \angle ADB = b \quad \ldots$(i)

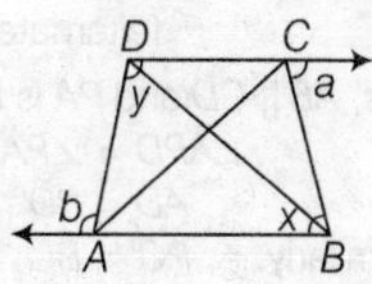

In ΔCBD,

$\angle CBD + \angle CDB = a \quad \ldots$(ii)

On adding Eqs. (i) and (ii), we get

$(\angle ABD + \angle CBD) + (\angle ADB + \angle CDB) = a + b$

$\Rightarrow \quad x + y = a + b$

16. Since, E and F are mid-points of AB and CD respectively but $AB = CD$.

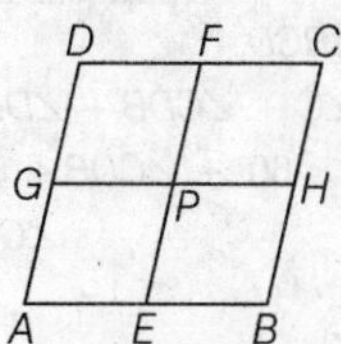

$\therefore \quad \dfrac{1}{2}AB = \dfrac{1}{2}CD$

$\Rightarrow \quad BE = CF$

Also, $\quad BE \parallel CF$

So, $BEFC$ is a parallelogram.

$\Rightarrow \quad BC \parallel EF$ and $BE = PH \quad \ldots$(i)

Now, $\quad BC \parallel EF$

$\Rightarrow \quad AD \parallel EF$

[since, $ABCD$ is a parallelogram]

So, $AEFD$ is a parallelogram.

$\therefore \quad AE = GP \quad \ldots$(ii)

But E is mid-point of AB.

$\therefore \quad AE = BE$

From Eqs. (i) and (ii), we get

$GP = PH$

Hence, P divides GH in $1:1$.

B. Properties of Parallelogram and Mid-point Theorem

1. Here, D and E are mid-points of AB and AC respectively.

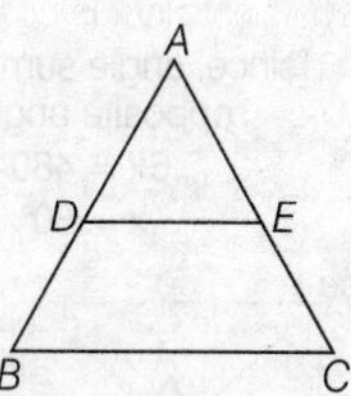

According to the mid-point theorem,

$DE \parallel BC$ and $DE = \dfrac{1}{2}BC$

Hence, $BCED$ formed is a trapezium.

2. Since, length of diagonal is always less than sum of its two non-parallel sides.

i.e. $\quad d < (7 + 4) \Rightarrow d < 11\text{cm}$

3. All angles are $90°$ because when diagonals of a parallelogram are equal, then it is either rectangle or square. So, all angles are $90°$.

4. $\because \quad AB = CD$

$\Rightarrow \quad y + 1 = 2x + 5$

$\Rightarrow \quad y = 2x + 4 \quad \ldots$(i)

Also, $\quad AD = BC$

$\Rightarrow \quad y + 5 = 3x - 4$

$\Rightarrow \quad y = 3x - 9 \quad \ldots$(ii)

From Eqs. (i) and (ii), we get

$2x + 4 = 3x - 9 \Rightarrow x = 13$

$\therefore \quad y = 30$

Now, $AB = 31$ cm, $BC = 35$ cm

$\therefore \quad AB : BC = 31:35$

6. Except (b), all others are squares.

7. According to the mid-point theorem, In ΔACD,

$PQ \parallel AC$

[since, P and Q are mid-points of AD and DC]

and $\quad PQ = \dfrac{1}{2}AC$

$\therefore \quad \dfrac{PQ}{AC} = \dfrac{1}{2}$

Now, $PQ : AC = 1:2$

9. In the following figure, $ABCD$ is a parallelogram.

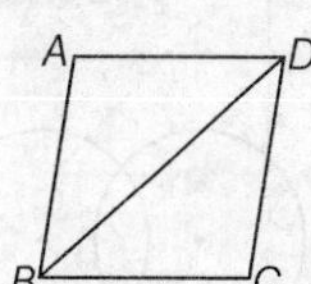

Its diagonal BD or AC divides it into two congruent (identical or equal) triangles.

10. By all the three ways, the area of divided field is equal. So, they can choose any of the given three ways.

11. I. True

Let smallest angle be x.

$\therefore$ Other angle $= 2x - 60°$

Now,

$$x + x + (2x - 60°) + (2x - 60°) = 360°$$

[since, angle sum property and opposite angles are equal]

$\Rightarrow \quad 6x = 480°$

$\therefore \quad x = 80°$

II. False

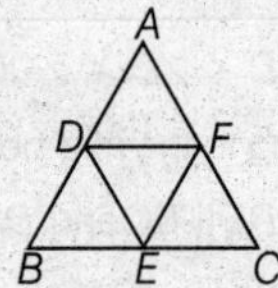

It divides it into four equal triangles.

III. False

$$CD = \frac{1}{2}AB$$

Here, AB is not given.

So, CD can't be calculated.

IV. False

$\because AB \parallel CD, CD = \frac{1}{2}AB$

But AD not $\parallel$ CB.

Hence, $ABCD$ is not rectangle.

V. True

$\because \quad \angle BAC = \angle CAD = 35°$

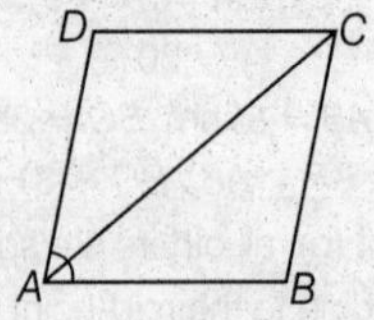

$\therefore \quad \angle DAB = 70°$

Now, $\quad \angle ABC = 180° - 70° = 110°$

12. I. 1.5 cm

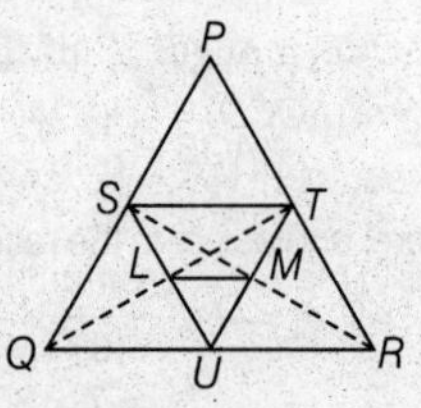

In ΔPQR, S and T are mid-points of PQ and PR, respectively.

$\therefore \; ST \parallel QR$ and $ST = \frac{1}{2}QR = QU$

$\because \quad ST \parallel QU$ and $ST = QU$

So, $STQU$ is a parallelogram whose diagonals QT and SU intersect at L, therefore L is the mid-point of SU.

Similarly, M is the mid-point of TU.

$\therefore \quad LM = \frac{1}{4}QR = \frac{1}{4} \times 6 = 1.5$ cm

II. 4 cm

$\because \quad \angle PAB = \angle APD$

[alternate interior angles]

As, $AB \parallel CD$ and PA is transversal.

$\therefore \quad \angle APD = \angle PAD$

$\Rightarrow \quad AD = PD$

Similarly, $\quad PC = BC = 4$ cm

III. 40°

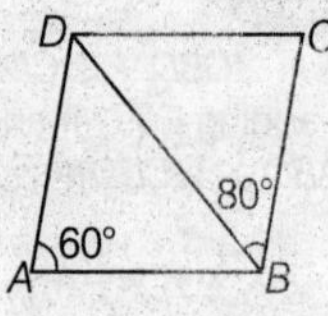

$\because \angle A = 60° = \angle C$

[opposite angles are equal]

In ΔBCD,

$\angle C + \angle CDB + \angle DBC = 180°$

$\Rightarrow \quad 60° + \angle CDB + 80° = 180°$

$\therefore \quad \angle CDB = 40°$

IV. 6 cm

Here, $BC = 2DE$

$= 2 \times 3 = 6$ cm

[by mid-point theorem]

13. We know that,

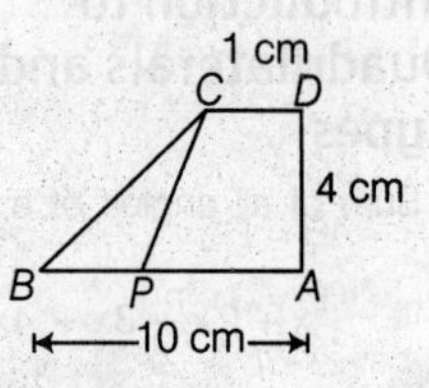

Area of trapezium

$= \frac{1}{2} \times$ Sum of parallel sides $\times$ Height

$= \frac{1}{2} \times 4 \times (10 + 1) = 22\text{ cm}^2$

$\because$ ar (trapezium $APCD$) = ar (ΔCPB)

$= \frac{22}{2} = 11\text{ cm}^2$

In ΔCPB,

$AD = 4$ cm

$PB = x$ cm [let]

$\therefore \quad \frac{1}{2} \times x \times 4 = 11$

$\Rightarrow \quad x = \frac{11}{2} = 5\frac{1}{2}$ cm

$\therefore \; \frac{1}{2}$ar (trapezium $ABCD$) = ar (ΔCPB)

$\therefore$ Required difference $= 22 - 11 = 11\text{ cm}^2$

14. $\because$ Diagonal of a square = 2

$\therefore$ Length of square $= \sqrt{2}$

Now, length of rectangle $= 3\sqrt{2}$

and breadth of rectangle $= 2\sqrt{2}$

$\therefore$ Diagonal of rectangle

$= \sqrt{(3\sqrt{2})^2 + (2\sqrt{2})^2}$

$= \sqrt{18 + 8} = \sqrt{26}$

7 Circle

A. Introduction to Circle and Basic Terminology

3. Since, two circles are congruent i.e. their radii are equal.

$\therefore$ Diameter of second circle

$= 2 \times$ Radius $= 10$ cm

5.

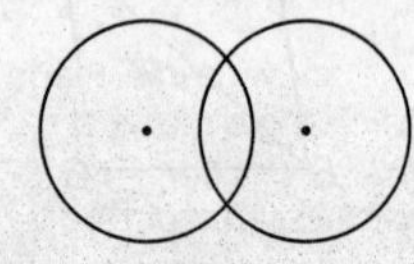

7. Length of two chords equidistant from centre is equal.

8.

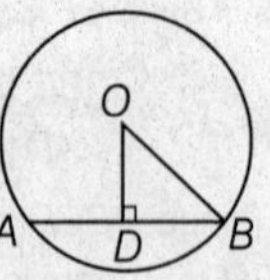

As seen, ODB is a right angled triangle and by property, we know that perpendicular from the centre to the chord bisects the chord in equal part.

$\therefore \quad AD = BD = \frac{24}{2} = 12$ cm

$\therefore \; OD = \sqrt{13^2 - 12^2}$

[by Pythagoras theorem]

$= \sqrt{169 - 144} = \sqrt{25}$ cm $= 5$ cm

9. Given, $DE = 8$ cm and $CG \perp DE$

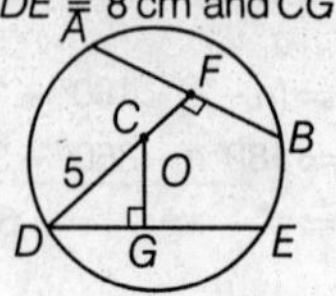

$\Rightarrow \quad DG = GE$

[since, perpendicular from the centre to the chord bisects the chord in equal part]

$\Rightarrow \quad DG = \frac{1}{2}DE = 4$ cm

In ΔCGD,

$$CD^2 = CG^2 + DG^2$$

$$\Rightarrow \quad 5^2 = CG^2 + 4^2$$

$$\Rightarrow CG^2 = 3^2 \Rightarrow CG = 3 \text{ cm}$$

Also, $CG = CF$

As, $AB = DF$

$\therefore \quad CF = 3$ cm

10. Since, $\angle ABD + \angle ABC = 90° + 90°$
$= 180°$

11. All are correct.

12. If they lie on same side of centre.

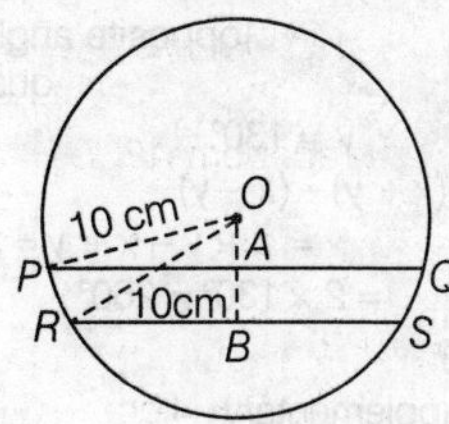

From the above figure,

$PQ = 16$ cm

$RS = 12$ cm

So, in ΔOAP, $AO = \sqrt{10^2 - 8^2}$
$= 6$ cm

In ΔORB, $OB = \sqrt{10^2 - 6^2} = 8$ cm

$\therefore$ Distance between chords

$AB = 8 - 6 = 2$ cm

If they lie on opposite side of the centre.

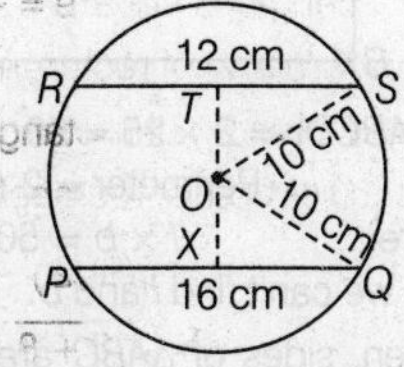

From the above figure,

$r = 10$ cm, $PQ = 16$ cm,

$RS = 12$ cm

Then, $\quad RT = ST = \frac{12}{2} = 6$ cm

In ΔOST, $\quad OT = \sqrt{10^2 - 6^2} = 8$ cm

In ΔOXQ, $OX = \sqrt{10^2 - 8^2} = 6$ cm

$\therefore$ Distance between chords

$XT = 8 + 6 = 14$ cm

13.

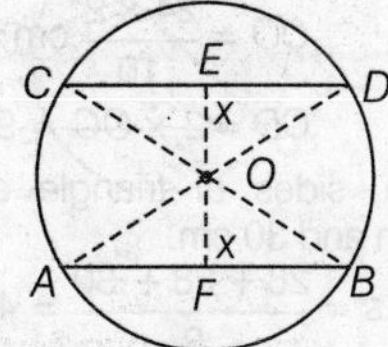

In ΔOCD and ΔOAB,

$OC = OD = OA = OB$ [radii]

$\angle COD = \angle AOB$

[vertically opposite angles]

$\therefore \Delta OCD \cong \Delta OAB$ [by SAS criterion]

$\Rightarrow$ ar(ΔOCD) = ar$(\Delta OAB) = 12\text{cm}^2$

14. Given that, $AB = 12$ cm, $r_1 = 10$ cm, $r_2 = 8$ cm, $OO' = ?$

and $AT = BT = 6$ cm

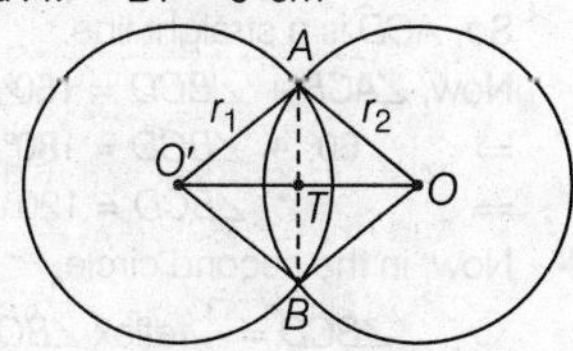

In

$\Delta O'AT, O'T = \sqrt{10^2 - 6^2} = 8$ cm Now,

in ΔATO, $OT = \sqrt{8^2 - 6^2}$

$= \sqrt{64 - 36} = \sqrt{28}$ cm

$\therefore \; OO' = O'T + OT = (8 + \sqrt{28})$ cm

15. The length of other chord is also 16 cm.

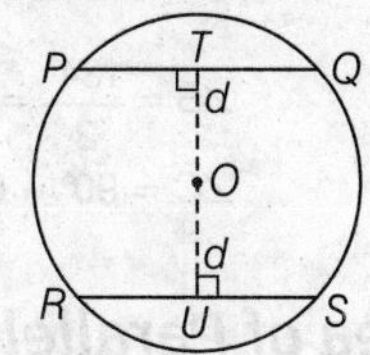

Given, $\quad OT = OU$

$\therefore \quad PQ = RS$

[chords equidistant from the centre are equal]

16. $\because \angle AOB = 60°$ [given]

$\therefore \quad OA = OB$ [radii of circle]

$\therefore \angle OAB + \angle OBA + \angle AOB = 180°$

$\Rightarrow \angle OAB + \angle OBA + 60° = 180°$

$\Rightarrow \angle OAB + \angle OBA = 120°$

$\Rightarrow \angle OAB = \angle OBA = 60°$

Hence, ΔOAB is an equilateral triangle.

$\therefore AB = 5$ cm

18.

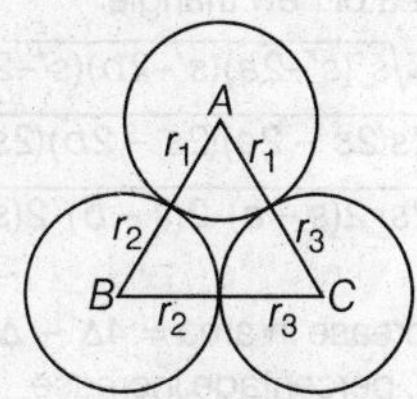

Given, $\quad AB = 7$

$BC = 8$ and $AC = 5$

$\therefore \quad r_1 + r_2 = 7 \quad$ ... (i)

$r_2 + r_3 = 8 \quad$ ... (ii)

and $\quad r_3 + r_1 = 5 \quad$ ... (iii)

From Eqs. (i) and (iii),

$r_2 - r_3 = 2 \quad$ ... (iv)

From Eqs. (ii) and (iv),

$2r_2 = 10$

$\Rightarrow \quad r_2 = 5$

$\Rightarrow \quad r_1 = 2$

and $\quad r_3 = 3$

$\therefore$ Required ratio $= 2 : 5 : 3$

B. Arc Properties of a Circle and Cyclic Quadrilateral

2. In ΔOAB,

$\angle OAB = \angle OBA$ [$\because OB = OA$ = radii]

$\therefore \quad \angle OBA = 40°$

Now, in ΔBOC,

$\angle OCB = \angle OBC = 30°$

$\therefore \quad \angle ABC = 40° + 30° = 70°$

$\therefore \quad \angle AOC = 2\angle ABC = 140°$

[since, angle made at centre by a chord is twice the angle made at any other point on circumference]

3. In ΔCDE,

$\angle D + \angle C + \angle DEC = 180°$

Now, $\angle DEC = 180° - 130° = 50°$

[by linear pair]

$\therefore \quad \angle D = 180° - (50° + 20°) = 110°$

$\therefore \quad \angle A = \angle D = 110°$

[since, angles in the same segment of a circle are equal]

4. In other cases, the length of arcs are same.

5. Since, the arc subtends 90° at centre.

Also, it is equal to $\frac{1}{4}$ circumference

$= \frac{1}{4} \times 2\pi r = \frac{1}{4} \times 40 = 10$cm

[$\because$ circumference $(2\pi r) = 40$cm]

6. In ΔBDE,

$\angle ABD = 180° - (120° + 45°)$

[$\because \angle A = \angle D = 45°$]

$= 15°$

7. $\because \quad 3x + x = 180° \Rightarrow x = 45°$

and $5y + y = 180° \Rightarrow y = 30°$

$\therefore \; x : y = 45° : 30° = 3 : 2$

8. Since, $102° + \angle y = 180°$

[by cyclic quadrilateral]

$\therefore \quad \angle y = 78°$

$\Rightarrow \; \angle x = 2\angle y = 156°$ [central angle]

9. $\because \quad \frac{\text{arc } AXB}{\text{arc } BYC} = \frac{1}{3} \Rightarrow \frac{\angle AOB}{\angle BOC} = \frac{1}{3}$

$\Rightarrow \angle AOB + \angle BOC = 180°$

[by linear pair]

$\Rightarrow \angle AOB + 3\angle AOB = 180°$

$\therefore \quad \angle AOB = 45°$

$\therefore \quad \angle BOC = 3 \times 45° = 135°$

10. Since, $\angle 4 = 35°$

[since, angle opposite to equal sides are equal]

$\therefore \quad \angle 5 = 180° - 35° - 35° = 110°$

and $\angle 6 = \frac{1}{2}\angle 5 = 55°$

11. As we know, angle made at centre is twice of angle made at other point on remaining part of circle.

$\therefore \angle AOC = 2\angle APC$

$\Rightarrow 140° = 2x$

$\therefore \quad x = 70°$

In cyclic quadrilateral $APCB$,

$\angle P + \angle B = 180°$

$\Rightarrow x + y = 180°$

$\Rightarrow 70° + y = 180°$

$\Rightarrow y = 110°$

$\therefore y - x = 110° - 70° = 40°$

12. In the given figure, $ABCD$ is a rectangle and we know diagonal of a rectangle divide it into two equal triangles.

i.e. $AB \parallel CD$

$\Rightarrow AC \parallel BD$

Since, AB and CD are equidistant from centre.

$\therefore AB = CD$

Similarly, $AC = BD$

Hence, $ABCD$ is a rectangle i.e. two triangles are congruent and have equal area.

13. (a) $\rightarrow$ Angle $= 60°$

(b) $\rightarrow \theta = 2 \times 30° = 60°$

(c) $\rightarrow \theta = 60° \times 2 = 120°$

(d) $\rightarrow \theta = 60°$

14. $\because$ Ratio of areas of regions 1 and 2 $= 2 : 1$

$\therefore$ Angle $\theta = 2 \times 45° = 90°$

15. $\because \angle ACB = \frac{1}{2}\angle APB = \frac{120°}{2} = 60°$

[since, angle at centre is twice of the angle made at other point on remaining part of circle]

So, ACD is a straight line.

Now, $\angle ACB + \angle BCD = 180°$

$\Rightarrow 60° + \angle BCD = 180°$

$\Rightarrow \angle BCD = 120°$

Now, in the second circle,

$\angle BCD = \frac{1}{2}$ reflex $\angle BQD$

$\Rightarrow 120° = \frac{1}{2}(360° - x)$

$\therefore x = 120°$

16. $\because \angle B - \angle C = 44°$

and $\angle B + \angle C = 90°$

[since, BC is diameter and $\angle A = 90°$]

$\therefore \angle B = \frac{134°}{2} = 67°$

and $\angle C = 90° - 67° = 23°$

$\therefore \angle B = 10x + 17° = 67°$

$\Rightarrow x = 5$

$\angle C = 15y - 7 = 23°$

$\therefore y = 2$

17. Since, $ABCD$ is a cyclic quadrilateral

$\therefore x + z = 180°$

and $\angle E = \angle D = 45°$

$\Rightarrow z = 45°$

$\therefore x = 180° - 45° = 135°$

Also, $y = 2z$

[since, angle at the centre is twice angle at remaining part of cir

$\therefore x + y - z = x + 2z - z = x + z = 180°$

18. $\because 50° + y = 180°$

[opposite angle of cy quadrilate

$\therefore y = 130°$

$\therefore (x + y) - (x - y) = x + y - x + y = 2y = 2 \times 130° = 260°$

21. I. 90°

II. supplementary

III. centre

V. quadrant of circle

8 Area of Parallelograms and Triangles

A. Area of Triangle using Heron's Formula (Various Types of Triangles and Perimeter of Plane Figures)

1. Sides of triangle are in the ratio 3 : 5 : 4. [given]

i.e. sides are $3x$, $5x$ and $4x$.

Perimeter= 144 cm [given]

i.e. $2s = a + b + c$

$\Rightarrow 144 = 3x + 5x + 4x$

$\Rightarrow 144 = 12x$

$\Rightarrow x = \frac{144}{12}$

$\Rightarrow x = 12$ cm

$\therefore$ Sides are 36 cm, 60 cm and 48 cm.

$\because 2s = 144$

$\Rightarrow s = \frac{144}{2}$

$\Rightarrow s = 72$

$\therefore$ Area of triangle

$= \sqrt{s(s-a)(s-b)(s-c)}$

$= \sqrt{72(72-36)(72-48)(72-60)}$

$= \sqrt{72 \times 36 \times 24 \times 12} = 864 \text{ cm}^2$

2. $\because s = 35$ cm [given]

$\therefore$ Perimeter $= 2 \times 35 = 70$ cm

$\because 2s = a + b + c$

3. Two congruent triangles always have equal areas.

4. Let sides of a triangle be a, b and c.

Now, $\frac{a+b+c}{2} = s$ ...(i)

$\Delta = \sqrt{s(s-a)(s-b)(s-c)}$

Let sides of new triangle be $2a$, $2b$ and $2c$.

$\therefore s' = \frac{2(a+b+c)}{2} = a + b + c = 2s$ [from Eq.(i)]

$\therefore$ Area of new triangle

$\Delta' = \sqrt{s'(s'-2a)(s'-2b)(s'-2c)}$

$= \sqrt{2s(2s-2a)(2s-2b)(2s-2c)}$

$= \sqrt{2s \cdot 2(s-a) \cdot 2(s-b) \cdot 2(s-c)}$

$= 4\Delta$

$\therefore$ Increase in area $= 4\Delta - \Delta = 3\Delta$

Now, percentage increase

$= \frac{3\Delta}{\Delta} \times 100 = 300\%$

5. Given, perimeter of triangle = 30 cm [given]

Sum of two equal sides = 24 cm

$\therefore$ Third side $= 30 - 24 = 6$ cm

So, $s = \frac{30}{2} = 15$ cm

$[\because 2s = a + b + c]$

$\therefore$ Area of triangle

$= \sqrt{15(15-12)(15-12)(15-6)}$

$= \sqrt{15 \times 3 \times 3 \times 9}$

$= 9\sqrt{15} \text{ cm}^2$

6.

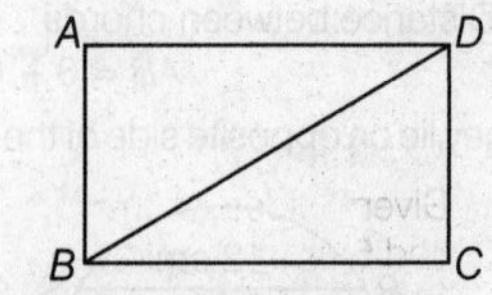

$ar(ABCD) = 2 \times 25 = 50 \text{ cm}^2$

$\therefore$ Perimeter $= 2(l + b)$

Here, $l \times b = 50$

So, we can't find l and b.

7. Given, sides of ΔABC are 6 cm, 8 and 10 cm.

$\therefore s = \frac{8 + 10 + 6}{2} = 12$ cm

Now, area of Δ

$= \sqrt{12(12-10)(12-8)(12-6)}$

[by Heron's formu

$= \sqrt{12 \times 2 \times 4 \times 6}$

$= \sqrt{4 \times 3 \times 2 \times 4 \times 3 \times 2}$

$= 4 \times 3 \times 2 = 24 \text{ cm}^2$

Also, area of triangle

$= \frac{1}{2} \times AB \times CO = 24$ c

$\Rightarrow CO = \frac{24 \times 2}{10}$ cm $= 4.8$ cm

$\therefore CD = 2 \times OC = 9.6$ cm

8. Given, sides of triangle are 26 28 cm and 30 cm.

Now, $s = \frac{26 + 28 + 30}{2} = 42$ cm

$\therefore$ Area of triangle

$= \sqrt{42(42-26)(42-28)(42-30)}$

$= \sqrt{42 \times 16 \times 14 \times 12}$
$= \sqrt{14 \times 3 \times 4 \times 4 \times 14 \times 4 \times 3}$
$= 336 \text{ cm}^2$

Now, area of parallelogram
$= \text{Base} \times \text{Height} = 336 \text{ cm}^2$

$\therefore \quad h = \frac{336}{28} = 12 \text{ cm}$

9.

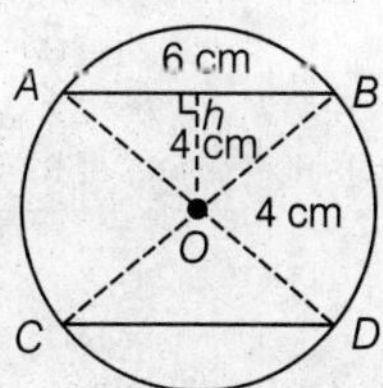

$AB = CD = 6 \text{ cm}$
[since, chords equidistant from centre are equal]

Now, $s = \frac{4+4+6}{2} = 7 \text{ cm}$

$\therefore$ Area of triangle
$= \sqrt{7(7-4)(7-4)(7-6)}$
$= \sqrt{7 \times 3 \times 3 \times 1} = 3\sqrt{7} \text{ cm}$

Also, area of triangle
$= \frac{1}{2} \times AB \times h = 3\sqrt{7} \text{ cm}$

$\Rightarrow \quad \frac{1}{2} \times 6 \times h = 3\sqrt{7} \text{ cm}$

$\Rightarrow \quad h = \sqrt{7} \text{ cm}$

$\therefore$ Distance between AB and CD
$= 2 \times \sqrt{7} = 2\sqrt{7} \text{ cm}$

10. Assertion
Given, sides of triangle = 3 cm, 4 cm and 5 cm.

Then, $s = \frac{3+4+5}{2} = \frac{12}{2} = 6 \text{ cm}$

$\therefore$ Area of triangle
$= \sqrt{s(s-a)(s-b)(s-c)}$
$= \sqrt{6(6-3)(6-4)(6-5)}$
$= \sqrt{6 \times 3 \times 2 \times 1}$
$= \sqrt{2 \times 3 \times 3 \times 2} = 2 \times 3 = 6 \text{cm}^2$

Reason If $2s = (a+b+c)$, then area of triangle
$= \sqrt{s(s-a)(s-b)(s-c)}$

11. We have,
Sides of ΔOBC as 7 cm, 6 cm and 7 cm.

$\therefore \quad s = \frac{7+6+7}{2} = 10 \text{ cm}$

Area of ΔOBC
$= \sqrt{10(10-7)(10-7)(10-6)}$
$= \sqrt{10 \times 3 \times 3 \times 4}$
$= 3 \times 2\sqrt{10} = 6\sqrt{10}$

Also, area of $\Delta OBC = \frac{1}{2} \times x \times 6$

$\Rightarrow 6\sqrt{10} = \frac{1}{2} \times x \times 6$

$\Rightarrow 2\sqrt{10} = x$

$\Rightarrow \quad x = 6.3 \text{ cm}$

B. Area of Circle and Parallelogram (Using Area of Triangle and Its Properties)

1. Perimeter of circle,
$2\pi r = 132 \text{ cm}$ [given]

$\Rightarrow \quad \pi r = \frac{132}{2}$

$\Rightarrow \quad \pi r = 66 \Rightarrow r = 21$

$\therefore$ Area of circle $= \pi r^2 = \pi r \times r$
$= 66 \times 21$
$= 1386 \text{ cm}^2$

2. Circumference of circle $= 2\pi r$
$= 2 \times \frac{22}{7} \times \frac{14}{2} = 44 \text{ cm}$

3. $OCDE$ is divided by OD into two equal triangles.

$\therefore \quad \text{ar}(\Delta ODE) : \text{ar}(OCDE) = \frac{1}{2}$

4.

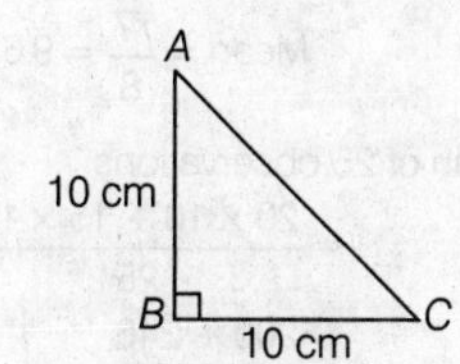

$AB + BC = 20 \text{ cm}$
$\therefore \quad AB = BC = 10 \text{ cm}$
$\Rightarrow \quad AC = 10\sqrt{2} \text{ cm}$
[by Pythagoras theorem]

$\therefore$ Area of ΔABC
$= \frac{1}{2} \times 10 \times 10 = 50 \text{ cm}^2$

or use $\sqrt{s(s-a)(s-b)(s-c)}$

5. Given that the triangle is an equilateral triangle with sides equal to 6 cm.

$\therefore \quad s = \frac{a+b+c}{2} = \frac{18}{2} = 9$

$\therefore$ Area of triangle
$= \sqrt{s(s-a)(s-b)(s-c)}$
$= \sqrt{9(3)(3)(3)}$
$= \sqrt{9 \times 9 \times 3} = 9\sqrt{3}$

Area of parallelogram
$= 2 \times \text{Area of triangle}$
[since, they are on the same base and between same parallel lines]
$= 18\sqrt{3}$

6. I. Longest chord = Diameter = 14 cm
$r = 7 \text{ cm} \quad [\because 2r = d]$

$\therefore \quad C = 2\pi r = 2 \times \frac{22}{7} \times 7 = 44 \text{ cm}$

II. Area of circle, $\pi r^2 = 154 \text{ cm}^2$

$\therefore \quad r^2 = \frac{154 \times 7}{22} = 7^2$

$\Rightarrow \quad r = 7$

$\therefore \quad C = 2\pi r = 2 \times \frac{22}{7} \times 7$
$= 44 \text{ cm}$

7. In ΔQTR,

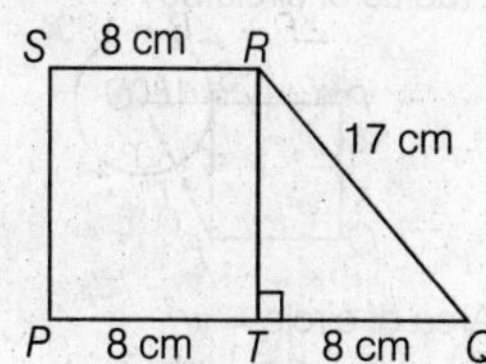

$QR^2 = QT^2 + RT^2$

$\therefore \quad RT^2 = 17^2 - 8^2$
$= 289 - 64 = 225$

$\Rightarrow \quad RT = 15 \text{ cm}$

$\therefore$ Area of trapezium
$= \frac{1}{2}(8+16) \times 15$
$= 12 \times 15 = 180 \text{ cm}^2$

8. Given, $AL = BM = 4 \text{ cm}$
$LM = 7 \text{ cm}$

In ΔADL,
$AD^2 = AL^2 + DL^2$

$\Rightarrow \quad 25 = 16 + DL^2$

$\Rightarrow \quad DL = 3 \text{ cm}$

Similarly,
$MC = \sqrt{BC^2 - BM^2} = 3 \text{ cm}$

$\therefore \quad x = CM + ML + LD = 3 + 7 + 3$
$= 13 \text{ cm}$

Now, ar(trapezium $ABCD$)
$= \frac{1}{2}(AB + CD) \times AL$
$= \frac{1}{2} \times 20 \times 4 = 40 \text{ cm}^2$

9.

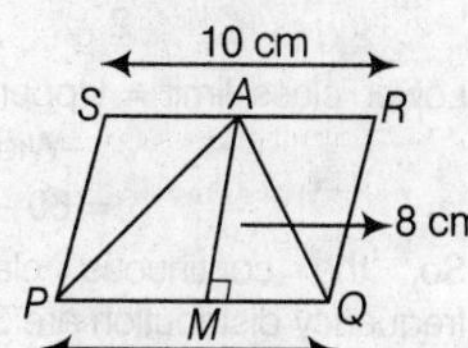

Given, $PQRS$ is a parallelogram with $RS = PQ = 10 \text{ cm}$ and $AM = 8 \text{ cm}$.

$\therefore$ Area of $\Delta APQ = \frac{1}{2} \times b \times h$
$= \frac{1}{2} \times 10 \times 8 = 40 \text{ cm}^2$

Now, area of parallelogram
$= 2 \times \text{Area of triangle}$
[since, they are on same base and between same parallel lines]
$= 2 \times 40 = 80 \text{ cm}^2$

$\therefore$ Area of region where pulses are to be grown
$= \frac{1}{2} \times 80 \text{ cm}^2 = 40 \text{ cm}^2$

11. Use the property that triangle and parallelogram on the same base and between same parallel lines and solve it.

12. Let radius of circle be r.

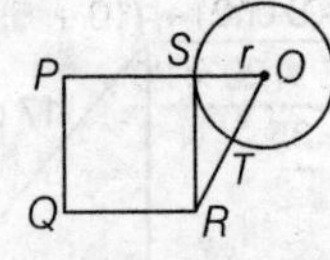

$\therefore$ Area of circle $= \pi r^2$

Now, $OR = OT + TR = r + r = 2r$

$\therefore \quad SR = \sqrt{3}r$

[by Pythagoras theorem]

Now, area of $PQRS = 3r^2$

$\therefore$ Required ratio $= \dfrac{\pi r^2}{3r^2} = \dfrac{\pi}{3}$

13. Let radius of outer circle be r.

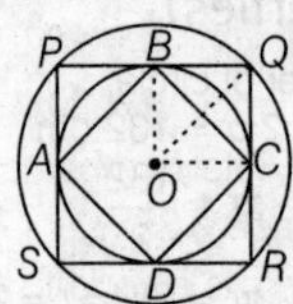

$\therefore$ Perimeter $= 2\pi r$

But $\quad OQ = BC = r$

[diagonals of square $BQCO$]

$\therefore$ Perimeter of $ABCD = 4r$

Now, required ratio $= \dfrac{2\pi r}{4r}$

$= \dfrac{\pi}{2}$

9 Statistics

A. Introduction to Statistics–Different Terminology, Bar Graphs Representation and Frequency Distribution

1. Range = Greatest value – Least value

$= 92 - 5 = 87$

3. Class $= \left(25 - \dfrac{5}{2}\right) - \left(25 + \dfrac{5}{2}\right)$

$= 22.5 - 27.5$

4. Maximum value $= 87 + 16 = 103$

5. $\because$ Upper limit – Lower limit = 6

Also, $\dfrac{\text{Upper limit} + \text{Lower limit}}{2} = 10$

$\therefore \quad$ Lower limit $= \dfrac{20-6}{2}$

$= \dfrac{14}{2} = 7$

6. Lower class limit = Upper class limit –Width of class

$= 60 - 5 = 55$

So, the continuous classes in a frequency distribution are 35-40, 40-45, 45-50, 50-55 and 55-60.

$\therefore$ Lower limit of lowest class = 35

9. $\because$ More than 100 g means number < 100 -120 to 160 -180 >

i.e. $\quad 17 + 10 + 4 + 1 = 32$

10. Range cannot be calculated.

11. $\because$ Number of students having heights shorter than 165 cm

$= 12 + 9 + 14 = 35$

and total number of students = 50

$\therefore$ Required per cent

$= \dfrac{35}{50} \times 100 = 70\%$

15. $\because$ (Export + Import) from 2007-08

$= 10 + 18 = 28$

and (Export + Import) from 2009-10

$= 11 + 20 = 31$

Now, change $= 31 - 28 = 3$

$\therefore \quad$ Per cent change $= \dfrac{3}{28} \times 100$

$= 10.71\%$

B. Measure of Central Tendencies–Mean, Median, Mode and Relation among Them

1. Since, the prime numbers between 1 and 20 are 2, 3, 5, 7, 11, 13, 17 and 19.

$\therefore \quad$ Mean $= \dfrac{77}{8} = 9.6$

2. Mean of 25 observations

$= \dfrac{20 \times 10 + 15 \times 16}{25}$

$= \dfrac{200 + 240}{25}$

$= \dfrac{440}{25} = 17.6$

3. Since, 10 students scored 75 marks.

$\therefore \quad$ Total marks $= 75 \times 10 = 750$

Since, 12 students scored 60 marks.

$\therefore$ Total marks $= 12 \times 60 = 720$

Since, 8 students scored 40 marks.

$\therefore \quad$ Total marks $= 8 \times 40 = 320$

Since, 3 students scored x marks.

$\therefore \quad$ Total marks $= 3 \times x = 3x$

Now, total number of students

$= 10 + 12 + 8 + 3 = 33$

$\therefore x = \dfrac{33 \times 57 - (750 + 720 + 320)}{3}$

$= 30.33 \approx 30$

4. Here, $\bar{x} = \dfrac{x_1 + x_2 + \cdots + x_n}{n}$

$\bar{y} = \dfrac{y_1 + y_2 + \cdots + y_n}{n}$

$\bar{z} = \dfrac{x_1 + x_2 + \dots + x_n + y_1 + y_2 + \cdots + y_n}{2n}$

$= \dfrac{x_1 + x_2 + \dots + x_n}{2n} + \dfrac{y_1 + y_2 + \dots + y_n}{2n}$

$\therefore \quad \bar{z} = \dfrac{1}{2}\bar{x} + \dfrac{1}{2}\bar{y}$

$= \dfrac{1}{2}(\bar{x} + \bar{y})$

5. $\because$ Mean

$= \dfrac{x_1 \times f_1 + x_2 \times f_2 + \cdots + x_n \times f_n}{f_1 + f_2 + \cdots + f_n}$

$\Rightarrow 20 = \dfrac{\begin{bmatrix} 15 \times 2 + 17 \times 3 + 19 \\ \times 4(20 + p) \times 5p + 23 \times 6 \end{bmatrix}}{2 + 3 + 4 + 5p + 6}$

$\Rightarrow 20 = \dfrac{\begin{bmatrix} 30 + 51 + 76 \\ + (20 + p) \times 5p + 138 \end{bmatrix}}{15 + 5p}$

$\Rightarrow \quad 300 + 100p = 157 + 100p + 5p^2 + 138$

$\Rightarrow \quad 5p^2 = 300 - 157 - 138$

$\Rightarrow \quad 5p^2 = 5$

$\Rightarrow \quad p^2 = 1$

$\therefore \quad p = 1$

6. Since, the median of the observations 11, 12, 14, 18, $(x + 2)$, $(x + 4)$, 30, 32, 35 and 41 is 24.

Number of observations = 10 [even]

$\therefore$ Median

$= \dfrac{\text{5th observation} + \text{6th observation}}{2}$

$\Rightarrow \quad 24 = \dfrac{x + 2 + x + 4}{2}$

$\Rightarrow 2x + 6 = 48$

$\therefore \quad x = 21$

7. Write the given observations in ascending order.

x	1	2	3	4	5	6	7
f	1	4	12	9	2	1	1
cf	1	5	17	26	28	29	30

$\therefore \quad$ Mode = 3 [12 times present]

Median $= \dfrac{\text{15th term} + \text{16th term}}{2}$

$= \dfrac{3 + 3}{2} = 3$

[since, 15th and 16th terms lie in $1 + 4 + 12 = 17(f)$]

We know that,

Mode = 3 × Median – 2 × Mean

$\therefore$ $\text{Mean} = \dfrac{3 \times \text{Median} - \text{Mode}}{2}$

$= \dfrac{3 \times 3 - 3}{2}$

$= \dfrac{6}{2} = 3$

10. $\because$ Mean

$= \dfrac{x_1 \times f_1 + x_2 \times f_2 + \cdots + x_n \times f_n}{f_1 + f_2 + \cdots + f_n}$

$\Rightarrow 7.5 = \dfrac{3 \times 6 + 5 \times 8 + 7 \times 15 + 9 \times p + 11 \times 8 + 13 \times 4}{6 + 8 + 15 + p + 8 + 4}$

$\Rightarrow 7.5 = \dfrac{18 + 40 + 105 + 9p + 88 + 52}{41 + p}$

$\Rightarrow \quad 303 + 9p = 307.5 + 7.5p$

$\Rightarrow \quad 303 - 307.5 = 7.5p - 9p$

$\Rightarrow \quad -4.5 = -1.5p$

$\therefore \quad p = \dfrac{4.5}{1.5} = 3$

11. $\because$ Original range = 93 − 30 = 63

$\because$ New range = 93 − 46 = 47

12. $\because \sum_{i=1}^{n} (x_i - 2) = 110$

$\Rightarrow \quad (x_1 - 2) + (x_2 - 2) + \cdots + (x_n - 2) = 110$

$\Rightarrow \quad x_1 + x_2 + \cdots + x_n = 110 + 2n$

$\Rightarrow \quad s - 2n = 110 \qquad \ldots(i)$

Similarly,

$\sum_{i=1}^{n} (x_i - 5) = 20$

$\Rightarrow \quad s - 5n = 20 \qquad \ldots(ii)$

From Eqs. (i) and (ii), we get

$3n = 90$

$\Rightarrow \quad n = 30$

13. $\because$ (15 + 1) = Total number and mean age = 25 yr

None of them is sufficient.

14. Given, $x_1 + x_2 + \ldots + x_7 = 7 \times 18 = 126 \ldots(i)$

and $x_7 + x_8 + \ldots + x_{13} = 7 \times 20 = 140 \ldots(ii)$

On adding Eqs. (i) and (ii), we get

$x_1 + \ldots + 2x_7 + \ldots + x_{13} = 266 \ldots(iii)$

Also, $x_1 + \ldots + x_{13} = 13 \times 19 = 247 \quad \ldots(iv)$

From Eqs. (iii) and (iv), we get

$x_7 = 19$

15. Number of boys = 30

Number of girls = 10

Mean age of boys = 20 yr

$\therefore$ Total age of boys = 20 × 30 = 600 yr

Mean age of girls = 18 yr

$\therefore$ Total age of girls = 18 × 10 = 180 yr

$\therefore$ New mean age

$= \dfrac{(10 + 5) \times 18 + (30 - 10) \times 20}{(30 - 10) + (10 + 5)}$

$= \dfrac{15 \times 18 + 20 \times 20}{35}$

$= \dfrac{670}{35}$

= 19.14 = 19 yr (approx.)

[$\because$ 19.15 > 19]

16. $\text{Mean} = \dfrac{1 + 2 + 3 + 3 + 6 + 3}{6}$

$= \dfrac{18}{6} = 3$

17. $\because$ Number of students = 15

and number of teachers $= \dfrac{15}{3} = 5$

$\therefore$ Total number = 15 + 5 = 20

We have, 1, 2, 3,..., 20

$\therefore$ $\text{Median} = \dfrac{10\text{th} + 11\text{th}}{2} = 20$ yr

According to the question,

$1 \rightarrow 20$

and $2 \rightarrow 19$

New arrangement will be like this

20, 19, 18, ..., 1

Total number = 20 [same]

$\therefore$ $\text{Median} = \dfrac{10\text{th} + 11\text{th}}{2}$

= Previous median = 20 yr

10 Probability

1. Total number of bulbs = 100

and defective bulbs = 15

Now, non-defective bulbs = 100 − 15 = 85

$\therefore$ Probability (selecting a non-defective bulb) $= \dfrac{85}{100} = 0.85$

2. $\because \quad n(E) = 1$

$n(S) = 100$

$\therefore$ P(even prime number less than 20) $= \dfrac{1}{100}$

4. Sample space for tossing two coins

= {(H, H), (H, T), (T, H), (T, T)} = 4

Favourable outcomes for getting atleast one head

= {(H, H), (H, T), (T, H)} = 3

$\therefore$ P (getting atleast one head) $= \dfrac{3}{4}$

5. Probability that it will rain today = 0.84

So, on this basis, we can't predict whether tomorrow will rain or not.

i.e. impossible event.

$\therefore \quad P = 0$

6. **Hint** $P(E) = \dfrac{3}{14}$

7. Favourable outcomes (i.e. number divisible by 3 from 1 to 25)

= 3, 6, 9, 12, 15, 18, 21, 24 = 8

$\therefore$ Probability (getting number divisible by 3) $= \dfrac{8}{25}$

Now, P(not divisible by 3)

$= 1 - \dfrac{8}{25} = \dfrac{17}{25}$

8. Total number of bulbs = 145

Defective bulbs = 25

$\therefore$ Non-defective bulbs = 145 − 25 = 120

He will buy, if bulb is good.

$\therefore$ P (he will buy it) $= \dfrac{120}{145} = \dfrac{24}{29}$

9.

Outcomes	Frequency
3 heads	45
2 heads	90
1 head	80
No head	85

Atmost 3 heads

= (0 head + 1 head + 2 heads + 3 heads)

= 300

$\therefore$ P (getting atmost 3 heads) $= \dfrac{300}{300} = 1$

10. A. Age less than 35 yr

= 70 + 110 + 165

= 345

Total number of teachers = 1000

$\therefore$ P(age less than 35 yr)

$$= \frac{345}{1000} = \frac{69}{200}$$

B. Age more than 35 yr and less than 45 yr = 320 + 200 = 520

$\therefore$ P (age more than 35 yr and less than 45 yr) $= \frac{520}{1000} = \frac{26}{50}$

C. Age not less than 35 yr

$$= 320 + 200 + 135$$
$$= 655$$

$\therefore$ P (age not less than 35 yr)

$$= \frac{655}{1000}$$
$$= \frac{131}{200}$$

D. Age selected from youngest group = 70

$\therefore$ P (age selected from youngest group) $= \frac{70}{1000} = \frac{14}{200}$

11. Not a girl i.e. a boy.

P(not a boy) = 0.4

$\therefore$ P(boy) = 1 − 0.4 = 0.6

[$\because P$(boy) + P(not a boy) = 1]

$\therefore$ P (not a girl) = 0.6

12. Total number of balls = 54

$$P(\text{red ball}) = \frac{1}{3}$$

$$P(\text{grey ball}) = \frac{4}{9}$$

$$\therefore \quad P(\text{pink ball}) = 1 - \left(\frac{1}{3} + \frac{4}{9}\right)$$

$$= 1 - \frac{7}{9} = \frac{2}{9}$$

Now, number of pink balls

$$= \frac{2}{9} \times 54 = 12$$

Alternate Method

$$P(\text{red ball}) = \frac{1}{3}$$

$\therefore$ Number of red balls

$$= \frac{1}{3} \times 54 = 18$$

$$\left[\because P(E) = \frac{n(E)}{n(S)} \Rightarrow n(E) = P(E) \times n(S)\right] \text{an}$$

d P(grey ball) $= \frac{4}{9}$

$\therefore$ Number of grey balls

$$= \frac{4}{9} \times 54 = 24$$

$\therefore$ P (pink ball) = 54 − (18 + 24) = 12

[$\because P(A) + P(B) + P(C) = 1$]